*An introduction to*

# ORNITHOLOGY

# An introduction to ORNITHOLOGY

SECOND EDITION

George J. Wallace, Ph.D.
*Professor of Zoology*
*Michigan State University*
*East Lansing*

THE MACMILLAN COMPANY
COLLIER-MACMILLAN LIMITED, LONDON

Third Printing, 1969

Library of Congress catalog card number: 63–11812

The Macmillan Company
Collier-Macmillan Canada, Ltd., Toronto, Ontario

Printed in the United States of America

DESIGN BY R. A. KASELER

**To Martha Cooper Wallace**

for patience, encouragement, and material help

# PREFACE

The widespread acceptance given the first edition of *An Introduction to Ornithology* encourages me to bring it up to date with a new edition, to expand the area of coverage, and to make other alterations. In spite of the many new bird books published in the last decade, including prospective textbooks at both advanced and elementary levels, there is still a need for a book of this scope: introductory ornithology at the college or university undergraduate level.

The second edition of *An Introduction to Ornithology* is completely revised—only a few pages from the first edition remain unchanged. Two new chapters, one on behavior and one on locomotion, have been added and some other chapters or parts of chapters have had extensive revision. In general, the original plan of organization and scope of the book have been retained. However, the addition of about seven years of new literature, expanding geographic coverage to make it more nearly worldwide, plus other desirable inclusions, inevitably constitute a more comprehensive volume. A great number of the former illustrations are replaced or deleted and many new ones added. The result is a total of eighty-two new illustrations.

References are divided into short lists of selected references at the ends of the chapters and a longer general bibliography of foreign and regional publications and of literature cited. This division could present a problem in that the reader may have to consult both the chapter-end references and the literature cited in order to locate a citation. However, the former include selected books or standard references—not necessarily cited in the text—pertaining to the subject matter of the chapter, whereas the literature cited section lists the original papers consulted. Chapter-end references are repeated in literature cited only if the references were specifically cited in other chapters.

References were severely pruned. Many papers listed in the first edition were replaced by more recent ones on the same subject, since the more recent paper would list earlier works and be a guide to other pertinent literature. A good example is Elder's paper on the oil gland, which lists ninety-five earlier papers on the subject: citing this main reference here would lead a student to the other papers, which thus would require no further citation here. North American ornithological literature was surveyed through 1960; revision of most of the manuscript in 1961 precluded using many papers for that year.

Common names of North American birds follow the latest (1957) American Ornithologists' Union (A.O.U.) checklist. Scientific names of North American birds are not used in the book, because they are available in the identification guides almost universally used in college courses. However, standardized common names for foreign birds often are not available; hence, their scientific names are included. Ordinal and family names and their derivatives are used freely, for early familiarity with these terms is useful to the student.

For aid in preparing this book, I am deeply grateful to many people. R. M. Naik, of the University of Baroda, India, and Dale A. Zimmerman, of New Mexico Western College, prepared most of the new drawings; and Allan D. Cruickshank contributed many outstanding photographs. Other photographs and illustrations are acknowledged in the text.

Several persons, other than those who helped with the first edition, have gone over portions of the new edition: Peter Stettenheim helped with the section on feathers and plumages; John A. King read the chapter on behavior; Ormsby Annan checked the new account of photoperiodism; and John F. Mehner and Roland Clement made useful comments on the new sections on conservation. My appreciation is also extended to many unnamed correspondents, teachers, and readers of the book for various useful suggestions.

Once again, I am indebted to my wife for typing the new material, assisting with the dummy, proof reading, and preparing the index—the unrewarding labors associated with the development of a new book.

GEORGE J. WALLACE

*Michigan State University*

# CONTENTS

## Part I

# PART I

# I

# THE HISTORY AND CURRENT STATUS OF BIRD STUDY

Watching birds, either as a profession or as a pastime, has always been a popular pursuit of man. Observations on birds began in prehistoric times, have continued with increasing momentum through the centuries, and now, with the many modern aids and conveniences for field studies, bird watching has reached a new peak of popularity.

There are many things about birds that appeal to people. Among these are their beautiful colors, their welcome springtime songs, their fascinating habits, their strange migrations and apparent freedom to come and go, and the fact that most of them are of economic value to man. But perhaps above anything else for many people is the challenge that the identification of so many kinds offers the imaginative mind, the never-ending quest of seeking something new. Certainly one of the most important aspects of bird life is the enjoyment and stimulation that thousands of people in all areas of life derive from watching and learning about birds.

There are many material aids for the bird student of today. Though the pioneers in American ornithology were of necessity largely self-taught, usually working alone under extremely trying conditions, now illustrated field guides, high-power binoculars, color portraits of birds by skilled artists, and usually convenient library facilities make bird watching both easier and more enjoyable. Nearly every sizable community has a bird club with organized field trips led by local experts. Cooperative club projects, such as the Christmas counts, are becoming increasingly popular, and indoor programs of colored movies (travelogues and screen tours) are making millions of Americans more conscious of birds.

Offsetting these attractive advantages, however, is the fact that increasing demands for living space and industrial expansion tend to restrict bird life more and more and to make good birding areas less available; even public lands ostensibly dedicated to the preservation of natural resources are under constant pressure for greater economic development and expanded recreational facilities at the expense of simple observation and enjoyment of wildlife.

## Historical Background

That cognizance of birds began long ago is shown by the crude drawings and other signs of recognition of bird life associated with ancient cultures. The oldest known records are from the Paleolithic (Old Stone) Age. Sketches of a crane or heron and also of a stork have been found on the walls of caves inhabited by the Aurignacians in southern France and Spain some 17,000 to 18,000 years ago (Fisher, 1954). Later (9,000 to 6,000 B.C.) the Magdalenians, the last of the Old Stone Age, left remarkable examples of art work, including a swan carved on a pebble, two probable Great Auks sketched on a rock, and a reindeer antler carved in the form of a Capercaillie (a European grouse). Then came Neolithic man, also in Spain, portraying a considerably greater variety of bird life. A dozen recognizable kinds of birds have been identified among their drawings (Fig. 1a), including a flock of alert geese ready for the take-off (E. G. Allen, 1951).

The ancient Sumerians in Mesopotamia left a new type of art work (Fisher, 1954). One building dating about 3,100 B.C. depicted a row of birds, probably doves, carved in limestone, and a copper relief of an eagle clutching two stags. Almost contemporaneous (about 3,000 B.C.), but more advanced in the use of bird symbols, were the ancient Egyptians, whose hieroglyphic writings employed many bird characters, and whose carvings, paintings, and mummified specimens were left on monuments and in temples; those of the highly venerated Sacred Ibis (*Threskiornis aethiopica*) remain as testimony to a bird now nearly exterminated from the land where it once was worshiped. Moreau (1930) reports that about 90 species of birds were known in ancient Egypt. Among the early Chinese, also, birds figured in legends and appeared on stamps, tapestries, and wall

*Fig. 1. Examples of ancient art. (Compare with Fig. 4r.) a. Sketches from cave drawings of Neolithic man in Spain,* 6000–4000 B.C. *(From E. G. Allen's "History of American Ornithology,"* Trans. Amer. Philosophical Society.*) b. Ocellated Turkey and King Vulture, Mayan culture. (From G. M. Allen's* Birds and Their Attributes, *copyright 1925 by Marshall Jones Company, Francestown, N. H.)*

paintings, though art work in tapestries reached a higher development in France at a much later date (Fig. 2r).

The Mayas of Central America, who had developed a remarkable degree of skill in wood and stone art long before white men arrived, left impressive carvings (Fig. 1b) of the King Vulture, Ocellated Turkey, and Great Horned Owl. Both the Mayas and the ancient Aztecs worshiped the Quetzal, which is now the national emblem of Guatemala. Sculptures in stone (Fig. 21), apparently by early Indians in South America, are also remarkable.

Biblical references to birds are numerous. About 30 different species are designated by name, though the exact number is impossible to determine because of the vague terminology often employed. Doves are referred to most frequently, but eagles and other birds of prey, as well as ravens, apparently appealed to the people of Israel. Moses compiled a list of "clean" (fit to eat) and "unclean" fowl. One passage (Numbers 11:31), whose interpretation has caused some controversy, relates: "And a wind went forth from the Lord and it brought quails (Fig. 3) from the sea, and dropped them by the camp, all around the camp one day's journey in each direction so that they covered the ground to the height of two cubits." If the people in the wilderness numbered "600,000 footmen" (v. 21) and the "least gathered ten homers" (v. 32), the harvest would be 66 million bushels of quail (F. Allen, 1948).

Perhaps the oldest published reference to migration is Job 39:26, "Doth

*Fig. 2. Left, fantastic sculptures in stone, of unknown origin, in the archaeological park in San Augustin, Colombia, include this raptorial bird (probably* Oroaetus isidori, *the Crested Eagle) clutching a serpent. It dates back at least to the tenth century and was probably carved by ancient Indians. (From a Kodachrome by Mrs. George Wallace.) Right, a tapestry depicting a heron from the Hunt of the Unicorn from southern France in the fifteenth century. Similar tapestries in China date back 4,000 years. (Photo, courtesy of the Metropolitan Museum of Art, the Cloisters Collection, Gift of John D. Rockefeller, Jr., 1937.)*

the hawk fly by thy wisdom and stretch her wings toward the south?" Equally famous, however, is the passage (Jeremiah 8:7), ". . . The stork in the heaven knoweth her appointed times and the turtle [dove] and the crane and the swallow observe the time of their coming."

Although there were probably many prehistoric observations on birds, classical studies had their origin with Aristotle and other Grecian scholars, more than three hundred years before the Christian Era (E. G. Allen, 1951). Aristotle devised a crude yet remarkable classification for the known birds, conducted anatomical studies by actual dissection, and even studied bird embryos, long before the invention of the microscope. In his classification he recognized or accounted for about 170 kinds, probably more than were known in any of the European countries throughout the Dark Ages at a much later date. Roman scholars, particularly Pliny the Elder, compiled additional information on birds, but none had the discriminating acumen of Aristotle; many of the writings of Pliny, in fact, are of unreliable data furnished by travelers about strange birds in strange lands.

Ornithology, as all sciences except perhaps medicine, suffered a relapse

*Fig. 3. Migratory Quail* (Coturnix coturnix), *believed to be the "bread of heaven" which fed the Israelites in the Land of Canaan, are now extensively used in experimental work because they are hardy in captivity and are prolific breeders. (Photo by the Mich. Dept. of Conservation.)*

during the Dark Ages when scientific pursuits were considered antireligious. The occasional scholar who attempted such studies was often persecuted. Further development of bird lore awaited the coming of the Renaissance in the twelfth century, when an awakening appreciation of living things and consequent studies of bird life blossomed into fuller flower in England, France, Germany, and other European countries. Particularly notable works were those of Turner (father of British ornithology) in 1544, and of Willoughby and Ray (the first really scientific classification of birds) in 1676, eighty-two years before Linnaeus' binomial system of nomenclature (Beddall, 1957).

Birds played an interesting and often a life-saving role in the early history of America. Though we now know from archaeological investigations that prehistoric Indians made frequent use of birds for food, wearing apparel, and ornaments, the first published reference, appropriately enough, pertains to Columbus. With his rebellious crew on the verge of mutiny, he took new hope at the sight of land birds out at sea and actually changed his course to follow the birds to land (Tooke, 1961). Conceivably, birds may have altered early American history, as otherwise Columbus might have landed elsewhere or not at all. Other navigators often depended on birds for subsistence and, unfortunately, often visited and ruthlessly plundered relatively helpless island colonies; the formerly abundant but now extinct Great Auk (p. 344) stands as mute testimony of this. The Cahow or Bermuda Petrel, once fabulously abundant, is known to have saved some of the early colonists from starvation during the famine of 1614–1615, but as a result of exploitation and later settlement it is now nearly extinct (Murphy and Mowbray, 1951).

The first settlers in America found a rewarding abundance of game birds. Though the Turkey is the most symbolic of these, there were many native grouse, flocks of wild pigeons said to number billions of birds, and a seemingly inexhaustible supply of waterfowl. In the gold-rush era, the sale of murre eggs to feed the West Coast's swollen population precipitated gun battles over lucrative egg-collecting rights in the murre colonies (Ferry, 1952).

Not all the relations of early settlers in this country with birds were for food. Though the often desperate struggle for existence was their chief concern, both explorers and settlers often took a keen interest in the new and strange birds about them. Lists were compiled, records of observations made, and drawings and engravings of birds as well as several natural-history books were on the market long before Audubon. Many specimens, merely eviscerated and heavily salted, were packed with botanical collections, which were then in considerable demand, and shipped to Europe, though few of the bird specimens long survived such treatment. Then came the more critical and elaborate works of such men as Mark Catesby (1682–1749?), who produced a two-volume treatise on the *Natural History of Carolina, Florida and the Bahama Islands*; Alexander Wilson (1766–1813), who literally drove himself to early death in the desperate but not quite successful attempt to complete his nine-volume work of *American Ornithology* (his biographer, George Ord, completed the eighth and ninth volumes); and John James Audubon (1785–1851), whose greater artistic skill and other achievements have, perhaps unfortunately, overshadowed his accomplished predecessors (Fig. 4).

Birds have served many other useful purposes. Perhaps the oldest practical use of birds was of cormorants trained for fishing by the Japanese in the sixth century, a practice apparently adopted by the Chinese some 500 years later. Rings or straps were placed about the cormorants' necks to

*Fig. 4. Left, John James Audubon, pioneer ornithologist and artist (1785–1851), whose incomparable* Birds of America, *an elephant folio of 435 paintings, sometimes sells for more than $30,000. (Courtesy of Nat. Audubon Soc.) Right, Gyrfalcon* (Falco rusticolus). *An example of the artistic skill and meticulous detail that went into Audubon's work. (Photo from an Audubon painting.)*

prevent them from swallowing their prey, and they were trained (or forced by use of leashes) to return their catch to their owner's boat. Pigeons and a few other birds, such as frigate-birds in the Polynesian Islands and wild geese in the Orient, have been utilized as carriers of messages since early times. Falconry is also an ancient pastime (Fig. 5), originating in China about 2,000 B.C. and then spreading throughout Eurasia, where it was employed more as a sport of kings and nobles than as a means of procuring food. Less generally known is the ancient partnership between certain natives in Africa and their avian honey-guides (Fig. 6) which led the hunters to bee trees and allowed both bird and man to share the spoils (Friedmann, 1955).

Bird plumages have long been used both for ornament and for comfort (p. 313); the use of feathers for millinery purposes once threatened the extermination of some of the world's most colorful birds (p. 314). Guano deposits of certain sea birds are a valuable asset in some regions; those of the Guanay Cormorant on islands off the coast of Peru (Fig. 160)

*Fig. 5. Once a sport restricted largely to the nobility, now many people enjoy training hawks for falconry. Most states, however, require special permits for the taking and possession of hawks. Here a student works with a trained Prairie Falcon. (From L. C. Pettit's* Introductory Zoology, *copyright 1962, by The C. V. Mosby Company, St. Louis. Photo, courtesy of Mich. State Univ. Museum.)*

bring the Peruvian government an annual revenue of millions of dollars. The beneficial role of birds in relation to agriculture (Chapter 13) has received wide recognition; one concrete evidence of this is the famous monument to the gulls in Salt Lake City, erected by the appreciative Mormons after California Gulls had wiped out a plague of Mormon crickets (*Anabrus simplex*) that threatened to destroy their crops. A similar memorial in stone to a colony of swallows in Japan recognizes their economic value (Inoue, 1954), but the monument to the Passenger Pigeon in Wisconsin (Fig. 174) is more a symbol of regret for the passing of a species.

Americans have a rich background for the study of ornithology. The high standards set by Wilson and Audubon have been continued by a distinguished line of taxonomists and creative workers until museum cabinets and library shelves are well stocked with reference material. Energetic collectors and curators have assembled and catalogued large museum collections until birds have become the best known systematically of any

*Fig. 6. The honeyguides (Indicatoridae) of Africa, though social parasites with respect to nesting habits, are valued by some native tribes because the chattering birds lead the way to bee trees. When the honey is taken, some comb is left for the birds as a reward. This ancient partnership between birds and man is being lost in the more civilized parts of Africa. (Courtesy of Amer. Mus. Nat. Hist.)*

of the animal groups. In sharp contrast to the insects, for instance, there are probably few undiscovered species of birds, even in the remote corners of the earth. A good bird library numbers hundreds of volumes; several university and museum libraries, in fact, have over 3,000 volumes dealing with ornithology. New bird books probably average one a week, both in England and America, and the number of journal articles and bulletins on birds runs to a thousand or more per year. Thus, although there are open fields and many unanswered questions in ornithology, extensive library resources, great museum collections, and works of art provide a rich and attractive background for further investigation.

## Some Aspects of Modern Bird Study

### BIRD LISTING

Though ornithology has many professionally trained people working on taxonomic, physiological, natural-history, and management problems, for most people bird study is a recreation or hobby. Perhaps the most popular aspect of modern bird study, which now largely replaces the egg and specimen collecting which was a "must" a generation or so ago, is simply bird listing. Many people keep some sort of bird records, from those who start a spring list with enthusiasm with the first Robin and soon drop it, to those who religiously record daily or seasonal observations. A layman I know—a day laborer—has kept a daily record of every species of bird, including numbers of individuals, that he has seen in the past thirty-seven years, and now has valuable, meticulously kept notebooks on the arrival and departure and population changes of birds in his study areas.

DAILY OR TRIP LISTS. Classes in ornithology are usually required to keep a record of birds seen on each field trip and most other observers do so voluntarily. A careful record of birds seen—when, where, how many, and under what circumstances—may be of inestimable value for future reference. In the last two decades, however, record taking for many has become a competitive game of merely listing species. A common goal of beginners is to see 100 species in a day; experienced observers, working from dawn until dark, now often record more than 150, a feat not thought possible a few decades ago.

A good example (from the many available) of this type of "ornithological golf" is the accomplishment of the Delaware Valley Ornithological Club on May 15, 1960. A party of fifty-five observers, divided into thirteen groups, listed 232 species, a possible record; the largest single group count was 190 (Scott, 1960). Such feats probably have little scientific value, except that they usually disclose some new locality records and new data, but they provide wholesome recreation, and good training for beginners (Fig. 7).

ANNUAL LISTS. Students in bird classes usually keep a complete list for the term or semester during which the course is taken, but a more common practice among bird watchers is to keep an annual (January to December) list. Such a list may be strictly local, state-wide, or national in scope. Like the daily record, it may become highly competitive. In Michigan we find that an annual list of 200 species, for a single person, necessitates intensive field work in a wide variety of habitats, but "veterans" in Massachusetts, and in other coastal or southern states, sometimes exceed 300 in a year. Coastal regions, of course, have the advantage of supplementary sea birds; southern states have their own avifauna plus most of the northern species in transit or in winter.

Birding on a national scale has also become popular among the few who can manage such an undertaking. Guy Emerson, a New York business

*Fig. 7. A class of beginners at a Nature Counselors' Training Camp in Michigan gets acquainted with local birds. (Photo by Homer D. Roberts, courtesy of* Jack-Pine Warbler.)

man whose trips take him to far corners of the country at strategic times, set a precedent in 1939 when he recorded 497 species. In 1953, however, Roger Peterson and his English companion, James Fisher, staged a well-planned sight-seeing and birding trip designed in part to wreck Emerson's long-standing record (Peterson and Fisher, 1955). In a spring tour of the perimeter of North America, from Newfoundland to Florida and the Gulf coast, then along the Pacific coast from California to Alaska, they recorded 536 species between April 11 and July 12, not including species seen on a detour into Mexico. Peterson extended his list for the year to 572. This record did not stand for long, however, for in 1956 another Englishman, Stuart Keith, following the route taken by Peterson and Fisher three years earlier, recorded 594 (Keith, 1961). Emerson (1940) had predicted that 591 species north of Mexico might be possible.

LIFE LISTS. The ultimate in bird listing is the life list. Here the late Ludlow Griscom, former curator of research at the Museum of Comparative Zoology at Harvard and long accepted dean of the bird-listing fraternity, still stands supreme. His list of birds identified in the field, including 400 added on an African tour by jeep and wheel chair in 1958 the year before his death, exceeded 3,000 species.

Life lists need not be on such a global or exhaustive scale, however. Few people have seen all the birds in their home state and probably no one has seen all the species known in North America.

### THE CHRISTMAS COUNT

Prominent among the more highly organized bird-watching events is the annual Christmas count, initiated on a modest scale in 1900 by the American Museum's great naturalist, Frank M. Chapman, and conducted for the past sixty years by the National Audubon Society. From this modest beginning (twenty-seven people at twenty-five stations), the counts have increased in popularity and magnitude until on the recent sixtieth count, thousands of participants in forty-eight states, District of Columbia, Hawaii, and seven Canadian provinces submitted 594 usable reports and recorded 501 species of birds (Cruickshank, 1960). A few people who were on the original count in 1900 are still participating; C. H. Rogers, curator of birds at Princeton University, has not missed a single census in the sixty-year period. Harry McConnell of Cadiz, Ohio, began counts on his own two years earlier, but did not send in his records until 1901. His record-setting participation ceased with the fifty-sixth count.

### AUDUBON FIELD NOTES

More useful scientifically are the other records published in *Audubon Field Notes* by the National Audubon Society in collaboration with the United States Fish and Wildlife Service. These include, in addition to the annual Christmas count, seasonal records for spring, summer, fall, and winter (four issues), plus the breeding-bird censuses. Any qualified observer in North America can contribute to the mass of information thus obtained. Observations are turned in to a regional editor, who prepares the regional records for submission to the national editors, who then prepare the final copy. Many useful data on distribution, migration, and abundance, as well as on the changing status of many forms, are obtained in this way (Fig. 8).

### OTHER ACTIVITIES

Photography is a popular and useful ornithological activity; it can be pursued by amateurs merely as a pastime, or employed by research workers in more critical studies. Slides and movies of birds are almost indispensable

*Fig. 8. Bird watchers in the Sacramento Valley, California, study a flock of geese, identify the species (mainly White-fronted and Snow Geese), and try to estimate numbers. (Photo by Allan D. Cruickshank.)*

for local club meetings; if they meet the high standards necessary for screen tours, they can be a source of income.

Bird banding, a federally sponsored program (p. 415), is engaged in by about two thousand licensed cooperators, who, often in spare-time back-yard projects, have helped to solve some of the riddles of migration, and have secured useful data on molts, plumages, longevity, and habits.

Attracting birds is a pursuit of more interest to many home owners who try to entice birds to their premises with nest boxes (Fig. 9), bird baths, feeding stations, and plantings of fruit-bearing shrubs and sheltering evergreens (pp. 360–365).

Falconry (Fig. 5), pigeon racing, and cockfighting are by no means lost arts, but cockfighting is now illegal in most states, though still popular in Mexico and parts of the Orient.

Birds as pets are also more popular in the Orient and aviculture is more advanced in European countries than in America, but traffic in cage birds in this country is a big business, with canaries, parakeets, and exotic finches in great demand.

*Fig. 9. One of the chief means of attracting birds to the home grounds is the erection of nest boxes for hole-nesting species. The House Wren, shown here, is quick to adopt man-made substitutes for the natural cavities in which it otherwise nests. (Photo by Allan D. Cruickshank.)*

Another aspect of bird watching that should not be overlooked is the hunting fraternity of more than 10 million people. Though many hunters have but slight critical interest in the birds they pursue, others enjoy stalking and studying their quarry (Fig. 10). Waterfowl hunters in particular have a good opportunity of getting more than bag limits out of their sport, since ducks on the wing, or on the water, are a pleasure to watch, require knowledge and experience to identify, and, in the many problems associated with their management, are a challenge to sportsmen.

On the more technical side are the many research projects being conducted by institutional personnel, both staff and students. A survey of the

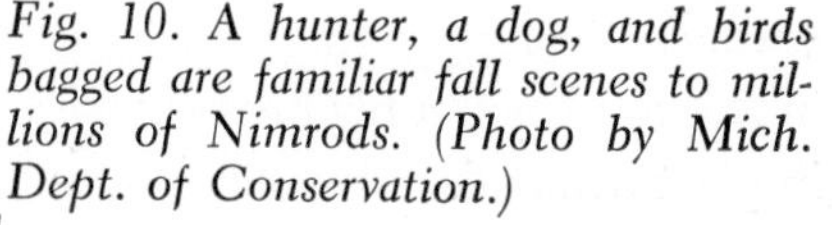

*Fig. 10. A hunter, a dog, and birds bagged are familiar fall scenes to millions of Nimrods. (Photo by Mich. Dept. of Conservation.)*

ornithological studies actively engaged in by students for advanced degrees during the spring of 1960 disclosed one hundred sixty-two projects in forty-three college and university departments. Life histories of different species have predominated in such studies, but the many titles in morphology, physiology, behavior, speciation, distribution, and ecology perhaps denote a trend away from the more traditional life-history investigations.

## *Who Watches Birds?*

Some of the reasons for the popularity of bird watching have already been indicated, but the habit as a whole is scarcely explainable. Bird watching brings together people from all walks of life. Fisher (1951), in describing the situation in England writes:

> All sorts of different people seem to watch birds. Among those I know of are a Prime Minister, a President, three Secretaries of State, a charwoman, two policemen, two Kings, two Royal Dukes, one Prince, one Princess, a Communist, seven Labour, one Liberal, and six Conservative Members of Parliament, several farm-labourers earning ninety shillings a week, a rich man who earns two or three times that amount in every hour of the day, at least forty-six schoolmasters, an engine-driver, a postman, and an upholsterer.

Of course the situation is similar in this country. Several presidents, particularly Jefferson and the two Roosevelts, were ardent bird watchers. Many professional men find recreation and relaxation in their keen interest in some phase of bird study. Still others—school teachers, youth leaders, farmers, and field men—find some knowledge and appreciation of birds a distinctly useful asset in their work. Barton (1955), from several sources of evidence, estimates that about 10 million Americans watch birds somewhat seriously, either at feeding stations or in the field, though less than a million have bought standard field guides to identification.

Contributions of these laymen to ornithology are of great magnitude; some are just incidental bits of useful knowledge, others long-term scholarly projects. A few of the latter, to select three well-known examples, are: (1) A. C. Bent's *Life Histories of North American Birds* (twenty volumes to date), compiled and largely written by a business man in Massachusetts before his death in 1954; (2) Mrs. M. M. Nice's *Studies in the Life History of the Song Sparrow*, a two-volume classic based on twelve years of study by a housewife in Ohio; (3) F. H. Kortright's *Ducks, Geese and Swans of*

*North America,* a widely used work written by a Toronto business man and sportsman. A list of the meritorious works of our "amateur" ornithologists would be a long one.

## *Professional and Semiprofessional Opportunities*

In spite of—perhaps to some extent because of—the substantial participation of the layman in the field of ornithology, there is an opportunity, though in a somewhat crowded and popular field, for professionally trained bird men. For where formerly professional careers in ornithology were open to few, mainly as taxonomists in museums, now there are opportunities for many, with an increased emphasis on the living bird. Birds have become leading subject matter in studies of speciation and evolution, distribution and ecology, and in animal behavior.

There are, in this country, perhaps a score of really large ornithological collections in municipal or university museums that require trained taxonomists as curators; the American Museum of Natural History, with a world-wide collection of more than 750,000 specimens, has a half dozen or more highly trained bird men on its staff. And there are countless smaller museums that have bird collections or exhibits that require curatorial care. In general, curatorial positions require a high degree of specialized training, if research is involved, but not necessarily where specimens (exhibits) are primarily for educational purposes.

Most of the large universities, and many smaller schools, have trained ornithologists in research or teaching capacities, though often the work with birds is part of a broader assignment. More than one hundred colleges and universities offer a course or courses in ornithology.

Summer biological stations offering introductory and advanced training in ornithology (Fig. 11) have increased in the last few decades; well-known stations of this nature now operate in Michigan, Ohio, Montana, Colorado, Minnesota, and Oklahoma. Field research stations are also expanding. Perhaps the best known are the tropical biological station at Barro Colorado in Panama, operated by the Smithsonian Institution, and the American Museum's southwestern research station in the Chiricahua Mountains in Arizona. An arctic research station and a tropical station in Mexico are in the planning stages.

The National Audubon Society (p. 425) has an office staff of more than fifty people and approximately another fifty field workers and sanctuary war-

*Fig. 11. A class in advanced ornithology looking for birds at the* W. K. *Kellogg Gull Lake Biological Station of Michigan State University. (Photo by Robert L. Fleming, Jr.)*

dens. The Society also operates summer camps in Maine, Wisconsin, and California, plus nature centers in Connecticut, Ohio, and California, for training teachers and field workers. One state society, Massachusetts, has a permanent staff numbering about sixty-five persons, operates twelve sanctuaries comprising nearly 5,000 acres, and has an annual operating budget of about $350,000 (Morgan, 1960). Several other states are attempting to follow the example set by Massachusetts. The National Park Service has greatly augmented its interpretive summer program with qualified naturalists at most of its thirty parks and at some of its monuments and historic sites. Sanctuaries, both public and private, usually employ ornithologists, although maintenance duties often supersede the ornithological in such places. Other trained or partly trained bird men find employment as camp leaders, city recreation directors, and keepers of zoos. Most of these positions, however, stress good public relations on a par with or above ornithological training.

Perhaps the most promising ornithological occupation from the standpoint of employment is in game-bird and waterfowl management or research

*Fig. 12. Game Division personnel trap and examine a Sharp-tailed Grouse. Box operates by a trap-door arrangement on top through which birds fall when they climb sloping sides for corn bait. (Photo by Mich. Dept. of Conservation.)*

in state or federal service (Fig. 12). These opportunities in wildlife fields have been well summarized by Turner (1948), using figures available in 1946. Since then, such opportunities have held up well or expanded, but unfortunately they fluctuate unpredictably with budgets. Graduate students often find summer employment in some of these state or federal agencies, and sometimes can continue research for advanced degrees as a part of their work.

Aside from these somewhat limited but challenging professional and semiprofessional opportunities, however, the study of birds has been, and probably will continue to be, a pursuit of the layman.

## *Selected References*


Allen, Elsa G. The History of American Ornithology before Audubon. *Trans. Amer. Phil. Soc.* (1951), **41**(3):387–591.

Allen, G. M. *Birds and Their Attributes.* Francestown, N.H.: Marshall Jones, 1925. Chapt. I.

Barton, Roger. *How to Watch Birds.* New York: McGraw, 1955.
Fisher, James. *Watching Birds.* London: Penguin Books, 1951. Chapt. I and III.
———. *A History of Birds.* Boston: Houghton, 1954.
Hickey, Joseph J. *A Guide to Bird Watching.* Reprint ed. Garden City, N.Y.: Garden City, 1953.
Moreau, R. E. The Birds of Ancient Egypt. In Nicoll's *Birds of Egypt,* by R. Meinertzhagen (London, 1930), **1**:58–77.
Peterson, Roger T. *Birds over America.* New York: Dodd, 1948.
———. *The Bird Watcher's Anthology.* New York: Bonanza, 1957.
———, and James Fisher. *Wild America.* Boston: Houghton, 1955.
Turner, David B. *Professional Opportunities in the Wildlife Field.* Washington, D.C.: Wildl. Mgt. Inst., Investment Bldg., 1948.

# 2

# THE BIRD:
## Characteristics, Origin and Classification

### Characteristics

A bird is a *vertebrate chordate* belonging to the class Aves. The *chordate* designation means that birds belong to a large division (phylum) of animals which includes all the forms possessing the common characteristics of a *notochord* (or backbone to replace the earlier notochord), a *dorsal nerve cord*, and *visceral arches* (gill bars or gill slits) in some stage of development. The *vertebrate* designation means that birds belong to a special subdivision (subphylum) of chordate animals that have replaced the primitive notochord by a series of vertebrae (backbone) as the chief axial support.

The class Aves comprises the well-defined group of animals which includes all the birds, and nothing except birds. Comparable vertebrate classes well known to the layman and fairly easily defined are the bony fishes (Class Osteichthys; the lampreys and the cartilaginous fishes are now placed in two other classes), the frogs, toads, and salamanders (Class Amphibia), the turtles, lizards, snakes, and crocodiles (Class Reptilia), and mammals (Class Mammalia). Each vertebrate animal has a number of diagnostic characteristics which determine the class in which it should be placed; the best known and most easily observed single characteristic for the vertebrate classes is the type of integumentary covering or outside wrapping—*dermal scales* in the fishes, a *scaleless glandular skin* in the amphibians, scales of a new type (*epidermal*) in reptiles, *hair* in mammals, and

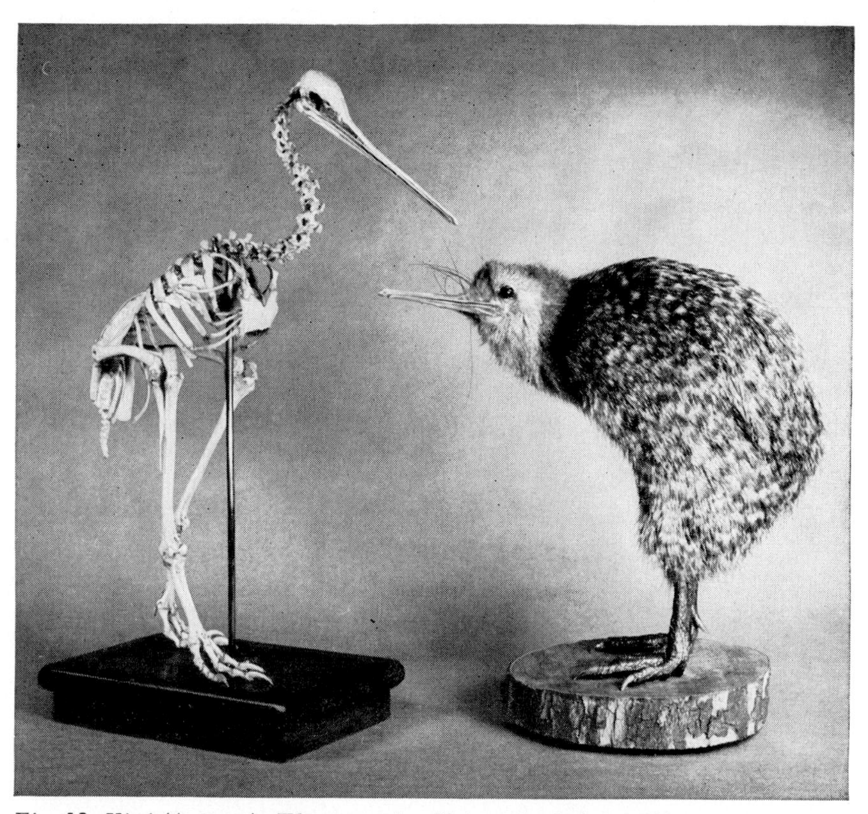

*Fig. 13. Kiwi* (Apteryx). *Three species (5 forms) of these odd creatures survive in small numbers in New Zealand. Note the hairlike plumage, nearly wingless condition, and odd feet and bill. They are nocturnal, nest in burrows, and unlike most birds have poor vision but keen smell. (Photo by Philip G. Coleman, courtesy of Mich. State Univ. Museum.)*

*feathers* in birds. Birds, then, are known by their feathers, and, although birds possess many other unique characteristics, their feathery covering is the only obvious feature not possessed by some other animal.

In spite of the great diversity found among the many different kinds of birds, they are perhaps the most homogeneous and most easily recognized class of animals on earth. For while many a layman has difficulty determining, or trying to remember, whether a whale is a mammal or a fish, an armadillo a reptile or a mammal, a glass snake a snake or a lizard, birds, with their characteristic beak, wings, and feathers, are so readily recognized that there probably is none anywhere that could be mistaken for anything else. Perhaps the most "unbirdlike" birds in the world are the kiwis (Fig. 13) with their somewhat hairlike feathers and nearly wingless condition, yet it is not likely that anyone would mistake one for a mammal.

Later chapters deal in more detail with the anatomy and biology of birds, but the main avian characteristics may be summarized here. The most obvious and distinctive of these, as already mentioned, is the possession of feathers. Other well-known avian characteristics are the development of the forelimbs as wings, usually for flight; a feathered tail that serves for balancing, steering, and lift; and a toothless horny beak. The skeleton exhibits many unique adaptations, mainly for flight and bipedal locomotion. A comparatively large four-chambered heart permits complete separation of arterial and venous blood, and an exceedingly rapid heart rate and high body temperature provide for the rapid metabolism characteristic of birds. Compact lungs closely appressed to the ribs are assisted by a remarkable system of air sacs; a special voice box, the syrinx, is developed at the base of the trachea. The digestive system lacks teeth for mastication of food but often has a crop for storing food items and a muscular gizzard for grinding hard materials. The brain of a bird is comparatively large, with well-developed optic lobes (associated with vision) and cerebellum for locomotor control and coordination, but the large cerebrum is relatively smooth and unfissured. Sight and hearing are exceedingly well developed, while taste and smell are comparatively degenerate. The nests, eggs, specialized care of the young, and often long migrations are well-known features associated with birds.

In size, living birds vary from the diminutive hummingbirds, many of which weigh less than four grams, to the bulky Ostrich which stands about 8 feet in height and weighs about 300 pounds. Comparative sizes of different species, however, are hard to evaluate, as different criteria (weight, height, length, wingspread, or over-all dimensions) may be used in expressing size. Table 1 gives some commonly used measurements of selected species, chiefly the larger forms, about which there are often controversial discussions on comparative dimensions.

Bond (1947) gives the male of the Bee Hummingbird (*Mellisuga helenae*) in the West Indies as the smallest of all birds (length about 2.5 inches). Although a male Ostrich at 300 pounds is by a wide margin the largest (heaviest) of living birds, several of the extinct flightless moas (*Dinornis*) and elephantbirds (*Aepyornis*) reached greater size. The largest flying bird known is a fossil form (*Teratornis incredibilis*) from Nevada (Howard, 1952). Bones of the forearm indicate that its wingspread was 16 to 17 feet, perhaps nearly double that of the related California Condor, though only slightly larger than a fossil oceanic bird (*Osteodontornis orri*) with an estimated wingspread of 14 to 16 feet (Howard, 1957).

***Table 1. Some Compartive Sizes of Birds***
*(Data from Standard References)*

| *Species* | *Weight (pounds)* | *Total Length (feet)* | *Wingspread (feet)* |
|---|---|---|---|
| Emperor Penguin | 57–94 (av. 70) | 3.5–3.8 | . . . . . . . . . . . . . . . |
| Wandering Albatross | 15–20 (av. 17) | 4.5 | max. 11.5, av. 10.1* |
| White Pelican | 17 | 4 –6 | 8 –nearly 10 |
| Great Blue Heron | 6–8 | 3.5–4.3 | 5.4–6.2 |
| Trumpeter Swan† | ♂–max. 38, av. 27.9<br>♀–max. 24.5, av. 22.6 | 5 –6 | 8–10 (or more?) |
| Whistling Swan† | ♂–max. 18.6, av. 15.8<br>♀–max. 18.3, av. 13.6 | 4 –4.6 | 6–7.3 |
| Canada Goose† | ♂–max. 13.8, av. 8.4<br>♀–max. 13.0, av. 7.3 | 3 –3.5 | 5–5.5 |
| California Condor‡ | 20–23 (av. 21.5) | 3.7–4.6 | 8.9–9.6 |
| Golden Eagle | 7–14.7 | ♂ 2.5–3<br>♀ 3 –3.5 | ♂ 6.2–7<br>♀ 6.8–7.8 |
| Bald Eagle | 7.2–11.5 | ♂ 2.5–2.8<br>♀ 2.9–3.1 | ♂ 6–7.1<br>♀ 6.6–7.5 |
| Wild Turkey† | ♂–max. 23.8, av. 16.3<br>♀–max. 12.3, av. 9.3 | 4 (♂) | 5 (♂) |
| Whooping Crane | 8.7–17.3 | 4.2–4.5 | 7.7 |
| Sandhill Crane (Greater) | 8.0–11.0 (av. 9.5) | 3.3–4.0 | 6.6–7.5 |
| Great Bustard | ♂–max. 30<br>(♀ smaller) | 3.8 | |
| Ruby-throated Hummingbird | 3–4 (grams) | 3.1–4.0 (inches) | 4.0–4.75 (inches) |

* Twelve-foot wingspread possible, 13-foot or over a myth (Murphy).
† Weights from Nelson and Martin (1953).
‡ Andean Condor is no larger; wingspreads of 11–14 feet in California form reported but not well verified.

## Origin and Fossil History

In origin, birds are believed to be derived from reptiles. Not only do the anatomy and embryology of reptiles and birds denote close kinship, but some noteworthy fossils actually link the two groups. At first glance it may seem incredible that a warmly feathered, highly organized bird, the embodiment of intense living and unrestrained freedom, could stem from a cold-blooded, earth-bound reptile, but of course both the birds and reptiles of early times were much different from those of today; in fact, birdlike reptiles and reptilelike birds existed together during the Mesozoic geological era, more than 100 million years ago.

The exact point of departure of birds from early reptiles is not clear from the fossil record. Apparently a group of stem reptiles (*cotylosaurs*) gave rise to the turtles, mammals, and several extinct reptilian lines (Fig. 14) at a very early date—the turtles in the Carboniferous Period and the mammals in the Triassic (Table 2). But they also gave rise to an exceedingly plastic and generalized group known as the *Pseudosuchia* (*thecodonts*), which were ancestral to all the later Jurassic and Cretaceous dinosaurs, the modern reptiles and the birds. Heilmann (1927) evokes a hypothetical group, the *Proaves*, as a connecting link between the rather generalized pseudosuchians and the first birds. Apparently the nearest living relatives of the birds are the crocodiles (Fig. 14).

Various other Mesozoic reptiles have been postulated as possible ancestors to the birds. These include (1) the *pterosaurs* or *pterodactyls*, bouyant, flying forms such as *Pteranodon* which had a wingspread of twenty feet or more and, necessarily for flight, had many other avian features; (2) the *Saurischia* (reptile-pelvis), which included some light-

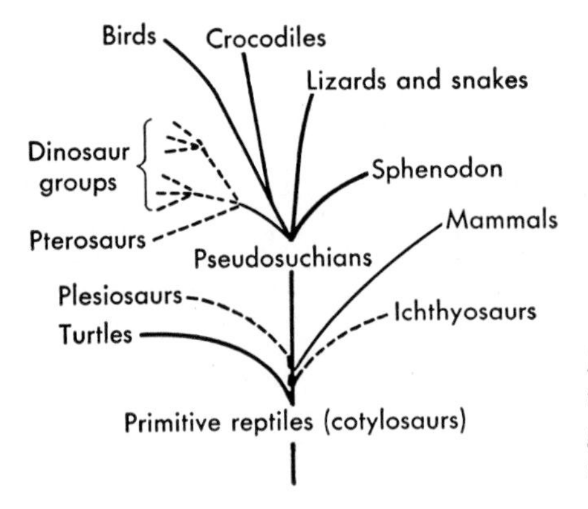


*Fig. 14. Family tree of the early reptiles showing origins of the higher groups. Broken lines represent extinct groups.*

*Table 2. Geologic Time Table*

| *Era* | *Periods and Epochs* | *Estimated Years Since Each Began* | *Birds and Other Life Characteristic of Periods* |
|---|---|---|---|
| CENOZOIC (*Age of Mammals*) | Quarternary | | |
| | Recent | 20,000 | Modern birds (30,000 forms); modern man |
| | Pleistocene | 1,000,000 | Several hundred fossil species, about half modern forms; primitive man; widespread extermination by climatic factors |
| | Tertiary | | |
| | Pliocene | 12,000,000 | Birds may have reached maximum abundance, some modern species |
| | Miocene | 28,000,000 | Some passerines; most non-passerine types represented |
| | Oligocene | 40,000,000 | Many gruiform types; buteos and a few modern genera |
| | Eocene | 60,000,000 | Diatrymids; ancestral(?) ostrich; primitive ardeid, anatid, tetraonid, scolopacid types; primitive owls and vultures |
| MESOZOIC (*Age of Reptiles*) | Cretaceous | 120,000,000 | Toothed divers (*Hesperornis, Ichthyornis*); primitive flamingos, cormorant; last of dinosaurs |
| | Jurassic | 155,000,000 | First birds (*Archaeopteryx*); dinosaurs dominant |
| | Triassic | 190,000,000 | Rise of ruling reptiles; first mammals; bony fishes |
| PALEOZOIC (*Age of Invertebrates*) | Permian | 215,000,000 | Life transitional between Paleozoic and Mesozoic |
| | Carboniferous | 300,000,000 | Age of amphibians; first reptiles |
| | Devonian | 350,000,000 | Age of fishes; first amphibians |
| | Silurian | 390,000,000 | First sharks (Chrondichthyes); first land animals |
| | Ordovician | 480,000,000 | First vertebrates (fishlike ostracoderms) |
| | Cambrian | 550,000,000 | Most invertebrate phyla present |
| PROTEROZOIC | | 925,000,000 | Simple marine invertebrates; sponge spicules |
| ARCHEOZOIC | | 1,500,000,000 | Presumptive origin of life, no fossils |

bodied, fleet-footed forms like *Struthiomimus* ("ostrich-mimic"); and (3) the *Ornithischia* (bird-pelvis), which included bipedal runners like the "duck-billed" dinosaurs. But apparently all these groups, though possessing many birdlike members, had already become highly specialized and died out without descendants during the Cretaceous, by which time birds were already well established. The loss of the clavicle (wishbone) in all these groups (except the ancestral *Pseudosuchia*) disqualifies them as ancestors of the birds; that is, since all flying birds possess a clavicle, it is very unlikely that their immediate ancestors would be without one.

## FOSSIL BIRDS

Unfortunately, bird remains are not as well represented among known fossils as are, for instance, the reptiles and mammals. Bird skeletons, because of their delicate structure, do not fossilize readily, and the living habits of birds are not conducive to preservation of specimens. So it is fortunate that several birds that lived during the Jurassic, perhaps 130 million years ago, have been recovered as fossils. One of these, a headless specimen now in the British Museum, was found in 1861 in the lithographic slate quarries in Bavaria then being mined extensively for writing stones. The bird was named *Archaeopteryx* ("ancient wing"). In 1877 a more complete specimen was found in the same region. It was named *Archaeornis* ("ancient bird") and is housed in the Berlin Museum. In 1956 a third specimen was found near the site of the 1861 fossil. Unfortunately, it was in a poor state of preservation and adds little to our knowledge but does help to clarify several formerly obscure points. All three specimens (plus an isolated feather found in 1861) are now usually referred to as *Archaeopteryx* and are considered conspecific (the same species) by some (de Beer, 1954; Swinton, 1960), but not by others (Wetmore, 1960; Savile, 1957).

*Archaeopteryx* (Fig. 15) was a medium-sized bird about the size of a pigeon but with a long lizardlike tail with lateral tail feathers, unlike any modern bird. Short, rounded wings with feathers probably enabled it to make short gliding flights, and claws on the wings suggest arboreal habits. The structure of the feet likewise indicate perching adaptations. The three fingers were separate, not fused as in modern birds. Other reptilian features include unfused pelvic bones and a lizardlike beak with teeth set in the jaws. Restorations depict the bird almost completely clothed with feathers but with scales over the head and neck.

*Fig. 15. Fossil remains of* Archaeopteryx, *discovered in Bavaria, Germany, in 1877. (From Hegner and Stiles,* College Zoology, *copyright 1951 by the Macmillan Company, New York.)*

The next oldest known bird fossils are from the Cretaceous geological period, some 35 million years later than the time of *Archaeopteryx*. These include rich finds in the shale beds of western Kansas and other prairie states, where inland seas inundated the land and left deposits when the waters receded. One of these was *Hesperornis* ("western bird"), a large, loonlike or cormorantlike bird (Fig. 16) perhaps five feet in length. Well-preserved specimens belonging to several genera are in the Peabody Museum at Yale University and at the University of Kansas. *Hesperornis* was apparently an aquatic bird, specialized for swimming and diving and presumably subsisting on fish. Like its Jurassic predecessors, it had teeth, which were unevenly set in the jaws. The neck was long and flexible, the

*Fig. 16.* Hesperornis, *a restoration showing teeth, absence of wings, laterally directed legs with lobed toes for swimming, and the peculiar (but largely imaginary) plumage. (Courtesy of Amer. Mus. Nat. Hist., from Hegner and Stiles,* College Zoology, *copyright 1951 by The Macmillan Company, New York.)*

tail shorter than in *Archaeopteryx* and more like modern birds, and the wings were reduced to a single pair of slender bones.

Another "find" from the same Cretaceous shales of Kansas was *Ichthyornis* ("fish-bird"), so called from its amphicoelous vertebrae. Reconstructions of skeletons have heretofore shown the birds with teeth, but now it is thought that the skulls supposed to belong here came from mososaurs (reptiles) associated in the same beds (Gregory, 1952). Apparently *Ichthyornis* resembled a gull somewhat in size and habits, was a strong flier with a keeled sternum and well-developed wings, and presumably lived on fish. Both *Ichthyornis* and *Hesperornis* disappeared when the inland seas receded, and left no descendants. Other Cretaceous birds include two primitive flamingos (*Scaniornis* and *Parascaniornis*) and a cormorant type (*Elopteryx*) from Europe.

Thus the entire Cretaceous record has so far yielded twenty or more forms—eight primitive divers (hesperornislike birds), eight ichthyornis types, two flamingos and a cormorant, plus a number of questionable items not positively identifiable.

During the Eocene epoch, dating back some 60 million years, bird remains, though still relatively scarce, show much better representation, including both strange types long extinct as well as the beginnings of definite lines that have persisted to the present day. An oft-cited example of an extinct line is *Diatryma*, a 7-foot flightless monster (Fig. 171), first recovered from the Eocene of Wyoming. Later discoveries revealed three additional species from Wyoming, New Mexico, and New Jersey, and two somewhat uncertain forms from Switzerland and France. Though suggestive of the Ostrich in size and perhaps habits, these giant fossils are believed to be more closely related to the shorebirds.

More modern types also prevailed in the Eocene. Deposits in this country have yielded heron, duck, grouse, sandpiper, crane, rail and owl types. In later deposits, particularly in the Miocene and Pliocene, examples of nearly all nonpasserine families in North America have been found. No modern species, or even genera, date back as far as the Eocene, but a lark-like bird (*Palaeospiza bella*) from the upper Miocene of Colorado and a "finch" (*Palaeostruthus hatcheri*) from the Miocene of Kansas show that some advanced types were in existence more than ten million years ago.

Bizarre forms also continued to appear and disappear throughout the Tertiary. Examples of these are *Phororhacos* (Fig. 17r), and several other cranelike giants from the Miocene and Oligocene of Patagonia (Argentina). These were large-headed, heavy-bodied, cursorial birds of prey, equaling or exceeding the Ostrich in size. Probably bird life reached its maximum

*Fig. 17. Left,* Diatryma, *a heavy-bodied giant from the Eocene of Wyoming, probably remotely related to the cranes and rails. Right,* Phororhacos, *giant bird of prey, suggestive of and probably remotely related to the Secretarybird (Fig. 148). (Courtesy of Amer. Mus. Nat. Hist.)*

development in the late Miocene and Pliocene periods (Wetmore, 1950), before unfavorable climatic conditions caused widespread extinction over much of the world.

Best known of the Pleistocene fossils are those from the asphalt pits at Rancho la Brea, California, where many birds as well as mammals became entombed and preserved. Fossil Lake in eastern Oregon and several beds in Florida have also yielded valuable Pleistocene remains. Altogether, from the Cretaceous down to recent times, more than 350 species of fossil birds have been recovered from North America, a little over half of them of species no longer living, the rest of modern forms. Wetmore (1950) figured the total for the entire world as 786 forms in 1950. However, known fossils are but a small fraction of the avifauna that must have existed in the past. Brodkorb (1960) calculates that more than a million species have evolved since the origin of the class Aves, of which less than one per cent exist today.

## Classification

The classification of living things is an attempt by biologists to place all plants and animals in an orderly arrangement, so that closely related species are grouped in ways to show their kinship. In the Animal Kingdom, such categories as *phyla, classes, orders, families, genera,* and *species,* and various modifications of these are designed to show this degree of relationship. The phyla, which are the largest units, are made up of classes; each class in turn is broken down into orders, then orders into families, genera, and species. Professional zoologists, working closely with many specimens, recognize *sub* and *super* categories of each of these groups, but these become rather confusing to the layman. Insofar as a linear arrangement and our incomplete knowledge permit, the groups, both large and small, are arranged in a phylogenetic sequence, that is, from the oldest and most primitive to the most advanced and most specialized. Actually a family tree with many branches (Fig. 18) is the only accurate way to express natural relationships, but in most cases our knowledge is inadequate for constructing such trees. Also considerable confusion exists as to what constitutes "old" and "primitive" and "advanced" and "specialized."

*Taxonomy* is the study or science of the classification of living things, including man's attempts to arrange them according to natural relationships. *Systematics* is usually used interchangeably with taxonomy, but

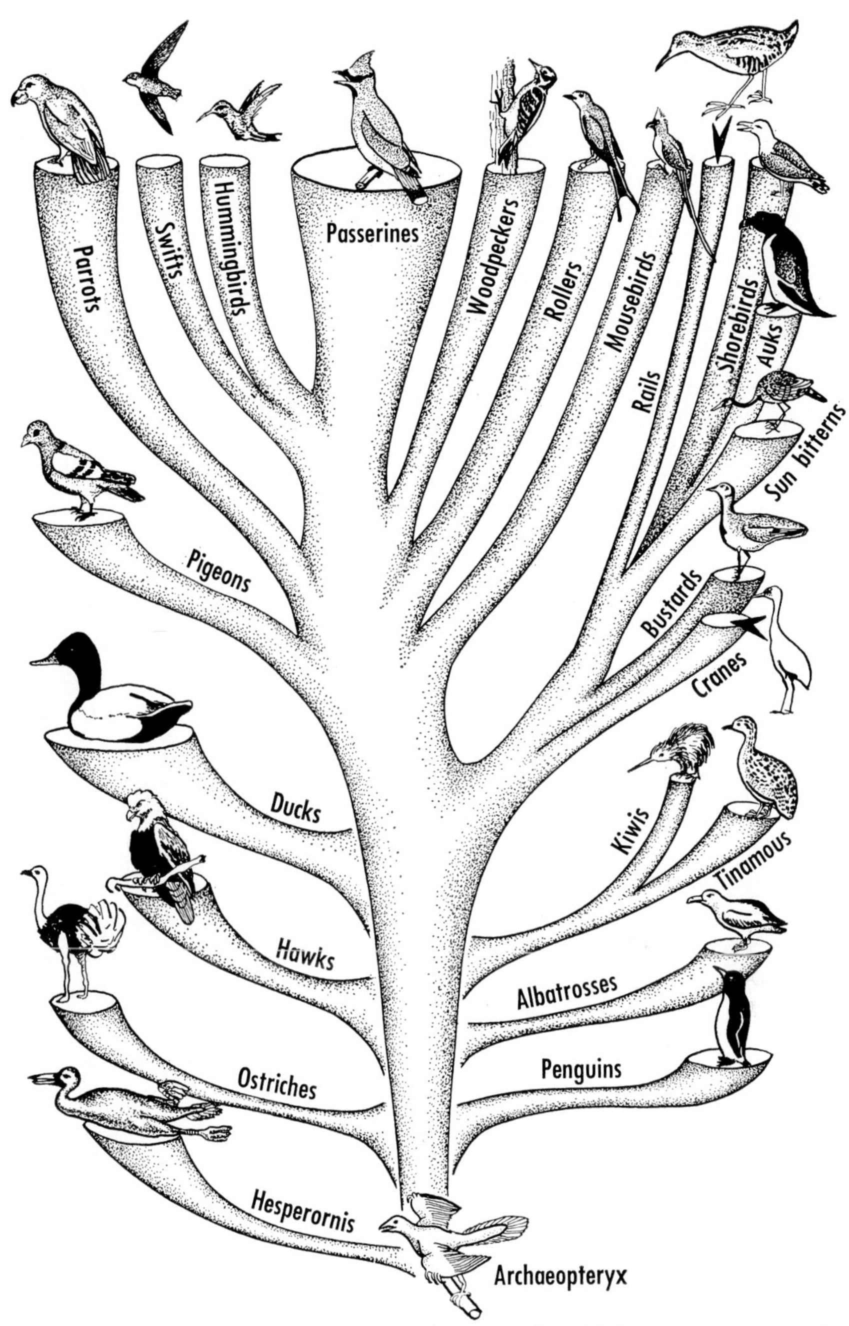


*Fig. 18. Hypothetical tree, showing probable relationships among some avian orders and families. Many of the relationships are uncertain, particularly in the lower branches (e.g., the position of the kiwis, tinamous, and ostriches). (Drawing by L. C. Pettit, courtesy of the C. V. Mosby Company, St. Louis.)*

according to Blackwelder (1959) the former should be used in the broadest possible sense while restricting the term taxonomy to work with the lower categories (genera, species, and subspecies). Applying names to things is called *nomenclature.* The need for such names was apparent to ancient peoples, but our currently used binomial nomenclature dates from 1758 when the Swedish botanist, Linnaeus, devised the plan of applying a scientific name (genus and species) to every plant and animal. This plan has been followed, with modifications, ever since. In 1895 an International Commission on Zoological Nomenclature was appointed which still functions in interpreting the complicated rules and procedures. In North America a committee of the American Ornithologists' Union (A.O.U.) decides what names should be used for North American birds.

### ORDERS

American classifications, following Wetmore (1960) and Peters (1931–1951), and some of those used in Europe, divide the class Aves into about 27 orders of living birds, with 6 others known only from extinct or fossil forms. Some Europeans, however, notably Stresemann (1959), use smaller ordinal units and recognize 51. Of the 27 orders used here, 20 are represented in North America. Three of these barely reach our borders (oceanic or tropical), so that most states have representatives of 17.

Avian orders often lack the sharp and sometimes obvious distinguishing characters associated with other vertebrates. Among the reptiles, for instance, the turtles belong to a well-defined reptilian order; and the carnivores, rodents, bats, and marsupials comprise well-known mammalian orders with easily observable distinguishing features, such as teeth and toes. Ordinal characters for birds, however, are often based on less obvious internal features, such as the structure of the palate and the arrangement of the bones of the skull. Internal features, especially of the skeleton, are presumed to be more stable and less subject to adaptive change than external features. The general structure of the bills and feet (not minor variations) is very useful (and more obvious), but has to be used with caution, in combination with other characters, because of adaptive convergence due to feeding habits (see p. 61).

Ordinal names of birds (in this country) end in *-formes.* They are often converted for convenient usage into anglicized terms such as *passeriform* (*passerine,* also used, stems from the older name Passeres) for perching birds, *columbiform* for pigeonlike, and *falconiform* for hawklike birds.

## FAMILIES

About 170 families of living birds are listed in most classifications, although much uncertainty exists about the status of some of them. An additional 41 fossil families have been listed by Wetmore (1960). The large number of avian families, especially in the Passeriformes, reflects the desire for dealing with reasonably small groups; otherwise many of the passerine families (perhaps all the songbirds) would be combined.

Family distinguishing characters, in addition to those that are internal and thus not obvious, include variations in the bill (the general structure is usually an ordinal character), the scutellation (scales) of the tarsus, and number and comparative length of the primaries. In the tube-nosed swimmers (Procellariiformes), for example, the four families are separated largely by the position of the nostrils. In the Falconiformes, variations in bills and feet are very helpful in setting up the 5 recognized families. Figure 19 illustrates some of these variations in the 4 North American families. In the less variable passerine groups, however, the bills and feet are not always sufficiently distinctive, but the length (or absence) of the outer (tenth) primary is sometimes useful in separating songbird families.

Family names of birds, as in all animal families, end in *-idae.* (Similarly, subfamily names end in *-inae* and superfamilies in *-oidea.*) As in the case of ordinal names, family names can be and often are converted for common usage into such terms as *fringillids* for the great and heterogeneous Fringillidae family, or *tyrannids* for the tyrant flycatchers (Tyrannidae), or *parulids* for the New World warblers (Parulidae). Such derivatives are more accurate designations than merely "warblers" or "flycatchers," of which there are unrelated Old World groups, while "sparrow" or "finch" family is very misleading because it includes buntings, grosbeaks, cardinals, and many other fringillids. Family names are based on a generic name (type genus) within the family (e.g., Gaviidae—loons—is based on the type genus *Gavia*).

Chapter 15 lists the 27 orders and 171 families of living birds. The beginning student, rather than trying to memorize these, should gradually familiarize himself with those found in his locality. Regional check-lists are usually available for this purpose.

*Fig. 19. Bill and foot characteristics of four falconiform families. From top to bottom: Turkey Vulture (Cathartidae), showing perforate nostril and comparatively weak foot with reduced hind toe; Red-shouldered Hawk (Accipitridae), showing imperforate nostril and more strongly developed, grasping foot; Osprey*

## GENERA, SPECIES, AND SUBSPECIES

The next commonly used unit in the subdivision of a family is the genus (plural, genera), a category composed of one to many closely related forms (presumably of common phylogenetic origin) known as species. Van Tyne and Berger (1959) merely define the genus as "a taxonomic group more comprehensive than the species but less comprehensive than the family (or subfamily)." Nomenclaturally the generic term is of special importance, since specific and subspecific names are attached to it, and family names, and sometimes ordinal names, are based on an included genus (e.g., *Gavia*, Gaviidae, Gaviiformes). Genera can be *monotypic*, of only one species, or *polytypic*, of two or more species. Genera are distinguished by minor variations (smaller than the family differences) in the bill, tarsus, feet, primaries, and to some extent color patterns.

Species, the real structural units in the classification, are defined by Mayr (1942) as ". . . groups of actually or potentially interbreeding natural populations, which are reproductively isolated from other such groups." This gives a biological concept, as opposed to the older morphological concept, to the definition of a species. Actually, in defining all taxonomic units, there are increasing attempts to utilize all available information, including morphological, ecological, and genetic. Sometimes details in life histories—nests, eggs, development of young, and breeding behavior—are useful in determining the closeness of relationships between different species, or between different groups. Even the nature of egg-white proteins (McCabe and Deutsch, 1952; Sibley, 1960) and serological studies (Stallcup, 1961) are used to help determine kinship.

The species is usually the smallest systematic unit recognized in the field, but specialists working closely with many individuals from different parts of a species' range are often able to sort them out into geographic groups—eastern, western, southern, desert, coastal—which are known as geographic races or subspecies. Unlike species, subspecies interbreed freely when they come together, and differ only in inconstant and overlapping measurements and intensity of color (duller, darker, paler, smaller). The first half of this century has witnessed a prodigious build-up of described

---

*(Pandionidae), showing strongly hooked beak, long claws, scaly sole and reversible outer toe; Prairie Falcon (Falconidae), showing circular nostril with bony central tubercle and beak with notch and tooth. (Drawings by R. H. Naik from specimens in Mich. State Univ. collections.)*

subspecies, creating a confusing situation in many animal groups (e.g., 36 races of Song Sparrows). Now the pendulum seems to be swinging the other way, with the suggestion of dropping or minimizing trinomials (subspecies names), but continuing with the study of geographic variations in populations without applying names to them (Borgmeier, 1957; Edwards, 1956; Pimentel, 1959).

The scientific name of a bird consists of the generic name, capitalized and put in italics (or underlined in script), followed by the species name and then the subspecies, if there are subspecies. Thus the full name for the Atlantic Song Sparrow is *Melospiza* (which designates the generic group to which the Song Sparrows and several other sparrows belong) *melodia* (for the species group or whole Song Sparrow complex) *atlantica* (for the coastal race), followed by the name of the describer, in this case Todd (*Melospiza melodia atlantica* Todd). If one wishes to speak of Song Sparrows without designating a particular race, only the binomial *Melospiza melodia* is used. It is now approved practice for field observers to use only the binomial, as the particular subspecies involved is usually difficult to determine, except by assumption on purely geographical grounds (Fig. 20).

The division of families into genera and species has varied greatly in the past. The current trend is to reduce the number of genera by lumping similar ones, and the number currently recognized is probably of no great moment to beginning ornithologists. The number of species, however, is of great interest, but unfortunately has been much confused by the failure

*Fig. 20. Screech Owls, like Song Sparrows, are divisible into numerous subspecies; 18 are recognized in North America north of Mexico, still others occur south of the border. This one is presumed to be an Eastern Screech Owl* (Otus asia asio) *because it was found in Michigan, but its subspecific identification could be determined only by careful study, usually by comparing it with other specimens in a good reference collection. (Photo by Dale A. Zimmerman.)*

to distinguish between species and subspecies, a situation aggravated by earlier ornithologists according specific rank to many birds now reduced to subspecies. Consequently one sees statements of the number of species of birds varying from about 8,000 to 30,000, depending on the number of subspecies included in the count.

Now, however, Mayr's (1946a) conservative count of about 8,600 distinct species seems to be generally accepted. His estimate of the total number of valid forms (including the subspecies) was about 28,500 in 1946 with the number of described subspecies increasing at the rate of about 200 per year. Consequently, we can say that the number of birds recognized in the world today is about 8,600 species and 30,000 forms (species and subspecies). The former number will probably remain relatively constant except for re-evaluations of the specific status of already known birds, as there are probably few undiscovered species anywhere in the world, but the number of subspecies is increasing rapidly as further exploration and work on museum collections continues.

The slowness of discovery of really new species—a feature that should be of interest to beginning students who so frequently "discover" a new bird—is well illustrated by work in North America. The last North American species of unquestionable status was described in 1889, when the Colima Warbler, a rare form of restricted distribution in Texas and northern Mexico, was discovered. In 1919 a new sparrow (the Cape Sable) was described from Florida, but its specific status has been questioned from time to time, although it is still retained as a full species in the A.O.U. check-list (1957). Much excitement was aroused in 1939 by the discovery of "Sutton's" Warbler (*Dendroica potomac*) in West Virginia, but further study of this new form, its sudden appearance and subsequent disappearance, led to the conclusion that it was probably a hybrid and not a true species.

Hence, we may conclude that the finding of any radically new North American birds is unlikely. New species from other parts of the world appear at the rate of one to several a year, the discoveries resulting from further exploration in the less known regions of the earth, or from working over old museum collections.

## Selected References

American Ornithologists' Union. *Check-List of North American Birds*. 5th ed. Lancaster, Pa.: Amer. Ornith. Union, 1957.

de Beer, Sir Gavin. *Archaeopteryx lithographica.* London: British Mus. Nat. Hist., 1954.

Hegner, Robert W., and Karl A. Stiles. *College Zoology.* New York: Macmillan, 1959. Chapt. 1, 22, and 29.

Heilmann, Gerhard. *The Origin of Birds.* New York: Appleton, 1927.

Mayr, Ernst. *Systematics and the Origin of Species.* New York: Columbia U.P., 1942.

———, E. Gorton Linsley, and Robert L. Usinger. *Methods and Principles of Systematic Zoology.* New York: McGraw, 1953.

Peters, J. L. *Birds of the World.* Cambridge, Mass.: Harvard U.P., 1931–1951. Vol. 1–7.

Storer, Robert W. The Classification of Birds. Chapt. III in A. J. Marshall's *Biology and Comparative Physiology of Birds.* New York: Academic, 1960.

Swinton, W. E. The Origin of Birds. Chapt. I in A. J. Marshall's *Biology and Comparative Physiology of Birds.* New York: Academic, 1960.

Van Tyne, Josselyn, and Andrew J. Berger. *Fundamentals of Ornithology.* New York: Wiley, 1959. Chapt. 12.

Wetmore, Alexander. *A Classification for the Birds of the World.* Smithsonian Misc. Coll. (1960), **139**(11):1–37.

# 3

# EXTERNAL FEATURES AND THEIR ADAPTATIONS

This chapter and the three following it deal with some of the anatomical and physiological features of birds. This first chapter in the series discusses the external parts, mainly the feathery covering and other epidermal derivatives. Since laboratory manuals and textbooks of anatomy commonly outline or describe organs and organ systems in detail, description of structures is minimized here, but considerable attention is given to the role that various morphological features play in the life of a bird.

## *Topography*

In descriptions of birds, reference is commonly made to regions of the body and to features of the bill, wings, feet, and tail. These body regions (e.g., *nape, jugulum, crissum*), feather groups (e.g., *primaries, rectrices*), and associated structures (e.g., *mandibles, hallux*) constitute the topography of a bird (Fig. 21).

## *Feathers*

### ORIGIN AND DEVELOPMENT

Phylogenetically, feathers are believed to have been derived from reptilian scales in Mesozoic times, when the elongated loose scales that

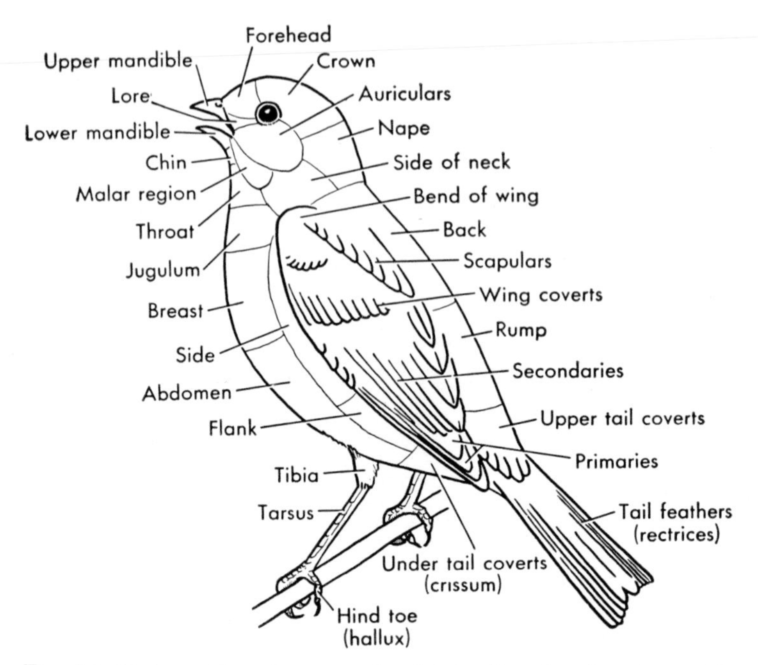


*Fig. 21. Topography of a passerine bird. (Drawing by Homer D. Roberts.)*

occurred on certain birdlike reptiles of that period may have developed fringed margins. Some such covering was indispensable for heat retention, and feathers probably developed more or less synchronously with warm-bloodedness, though some authors maintain that warm-bloodedness preceded feather development and occurred in the pterodactyls. Hence, development of feathers may have been an adaptational response to protect accelerated metabolism. Actually, the transition from reptilian scales to feathers has never been demonstrated, but Rawles (1960) states that transition from scales to feathers has been observed in domestic fowl. Scales and feathers have a common origin; both develop from similar germ buds which on the bare tarsus of the Bald Eagle, for instance, give rise to scales, and on the tarsus of a Golden Eagle, grouse, or owl give rise to feathers.

A feather begins its development as a *papilla* (Fig. 22) which thrusts up the overlying epidermis, the outer layer (of stratum corneum) forming the sheath of the feather, the inner layer composed of the future feather parts which arise from a germinating ring or collar at the base of the papilla. The central dermal pulp cavity contains blood vessels which carry nutrients and color pigments to the growing feather, but as the struc-

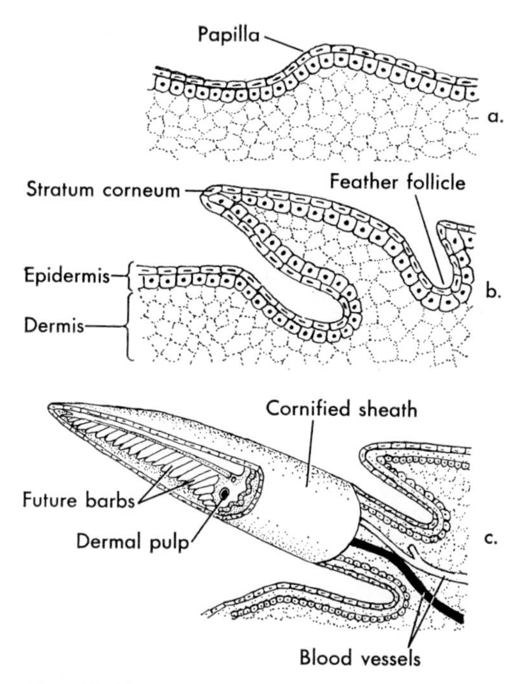


*Fig. 22. Development of a feather. a. Origin of the feather papilla. b. Continued growth of papilla. c. Unfolding of maturing feather. (From Storer's,* General Zoology, *copyright 1943 by McGraw-Hill Book Co., Inc., New York. Redrawn by R. M. Naik.)*

ture matures the surrounding sheath is shed or preened off, the feather parts unfold and harden, and the blood supply is shut off. The result is a structure composed entirely of dead cornified epidermis. The base of the feather is imbedded in a pit or *follicle* from which another feather will arise when the first is molted.

In early development two types of feathers are recognized: (1) *neossoptiles,* which constitute the downy plumage of newly hatched birds, and (2) *teleoptiles,* the adult-type feathers (probably including adult down in species that have adult down) which replace the neossoptiles. Papers by Lillie and co-workers (1932–1944) should be consulted by those who wish further information on the physiology of feather development.

## STRUCTURE

Figure 23 illustrates a flight feather and its parts. It consists of a flattened *vane* or *webs* (inner and outer) supported by a central *shaft* com-

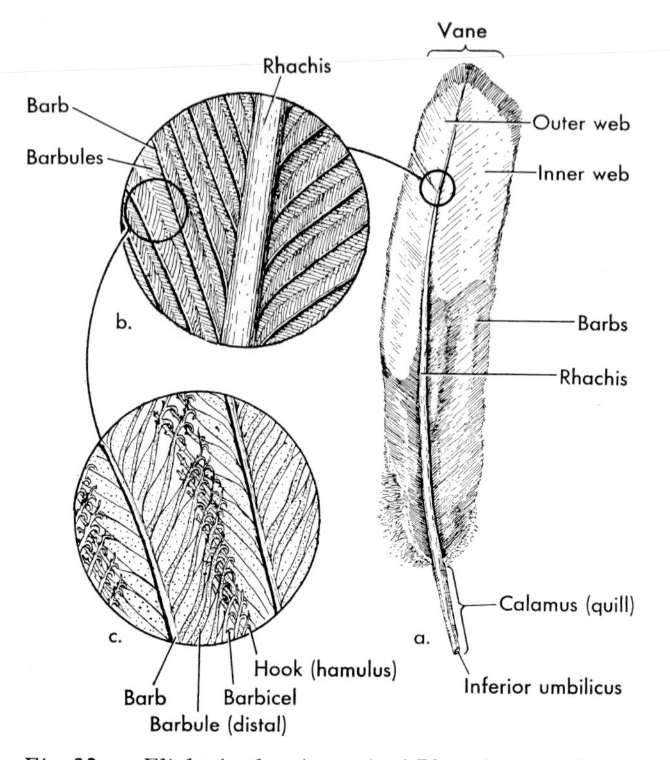


*Fig. 23. a. Flight feather (remex) of Plantain-eater (Musophagidae). b. Enlargement of portion of vane, showing arrangement of barbs and barbules. c. Further enlargement of barbs and barbules, showing interlocking arrangement. (Drawings by R. M. Naik.)*

posed of a pith-filled *rhachis* (webbed portion) and a tubular *quill* or *calamus* (webless portion). The *inferior* (lower) *umbilicus* is the opening into the calamus through which nutrients and pigments were originally supplied to the developing feather. A *superior* (upper) *umbilicus* occurs at the junction of the calamus and rhachis. In some birds a prominent *aftershaft* (Fig. 24b) is present, notably in the Emu, where it is nearly as long as the main feather, and in such galliform birds as grouse, pheasants, and quail, where it undoubtedly has real insulation value. The aftershaft is believed to be of a primitive character, but it has been independently lost, reduced, or retained in so many unrelated groups of birds that its evolutionary significance is not evident.

The outer and inner webs of the primaries are unequal, with the outer edge narrower than the inner. Both webs, but particularly the inner, are

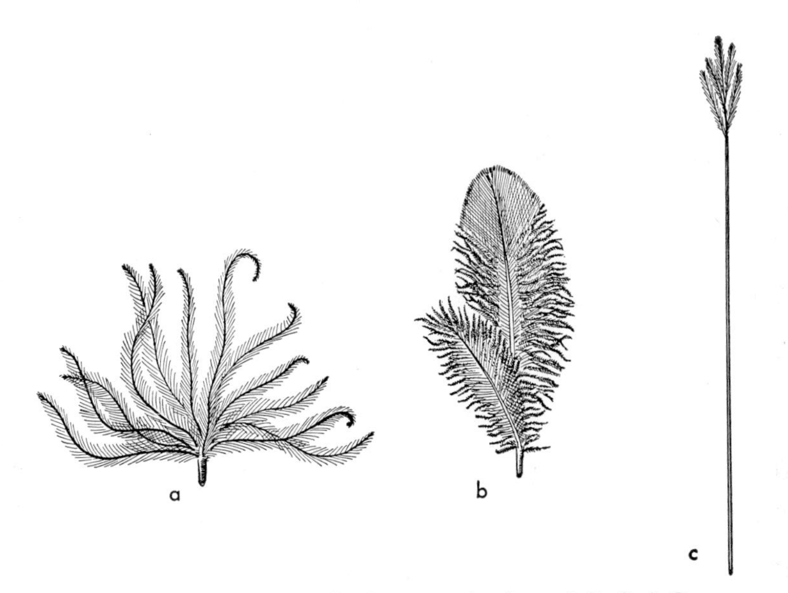


*Fig. 24. a. Down feather. b. Contour feather of Ruffed Grouse, showing aftershaft. c. Filoplume. (Drawings by Homer D. Roberts.)*

sometimes notched or emarginate toward the tip to provide for "slotting" which is of importance for many birds in flight (p. 114).

The webbed portion of the feather consists of a parallel series of closely spaced *barbs* (about 600 pairs in a pigeon primary) on either side of the rhachis, and each barb in turn gives rise to a series of *barbules* (several hundred pairs per barb) which overlap and interlock with the barbules of adjacent barbs. Figure 23c shows this interlocking mechanism, which consists of a series of microscopic *barbicels* with little hooks or *hamuli* on the *distal* or *anterior* barbules (those directed toward the tip of the feather) which overlap and hook onto the rolled edge of the *proximal* or *posterior* barbules (those directed toward the base of the feather). Both the distal and proximal barbules have barbicels, but only the distal have hamuli. This somewhat limited sliding arrangement of barbules gives flexibility to the feather while at the same time making it sufficiently rigid to be relatively impervious to air and water. The interlocking parts are readily pulled apart, as can be demonstrated by separating the barbs on a chicken feather, but they can be slipped in place again by pulling them through closed fingers. Birds repair such damaged feathers in preening by drawing them through their bill.

Some loosely plumaged flightless birds, such as the ostrichlike birds and the kiwis, lack this interlocking mechanism; still other species have a scarcity of barbules in certain feathers. The dorsal plumes of the egrets (Fig. 26), for instance, and the lax body feathers of many tropical birds are largely devoid of barbules.

The complete feather, then, is an exceedingly lightweight but durable and efficient structure, whose complexity is well illustrated by the many functional parts described above. A single pigeon primary consists of more than a million parts.

## FUNCTIONS OF FEATHERS

Feathers serve a variety of important protective and decorative functions. Feathers furnish the bird with an admirably lightweight yet durable covering; lightness is an obvious asset in flight, durability a protection against mechanical or physiological injury to the tender skin. Plumages are generally quite waterproof, for though a bird may deliberately soak itself in bathing, it can shed water effectively during rains. A duck's closely imbricated feathers, with the aid of secretions from the oil gland (p. 65), are structurally waterproof, but matting of the feathers by oil pollution causes a loss of trapped air so that a duck loses buoyancy and cannot stay afloat. Some birds, however, do not have a waterproof plumage. Cormorants and snake-birds, which pursue fish underwater, get thoroughly soaked with each plunge and then perch on rocks, piers, or trees to dry out. The related frigate-birds, which inhabit oceanic islands, avoid contact with water by gleaning food from the surface or by robbing other birds; if accidentally submerged, they may get waterlogged and drown. Tropical species with a lax plumage often get drenched, sometimes deliberately bathing, in the frequent showers characteristic of the rain forests, but dry out in the intermittent periods of sunshine. Leaf bathing, as described for Mockingbirds in California (Abbott, 1954), serves the same function; the birds fly into and rub against wet leaves.

Perhaps the most important physiological function of feathers is heat retention. Feathers are the most efficient type of insulation known, for birds maintain extremely high body temperatures, commonly 104° to 112°F., even in subzero weather. The feathers of a bird are full of dead air spaces, especially when fluffed out. Fluffing out the feathers, an arrangement made feasible by special muscles in the skin, increases the depth of insulating material by adding to the air spaces within the feathery layers. Thus heat loss is reduced to a minimum. Conversely, in warm weather, the feathers are often depressed or held close to the body to allow some escape of body heat. Feathers also function in courtship displays and for sex recognition (p. 46).

## KINDS OF FEATHERS

Feathers are commonly divided, on the basis of function and location, into the various kinds listed below:

1. *Contour* feathers—Typically, feathers with shaft and vane, covering body, wings, and tail.
    *a.* General body feathers.
    *b.* Wing feathers (*remiges*), divided in primaries and secondaries.
    *c.* Tail feathers (*rectrices*).
2. *Semiplumes*—Feathers with a prominent shaft but downy web, lacking the interlocking mechanism of contour feathers. Interspersed with and concealed by the latter.
3. *Down* feathers—Soft feathers with a minute shaft (except in adult duck down), the barbs usually arising as a fluffy tuft from the end of the quill; provides the natal covering of newly hatched birds and appears as an undercoat on some adult birds (Fig. 24a).
4. *Filoplumes*—Minute hairlike feathers with a slender barbless shaft and inconspicuous tuft of weak barbs and barbules at tip (Fig. 24c); occur among the contour feathers.
5. *Rictal* bristles—Hairlike feathers, with rudimentary barbs at base, around the *rictus* (base of bill) of such birds as flycatchers (Fig. 36c) and goatsuckers; may be modified contour feathers.
6. *Powder downs*—Feathers producing a powdery substance best seen as paired pectoral and pelvic yellowish patches on herons and bitterns; probably derived from disintegrating down that persists throughout life.

*Fig. 25. a. Ornamental head plume of Gambel's Quail. b. Flash patch of Ruby-crowned Kinglet (male). c. Topknot of Cardinal. (Drawings by Dale A. Zimmerman.)*

Obviously the prevailing feathers of a bird are the contour feathers. Though the chief function of these is to provide a warm protective covering and to serve as implements of flight (wing and tail feathers), on some parts of the body they become modified for a great variety of ornamental functions. On many birds the crown feathers (Fig. 25) are modified into crests or topknots (Cardinal), ornamental plumes (Gambel's Quail) or colored "flash" patches (kinglets). Other birds have special ruffs (Ruffed Grouse) or pinnae (Prairie Chicken) about the neck (Fig. 91), that are utilized in courtship displays. Special upper tail coverts in the peacocks, "aigrettes" or breeding plumes in certain herons and egrets (Fig. 26), highly specialized tail feathers in many birds, and the most fantastic decorations (probably modified contour feathers) of the birds of paradise (Fig. 93) serve a similar sexual purpose. Other modifications seem more practical, as in the spine-tipped rectrices of Chimney Swifts and woodpeckers which facilitate clinging to vertical surfaces; a long or broad tail fan may be both ornamental and useful in flight, as in pheasants and turkeys, and

*Fig. 26. Common Egret feeding young. The dorsal plumes (aigrettes) of egrets were once worth $32 an ounce in the millinery trade and nearly brought about extermination of the birds. (Photo by Allan D. Cruickshank.)*

as in the lengthened outer rectrices of the Barn Swallow which presumably give added grace and maneuverability.

Semiplumes are interspersed, rather sparingly in some birds, among the other body (contour) feathers, especially along the edges of the feather tracts. Sometimes they have been classed as contour feathers, sometimes as down, but various degrees of intergradation occur between the two types. When present in sufficient quantity, semiplumes add insulation and buoyancy.

Down feathers are of special importance as the natal covering in birds that are born in an advanced state of development (pheasants, ducklings) and as a dense undercoat in many aquatic birds. In ducks a special down is grown by the females in spring and plucked for lining the nest.

Powder-down feathers, already adequately described, are found in quite a few diverse groups of birds besides the herons and bitterns. Young herons, which lack a functional oil gland at first, constantly rub the bill over the powder-down tracts, suggesting that they function as a substitute for the oil gland in such birds.

## NUMBER OF FEATHERS

The number of feathers on a bird and its significance in relation to size, rate of metabolism, season of year, and phylogenetic relationship was largely neglected in biological studies of birds until 1933, when the Smithsonian Institution sponsored an ambitious feather-counting project. The initial counts, made on 153 birds of 79 species, mostly passerines, disclosed fewer feathers on the smaller birds, with the lowest number (940) on a Ruby-throated Hummingbird and the highest number (2,973) on a Robin, which was one of the largest birds used in the count. A male Hairy Woodpecker had 375 more feathers than a male Downy Woodpecker. Two Eastern Phoebes, collected at about the same time, had a difference of only two feathers. An interesting seasonal adaptation was that birds had their thinnest plumage in late summer and their densest covering in winter. An American Goldfinch in winter plumage had nearly a thousand more feathers than one in summer plumage.

Since these studies were made chiefly on passerine birds, the few counts available for nonpasserines are of interest. One of the earliest of these was undertaken by a dairyman to settle an argument as to how many feathers there are on a chicken. He counted 8,325 on a Plymouth Rock.

Another count on a Mallard hen disclosed 11,903 feathers. Apparently the highest count ever made was on a Whistling Swan which had 25,216 contour feathers. However, 80 per cent of these were of the small feathers on the head and neck, so that the rest of the body plumage was not notably dense. In fact, if body size is taken into consideration, it is found that the smaller birds generally have more feathers per unit of body weight than the larger birds, a fact no doubt correlated with the heat-retention needs of the smaller forms, which in general have a higher rate of metabolism (Hutt and Ball, 1938). Table 3 gives some sample feather counts for both passerine and nonpasserine birds. High feather counts on such birds as the Pied-billed Grebe, Pintail, American Coot, and owls are of particular interest; the grebe had more than twice as many feathers as the larger, more coarsely feathered eagle, no doubt reflecting the need for better insulation in aquatic birds.

*Table 3. Feather Counts of Representative Birds*

| *Species* | *Sex* | *Date* | *Number of Feathers* | *Reference* |
|---|---|---|---|---|
| Pied-billed Grebe | ♀ | Dec. 30 | 15,016 | Brodkorb, 1949 |
| Least Bittern | ♂ | May 20 | 3,867 | Brodkorb, 1949 |
| Whistling Swan | — | Nov. 5 | 25,216 | Ammann, 1937 |
| Mallard | ♀ | Mar. 19 | 11,903 | Knappen, 1932 |
| Pintail | ♂ | Jan. 28 | 14,914 | Brodkorb, 1949 |
| Bald Eagle | imm. | Jan. — | 7,182 | Brodkorb, 1955 |
| Plymouth Rock | — | — | 8,325 | Wetmore, 1936 |
| Coot | ♂ | Nov. 16 | 13,913 | Brodkorb, 1949 |
| Least Sandpiper | ♀ | Apr. 30 | 4,480 | Brodkorb, 1949 |
| Screech Owl | ♂ | Feb. 18 | 6,458 | Brodkorb, 1949 |
| Barred Owl | ♂ | June 24 | 9,206 | Brodkorb, 1949 |
| Common Nighthawk | ♀ | July 9 | 2,034* | Wetmore, 1936 |
| Common Nighthawk | ♀ | Apr. 30 | 3,332 | Brodkorb, 1949 |
| Ruby-throated Hummingbird | ♂ | June 11 | 940* | Wetmore, 1936 |
| Ruby-throated Hummingbird | ♀ | May 15 | 1,518 | Brodkorb, 1949 |
| Hairy Woodpecker | ♂ | Apr. 23 | 2,395 | Wetmore, 1936 |
| Downy Woodpecker | ♂ | Mar. 26 | 2,020 | Wetmore, 1936 |
| (Northern) Blue Jay | ♂ | Oct. 8 | 1,898* | Wetmore, 1936 |
| (Southern) Blue Jay (juv.) | ♀ | July 25 | 3,773 | Brodkorb, 1949 |
| Brown Thrasher | ♂ | June 11 | 1,960* | Wetmore, 1936 |
| Brown Thrasher (juv.) | ♀ | July 9 | 3,379 | Brodkorb, 1949 |
| House Sparrow | ♂ | July 2 | 1,359* | Wetmore, 1936 |
| House Sparrow | ♂ | July 5 | 3,138 | Staebler, 1941 |
| Brown-headed Cowbird | ♀ | July 2 | 1,622* | Wetmore, 1936 |
| Brown-headed Cowbird | ♂ | Feb. 21 | 4,297 | Wing, 1952 |

* There appears to be no ready explanation of why Wetmore's counts run so much lower than subsequent counts on the same species.

## PTERYLOSIS

The contour feathers of a bird, it may be noted by plucking a fowl or by examining a nestling Robin, are not evenly distributed over the whole body but are arranged in special tracts. These feather tracts are called *pterylae,* the featherless areas between the tracts are called *apteria;* together they account for the distribution or arrangement of feathers over the bird's body which is known as *pterylosis.* Both the feathered and the featherless areas are named according to the regions where they occur. There are eight (or more in many species) feather tracts, as designated in Fig. 27, usually with adjacent apteria.

The pterylae can be subdivided further. The *capital tract,* for instance, can be divided into *frontal, coronal, occipital, loreal,* and *auricular* regions to denote special parts of the head (R. E. Stewart, 1952b). In a few birds, such as the Ostrich and the penguins, feather tracts are lacking, and in densely plumaged birds the apteria are reduced and sometimes, as in the ducks, covered with down.

## PLUMAGES AND MOLTS

Birds periodically renew their plumage by shedding and replacing their old feathers in a process called *molting.* Nearly all birds have one com-

*Fig. 27. Feather tracts and apteria in the Yellowthroat. a. Dorsal view, showing subdivisions (regions) of the capital tract. b. Ventral view. (From R. E. Stewart,* Auk, *69, 1952. Redrawn by Homer D. Roberts.)*

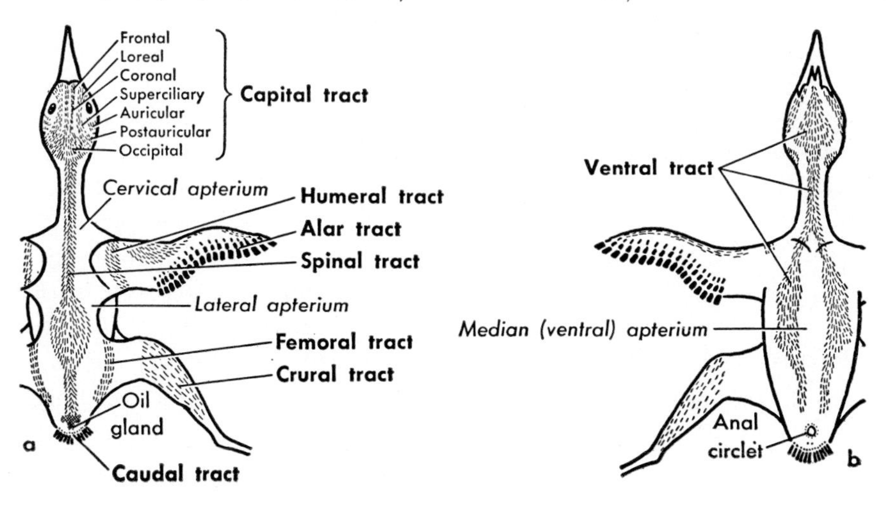

plete annual molt, usually in late summer after nesting, and some birds have an additional complete, nearly complete, or partial molt in the spring before the breeding season. The various plumages worn by birds at different ages and seasons and the molts producing them may be summarized as follows:

| *Plumage* | | *Molt* |
|---|---|---|
| Natal down | lost by | postnatal |
| Juvenal | lost by | postjuvenal |
| First winter | lost by | first prenuptial |
| First nuptial (breeding) | lost by | first postnuptial (annual) |

These four molts and plumages carry the bird through its first year. Then its second winter plumage may, in many cases, differ in appearance from the first winter plumage, and its second nuptial plumage may likewise differ from the first nuptial. Some birds require more than two years to reach maturity and thus may have third, fourth, and even fifth winter and nuptial plumages before assuming fully adult dress. The larger gulls commonly require three or four years to attain their immaculate white and gray-mantled plumage, and in Bald Eagles it is three to five years or more before the symbolic white of the head and tail is complete.

In many colorful passerines the second-year coat of feathers (first breeding season) may be a mixture of new (colorful) and old (brownish) feathers. The Indigo Bunting in its second year may be mottled with brownish, rather than uniformly blue, and its remiges and rectrices are brown rather than black. The Rose-breasted Grosbeak, American Redstart, and Scarlet Tanager have mixed feathering in their second year. The spring plumage of all birds is usually referred to as nuptial regardless of whether or not they are breeding, or in full plumage.

Recently Humphrey and Parks (1959) have called attention to many long known inconsistencies in the terminology used for molts and plumages and have proposed a new classification. Inconsistencies include use of age (natal, juvenal), sexual condition (nuptial), and time or season (annual, winter) in describing molts and plumages, whereas these terms often do not apply on a world-wide basis. "Nuptial," for example, is used for the plumage worn in the spring regardless of whether or not there has been a feather change, and regardless of whether or not the species in question is breeding. Seasonal terms, devised largely for the northern hemisphere, do not apply in other parts of the world. Pending further study, they propose to retain the present terms of natal and juvenal plumages, but to call the first winter plumage (and all subsequent plumages if there is no real feather change in the spring) the basic plumage which is attained by a prebasic (rather than postjuvenal) molt. However, in birds that have a real feather change in the spring, an additional term, the alternate plumage, attained by a prealternate molt, is proposed. Hence, the sequence of plumages and molts they propose is:

| | |
|---|---|
| Natal down | postnatal molt |
| Juvenal plumage | first prebasic molt |
| First basic plumage | first prealternate molt |
| First alternate plumage | second prebasic molt |

Using the old terminology, the following brief description explains the sequence, and some of the variations, in the molts and plumages of birds. The young are hatched with a covering of natal down (neossoptiles), completely investing the body in *precocial* (born in an advanced stage of development) birds like ducks and gallinaceous birds (Fig. 28), or more or less sparsely distributed in tracts, as in *altricial* (born in a more immature stage) birds. Some birds (e.g., woodpeckers, kingfishers, and some passerines) are born naked; usually these go directly into juvenal plumage without an apparent down stage. A few birds (the megapodes or mound builders in Australia) actually pass through the down stage in the egg and are covered with juvenal plumage and able to fly at hatching time. For further information on the natal plumages of North American passerines, see Wetherbee (1957).

The natal down is pushed outward (postnatal molt) on the tips of the

*Fig. 28. Sharp-tailed Grouse five days old. The young of precocial birds are born with a complete covering of natal down and can usually run from the nest soon after hatching. (Photo by Mich. Dept. of Conservation.)*

incoming juvenal plumage which first appears as stiff quills whose confining sheaths gradually rupture to unfold the juvenal feathers (Fig. 29). The familiar spotted plumage of a young Robin, with wisps of natal down still clinging to the other feathers, is a good example of this stage. Then, usually in late summer (July to September), follows a postjuvenal molt, in which the fluffy juvenal feathers are shed and replaced by the feathers of the fall and winter plumage. Most young birds complete their postjuvenal molt before migration, but most of the swallows and some of the *Empidonax* flycatchers (Mengel, 1952) migrate *before* molting. In Anna's Hummingbird in California, both the adults and young move to their wintering grounds (not a great distance) before undergoing their postnuptial and postjuvenal molts (Aldrich, 1956). At the other extreme, woodpeckers complete their postjuvenal molt in the nest cavity (Sibley, 1957).

The postjuvenal molt usually involves only the general body feathers, not the remiges and rectrices which are retained in most species until the following year. This feature often makes it possible to distinguish the young from adults in the fall, as the somewhat worn wing or tail feathers of the young, acquired soon after hatching in spring or early summer, may be distinguishable from the relatively unfrayed wing or tail feathers of the adults, acquired during the late summer molt. To use this slight distinction accurately, as in age determinations of game birds in the fall,

*Fig. 29. These Brown Thrashers are in juvenal plumage, but show wisps of natal down still adhering to the juvenal feathers. (Photo by Edward M. Brigham, Jr., courtesy of* Jack-Pine Warbler.)

one needs to be thoroughly familiar with the sequence of feather replacement in the species involved. There are some exceptions to the general rule of retention of the juvenal remiges and rectrices, however. The Yellow-breasted Chat (Dennis, 1958a) and the Common Yellowthroat (R. E. Stewart, 1952b), for example, replace their juvenal plumage completely, including wing and tail feathers, during the postjuvenal molt.

The next plumage change occurs in late winter or early spring, when a so-called prenuptial molt produces the nuptial (breeding) plumage. Relatively few birds have a complete molt at this time, though many have a partial replacement of feathers. In other species, the spring dress is acquired by fading (no feather change) or by the wearing off of buffy feather tips worn in winter. The breeding plumage of the brown-backed woodland thrushes, for instance, is only imperceptibly grayer (less brownish) than that worn in fall and winter. The male Bobolink's handsome black and white nuptial plumage, though acquired by an early prenuptial molt (February or March), is largely concealed by buffy feather tips which wear off before he reaches his summer home. Less perceptible is the wearing off of the gray-tipped feathers on the black throat of the House Sparrow. The American Goldfinch is one of the less usual cases of actual plumage replacement in spring. New body feathers, but not new remiges and rectrices, account for the striking change in this species from its dull winter plumage to the black and gold of spring and summer.

After the breeding season, in July, August, or September for most northern hemisphere species, birds undergo a complete postnuptial or annual molt in which all of the feathers, including the remiges and rectrices, are replaced. The molt is usually prolonged and gradual, lasting several weeks to several months. The Clark's Nutcracker, for instance, requires up to five months to complete the molt and may start it while still in breeding condition (Mewaldt, 1958). Many birds go into partial retirement at this time, cease singing and become relatively inactive, even fasting in some cases. Richdale (1951b) reports that a molting Yellow-eyed Penguin fasts for twenty-four days. Growing a completely new plumage undoubtedly imposes a severe physiological drain on the bird, which generally restricts its physical activities. Typically the feathers are shed a few at a time, region by region, so that the molting bird may appear somewhat ragged and unkempt, a patchwork of old and new feathers. The flight feathers are usually shed one after another in a definite sequence, more or less synchronously from each wing, with new feathers replacing those lost rapidly enough so that a bird is seldom deprived of flight during the molt. Exceptions occur among the ducks and rails, which shed all their flight feathers more or less at once and are temporarily unable to fly. The American Coot is largely flightless for about four weeks, and like other rallids skulks and hides in the marshes during this period (Gullion, 1953a).

The eclipse plumage in ducks, which is a dull, henlike plumage assumed by most drakes in the northern hemisphere during the summer, is quite exceptional among birds. It is usually considered an arrested fall and winter plumage, brought on prematurely by an early postnuptial molt in May or June, which is merged or overlaps with a hastened prenuptial molt so that the drake attains its breeding plumage (and sometimes starts courtship and mating) in the fall or winter instead of waiting until spring. Some authors suggest, however, that the eclipse may be a special molt acquired by male ducks to conceal and protect them during their flightless period; it, or a similar type of molt, is also now known in several families of Old World passerines (Van Tyne and Berger, 1959). There is considerable variation, however, among different ducks, as well as among individuals of the same species, so that drakes may be observed in nearly all stages of plumage in the summer and fall. The hens follow a more normal sequence of molts: a complete postnuptial in the summer, after nesting, and a prenuptial (body feathers and tail) in late winter or early spring, including the shedding of old down and the acquisition of a special nest down.

To a certain extent, birds can shed and replace damaged feathers irrespective of the regular molts, but perhaps it is more usual to retain broken stubs until the time for the next molt. *Pulled* primaries in a captive bird, for instance, or a lost tail, are rather quickly replaced, but a *clipped* wing deprives the bird of flight feathers until the next wing molt, which is usually an annual affair. A *pinioned* bird has the manus (hand) amputated and thus can never grow primaries. *Brailing* merely binds the manus to the forearm and prevents unfolding the wing. It is customary to clip, pinion, or brail only one wing, so that the bird has difficulty getting off the ground, or flies in low circles if it can rise at all. Some strong-winged birds, however, can manage labored flight even when clipped, pinioned, or brailed.

## *Plumage Coloration*

The extraordinarily varied plumage in birds, which runs a gamut of colors and color patterns surpassing in variety and vividness that of any other vertebrates, is due to (1) pigments (*biochromes*), consisting chiefly of *carotenoids* and *melanins*, and (2) structural colors (*schemochromes*) which result from the breaking up and reflection of the different components of white light by the physical structure of the feather. "These two fundamentally different color sources are often so interrelated that, in most cases, the observed coloration is the result of a combination of one or more pigments with structural colors" (Rawles, 1960).

The carotenoids (also called *lipochromes*) are responsible for most of the bright red, orange, and yellow colors in birds (melanins in the red-yellow color range are duller). These occur in a great variety of combinations and intensities, from the brilliant red of the Scarlet Tanager to the "washed out" red of the Hepatic Tanager, or the intense yellow of the American Goldfinch compared to the pale yellow of some of the strains of domestic Canaries. The fat-soluble carotenoids are carried by body fluids into the feather at the time of its formation and after keratinization sets in the fat solvent disappears, leaving the pigment concentrated in the barbs and barbules. Intensity of these colors can be controlled to some extent in domesticated birds by feeding carotenoid-rich foods.

The melanins are the most abundant and widely distributed pigments in birds. They are responsible for the dark pigments (dark browns, grays, and blacks), as well as the duller or lighter shades of red and brown (chestnut, tan). Melanins occur as granules, the darker shades usually in the form of rods or ovals, the lighter as smaller spheres (Rawles, 1960).

A third, less generally known group of pigments are called *porphyrins.* Two of these, found only in African plantain-eaters (Musophagidae), are of special interest. One is *turacin,* a deep red copper pigment found primarily in the wing feathers; the other is *turacoverdin,* a green pigment found in the body plumage.

Structural colors (schemochromes) are due to the physical properties of feathers, the various spectral or rainbow colors being either reflected or absorbed. The bright blue of the Blue Jay, various bluebirds (*Sialia*), or Indigo Bunting, for example, is due to blue light reflected from a layer of blue-producing cells which overlies the melanin-impregnated pigment cells found in the barbs of the feather (Fig. 30). Green feathers in parrots and other noniridescent greens are essentially the same except that a transparent *yellow* layer superimposed on the blue-producing cells modifies would-be blue to green. Looked at in *transmitted* light (instead of *reflected* light) of a microscope, blue feathers appear brown, and green feathers appear yellow, because only the true pigments are then evident. White feathers are devoid of pigments, so that all the light falling on them is reflected as white light; if all were absorbed the effect would be black.

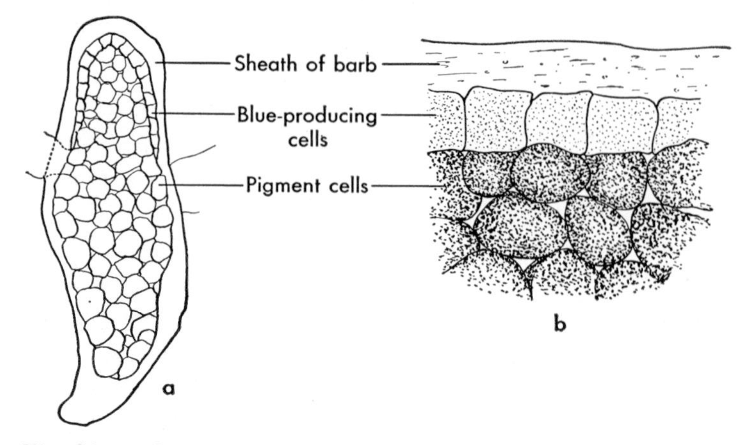


*Fig. 30. a. Cross section of barb of Blue Jay feather. b. Sagittal section of same, showing dorsal portion of sheath, layer of blue-producing cells and underlying pigment cells containing melanin granules. (From Gower,* Auk, **53**, *1936.)*

White plumage is of course normal for many birds—gulls, terns, swans, egrets, to mention only a few—but sometimes in other species the factors responsible for pigment production are lost and *albinism* results. This is particularly true of browns and blacks and is due to lack of melanin-producing cells (*melanophores*). Albinism may be *partial* (Fig. 31l), where the white is limited to certain feathers or regions; *total* (Fig. 31r), where the plumage is entirely white and the eyes red; or *imperfect,* where the pigment is very dilute, resulting in lighter than normal colors. Albinistic birds are usually short-lived because of physical and physiological defects, but Middleton (1960) reported a partial (nearly total) albino Robin which

*Fig. 31. Left, partial albino Robin. (From specimen in Mich. State Univ. Museum.) Right, total albino Robin. (Courtesy of L. H. Walkinshaw.)*

returned to his banding station in Pennsylvania for eight successive years.

The opposite of albinism, or the production of an excess of dark pigments, is known as *melanism,* and explains the dark phases found in birds like the Rough-legged Hawk which has a light or normal phase and a dark phase. Apparently increase in melanin production accounts for the darker geographic races in humid climates; Bowers (1959) has shown that the darker coastal race of the Wrentit in California has more and larger pigment granules than the lighter interior race. *Erythrism* (excess red pigment) is less common, but is well known because of its frequent occurrence in the Screech Owl, which has two color phases, red and gray, a condition known as *dichromatism.* Hrubant (1955) has shown that the gray phase is dominant, as matings of grays produced only grays (fifty-three cases) and no reds or intermediates and matings between red parents were required to produce reds. Sometimes a bird's plumage takes on a superficial hue due to some environmental factor, as when Sandhill Cranes become tinged with reddish brown from the soil (Fig. 32). This is known as *adventitious coloration.*

*Fig. 32. In Alberta, where this photograph was taken, Sandhill Cranes become reddish-brown in the spring from ferric oxide in the muskeg in which they probe with their bills. In preening, a reddish stain is transferred to the plumage. (Photo by L. H. Walkinshaw, courtesy of the Cranbrook Institute of Science.)*

Another familiar color phenomenon is *iridescence,* the interchanging colors so commonly observed on hummingbirds, grackles, and the necks of pigeons. This, in general, is due to interference or unequal dispersion and scattering of light from special feather structure, but iridescence may be modified somewhat by the nature of the underlying pigments.

## USES OF COLORS

During the past century, from Darwin down to present times, there have been many speculations, as well as extensive publications, attempting to explain the meaning and function of the various colors in birds, but these always involve the risk of anthropomorphic interpretations. Many birds are protectively or concealingly colored (*cryptic coloration*), having markings which simulate their surroundings (Fig. 33). Sparrows and marsh birds and many other ground-nesting species are often streaked, resembling the grasses among which they live. Vireos and warblers, often with shades of green and yellow predominating, resemble the foliage of the trees they inhabit and are difficult to detect, especially when they "freeze" in times of danger. Other cryptically colored birds illustrate the principle of *counter-shading,* that is, they are darkest above where they receive the most light and lightest below where they receive the most shadow. Shorebirds on a beach, with their light underparts and darker backs, illustrate this principle. *Disruptive* patterns, as in a Killdeer, may also serve to protect a bird by visually disrupting the birdlike shape.

Still other birds, not necessarily protectively colored, exhibit *deflective coloration,* with conspicuous plumage features which are said to startle,

*Fig. 33. Left, a White-tailed Ptarmigan, crouching among the boulders on Mt. Evans, Colorado, is a good example of concealing coloration. There are at least four ptarmigans in the scene at the right. (From Kodachromes by Mrs. George Wallace.)*

confuse, or deflect the aim of a predator. Thus the flashing white outer tail feathers of birds like juncos, or the white or brightly colored rump patches of the flickers or Killdeer, might divert the aim of a pursuing predator from a vital to a less vulnerable part of the intended victim's body. Observations tend to support these views, but they can be easily overemphasized.

Perhaps even less convincing are some of the theories designed to explain the strikingly marked or brilliantly colored plumages (*epigamic coloration*), which serve to attract mates in the breeding season. Darwin's theory of sexual selection, which presupposes that the females select the most strikingly colored males, has not stood the test of time, but there is no doubt that special markings on many male birds aid in sex recognition and probably sex attraction, and that brilliant plumages often function meaningfully in the elaborate mating season displays and rituals performed by certain birds. In some cases secondary sexual characters, as in peacocks and birds of paradise, have seemingly evolved beyond the point of any apparent practical use, yet having attained this high development it is not likely that such birds could return to simpler patterns and still complete their sexual cycles. Many special markings on birds, however, such as the head patterns and wing marks of sea birds and ducks, are probably primarily for species recognition rather than sex attraction.

Another aspect of coloration is purely utilitarian from man's standpoint. Much of the popularity of birds stems from their pleasing variety of harmonious colors, and of course colors are the chief but not the only criteria for identifying birds either in the field or in the laboratory. Plumages of birds can be very confusing to the beginner, not only because of the many differently marked species, but also because of the wide range of sexual, age, and seasonal variations within a species. Among the adults of some species, for instance, the sexes are marked alike (Blue Jay), or the males may possess some special marking (crown patches of kinglets or facial marks of flickers), or the males may be merely more brightly colored (Cardinal), or of an entirely different plumage (Bobolink). In rare cases the female is the more brightly marked, throughout the year, as in the Belted Kingfisher, or only during the breeding season, as in the phalaropes. Young birds are commonly marked or colored differently than the adults, sometimes differing only from the male (like the female Rose-breasted Grosbeak), sometimes differing from both male and female (Red-headed Woodpecker), while in other cases (crows, jays, titmice) the young and the adults are essentially alike. And as already mentioned, some birds have different first-year, second-year, and third-year plumages, such factors notoriously increasing the difficulties of identification in the gulls. Add to all these such traits as melanism, albinism, and dichromatism, and the beginning ornithologist is truly beset with identification problems.

## Other Integumentary Structures

Though a bird is so fully clothed with feathers that there is limited opportunity for development of other integumentary features, a few such structures occur. Among these are the combs, wattles, and facial decorations common to some gallinaceous birds (poultry, turkeys, pheasants), the pouches and gular sacs of pelicans and cormorants, the spurs on the tarsi of pheasants or on the wings of jaçanas (Jacanidae) and screamers (Anhimidae), and bare areas, often highly colored, on the face (toucans), head (Sandhill Crane), or head and neck (certain vultures). Such structures are usually derivatives of the epidermis, though some of them have a blood supply in the underlying dermis. In most cases they serve a secondary sexual or defensive function, and are regulated by hormones. The frontal shield of the American Coot, which is a continuation of the covering of the maxilla up over the forehead, develops a highly pigmented *callus* in the breeding season which is used for sex recognition and for territorial threats and displays (Gullion, 1951). Similarly the inflatable sacs on the neck of the Prairie Chicken (Fig. 91r) are composed of pigmented integument, but are connected (indirectly) with the lungs to act as a bellows in producing the booming sound heard on the bird's dancing grounds. The pouch of man-o'-war birds (Fig. 34) is a similar structure, but bright red in color, so that a colony of brooding males with inflated sacs is truly a spectacular sight.

*Fig. 34. In the man-o'-war birds, the males possess a bright red inflatable gular sac used for courtship and intimidation displays. The exact inflation mechanism of the pouch is not well known. (Courtesy of Amer. Mus. of Nat. Hist.)*

## *Bills and Feet*

The bills and feet of birds are of great interest to taxonomists because of their importance in determining phylogenetic relationships, and to ecologists because of the many adaptations they show. Perhaps such structures, particularly the bills, have been overused in determining relationships, since similarities may sometimes be deceptive. The similar bills of kingfishers and herons, for instance, do not express genetic relationship, but merely similar food habits, which is a good example of *convergent evolution*. The dissimilar bills of closely related mergansers and diving ducks, on the other hand, reflect different feeding habits and tend to mask genetic relationship, a case of *divergent evolution*. No doubt the large fringillid family, based in part on bill structure, is an artificial category.

The many fascinating adaptations illustrated by the greatly varied bills and feet of birds are of more interest to the beginning student, but these are largely a matter of observation in field and laboratory and need only be briefly summarized here. The development of the avian wing deprived birds of some of the normal functions of the quadruped forelimb, which had to be taken over by the bills and feet. Thus these structures play a diverse role in food gathering, nest building, defense, and aggressive fighting in addition to the more prosaic functions of merely eating and walking.

### BILLS

Figures 35 and 36 illustrate and the following paragraphs describe some of the adaptational modifications of the beaks in birds. The flattened bills of ducks are equipped with strainer plates (*lamellae*) for sifting out submerged food items, but mergansers have serrate mandibles to hold onto slippery fish. Hawks and owls possess powerful hooked beaks, operated by well-developed mandibular muscles, for tearing up prey. Semiaquatic shorebirds have long bills, extremely long in some, for probing into mud and water; the probing bill of the Woodcock, in addition, has a flexible tip on the upper mandible to facilitate seizing an earthworm deep underground. Woodpeckers have strong chisel-like beaks for drilling into wood for food or for nest construction, and have thickened, shock-absorbent bones of the head and strong neck muscles to make such poundings feasible. The effectiveness of the rapierlike probing bill of hummingbirds, amazingly modified to serve special needs in many tropical forms, is ob-

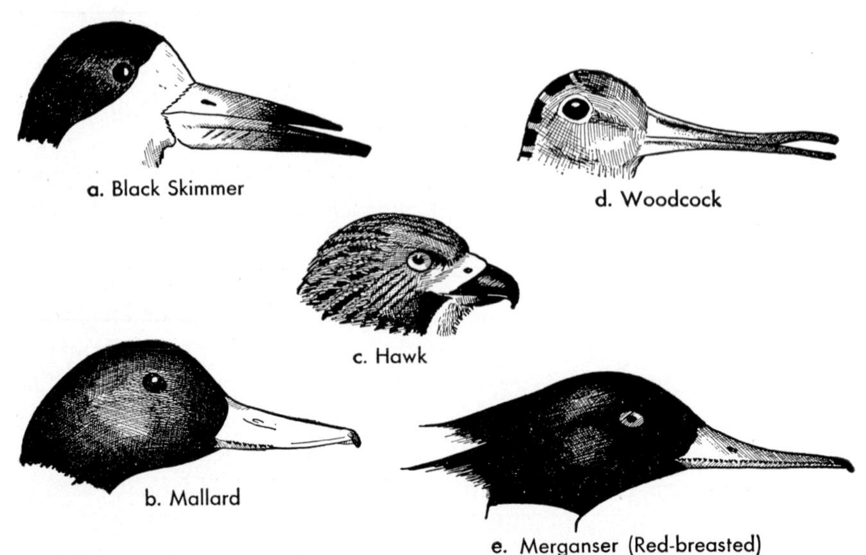


*Fig. 35. Adaptations of bills. a. Black Skimmer, for skimming and cutting surface of water. b. Mallard, with strainer plates for sifting bottom debris. c. Hawk, strongly hooked for tearing up prey. d. Woodcock, for probing in mud, with flexible tip on upper mandible. e. Red-breasted Merganser, with saw-toothed margins for holding fish. (Drawings by Homer D. Roberts.)*

*Fig. 36. Adaptations of bills. a. Downy Woodpecker, for drumming, and drilling in trees. b. Evening Grosbeak, for cracking seeds. c. Kingbird, strong and depressed (flattened) with notch at tip and rictal bristles at base (tyrant flycatchers snap up insects in the air with a loud click of the bill). (Drawings by Homer D. Roberts.)*

vious. Swifts and swallows, which scoop up their prey into open mouths while on the wing, have small bills while flycatchers which snap onto similar insect fare have strong, flattened, notched mandibles beset with rictal bristles at the base. Insectivorous foliage gleaners like warblers and vireos have small slender bills, whereas short stout bills for crushing seeds are characteristic of seed-eaters.

Like some fantastic plumage decorations, some peculiar bills have developed to a stage where they fail to show any readily apparent adaptational use, as in the enormous spongy beak of the toucans (Fig. 37) and

*Fig. 37. The enormous beak of a toucan seems unwieldy, but it is spongy in character and exceedingly light. Though its length serves a useful purpose in reaching for fruit and its bright colors may serve for sexual displays or species recognition, there is no readily apparent advantage for so large a bill. (Courtesy of N.Y. Zool. Soc.)*

the crested casque of the hornbills (Fig. 114). On the other hand, the dextrally curved beak of the Wrybill Plover (*Anarhynchus frontalis*) of New Zealand is said to function admirably for extracting prey from beneath the edges of stones which the bird circles in a clockwise direction. The peculiar bill of the Black Skimmer (Fig. 35a) serves the unique skimming purpose implied in the name; the thin, bladelike lower mandible cuts the surface of the water, and fish are seized and swallowed. The bills of the extinct Huias (Callaeidae) of New Zealand were even more remarkable: that of the male was straight and sharp for tunneling into dead wood for grubs, that of the female was slender and decurved for extracting prey the male could not reach. Then they shared the spoils in an unusual example of cooperative hunting.

### FEET

Similarly, the feet of birds (Figs. 38 and 39) are often modified to serve specific needs (see also Chapter 5 on Locomotion)—webbed or lobed for swimming in aquatic birds, long-toed for walking over aquatic vegetation in some marsh birds, strongly clawed for scratching in gallinaceous birds, strongly taloned for seizing prey in predatory birds, yoke-toed (*zygodactylous*) in woodpeckers for clinging to and climbing on vertical surfaces, and well adapted for perching in the great order of perching birds which have a long opposable hind toe for securely fastening the foot to a branch. A peculiar foot form for which no adaptational significance seems to have been suggested is illustrated by the Coraciiformes (kingfishers and related families); two and sometimes three of the toes are joined to form a com-

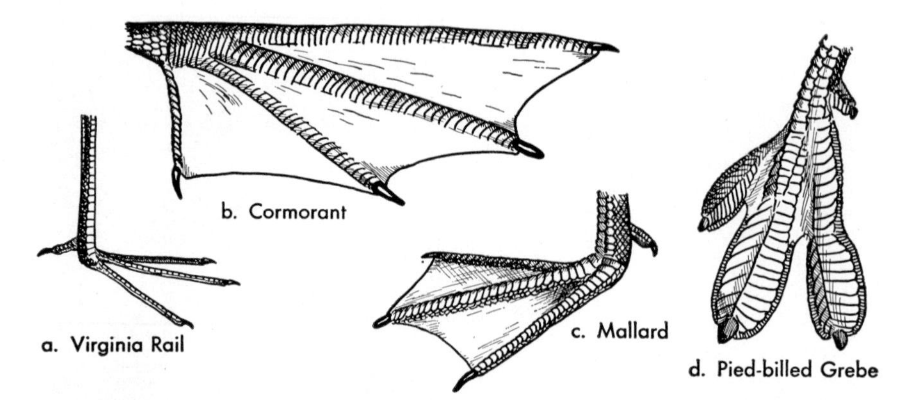


*Fig. 38. Adaptations of feet. a. Virginia Rail, long-toed for paddling over mud and marsh vegetation. b. Cormorant, a "pelecaniform" foot, with all four toes united in a web, for swimming. c. Mallard, three toes united in a web, for swimming and paddling. d. Pied-billed Grebe, toes broadly lobed with flattened nails, tarsus compressed, for swimming and diving. (Drawings by Homer D. Roberts.)*

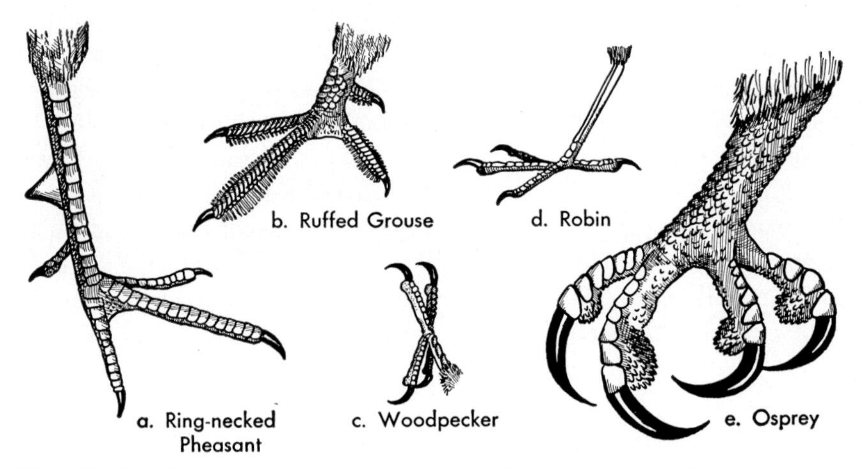


*Fig. 39. Adaptations of feet. a. Ring-necked Pheasant, for running and scratching, with a spur on the cock for fighting and for treading hens. b. Ruffed Grouse, showing fleshy fringes (winter only) on toes for walking on snow. c. Woodpecker, for clinging to and climbing on vertical surfaces, outer (fourth) toe permanently reversed (zygodactylous). d. Robin, for perching, with long incumbent hind toe (hallux). e. Osprey, for grasping fish, outer toe reversible. (Drawings by Homer D. Roberts.)*

mon sole, a condition known as *syndactyle.* Certain additional devices, as the fleshy fringes that develop on the sides of the toes of the snowshoelike feet of grouse in winter, serve important adaptational needs, and other developments, such as the long hind claw of the larks (Alaudidae) and certain fringillids, give extra support on snow or sand. The pectinate claw (comb) on the middle toe of the Poor-will is used for scratching the feathers of the head, as well as for straightening disarranged rictal bristles and possibly for combing out lice (Brauner, 1953).

## *The Oil Gland*

A bird has few integumentary glands; the sebaceous and sweat glands common to mammals are absent and heat regulation is taken care of by other means (Chapter 4). The one prominent gland on the exterior of a bird is the oil or preen gland (*uropygium*), a conical, bilobed elevation, often with a tuft of tiny feathers which serve as a wick around the opening, immediately in front of the tail. It secretes an oily substance which in many birds apparently serves as a "dressing" for the feathers during preening. Some birds—the ostrichlike birds, some parrots and pigeons—have no oil gland; in others, such as caprimulgids, it is probably largely functionless. Many other species, including flamingos, herons, toucans, skimmers, would have an awkward time trying to distribute the oil among the feathers by means of the bill, although they could do so by rubbing their head feathers over the oil gland and thus transferring the secretion to the rest of the body.

Law (1929), using a variety of tests on the feathers of a large number of species, concluded, in disagreement with some other workers, that birds do not waterproof their feathers, but that in preening they rub the beak over the oil gland to keep the covering of the bill in good condition. More recently, Elder (1954) reviewed the whole situation and showed by extensive experiments and observations that ducks, which have large oil glands, depend on the secretion to keep their plumage in good condition (without it the feathers become brittle, frayed, and nonrepellent for water) and to keep the bill and legs from chafing and peeling. Whitaker (1957b) observed a captive Lark Sparrow deliberately and repeatedly oiling its tarsi but *not* its plumage.

A series of studies by a Chinese investigator (Hou, 1929–1931) supports the belief that the oil gland also has an antirachitic function; experimental extirpation of the gland in some but not all birds is followed by rickets. In preening, oil is distributed over the feathers where it is activated by the rays of the sun and the irradiated material absorbed through the skin or obtained by the ingestion of feather particles. Removal of the oil gland does not cause rickets in the House Sparrow, however, suggesting a differential degree of need for vitamin D in different species, or that different species get their vitamin D in different ways (Friedmann, 1925).

Thus the oil gland serves at least three important functions, though apparently both usage and need vary greatly in different species: (1) it helps keep the plumage water-repellent, perhaps particularly in waterbirds which have the largest oil glands; (2) it lubricates the beak and tarsi, thus preventing chafing; and (3) it may provide a source of vitamin D in some species.

## *Selected References*


Allen, G. M. *Birds and Their Attributes.* Francestown, N.H.: Marshall Jones, 1937. Chapt. II, III, and IV.

Beebe, C. W. *The Bird: Its Form and Function.* New York: Holt, 1906. Chapt. 2 and 10–15.

Dwight, Jonathan, Jr. The Sequence of Plumages and Moults of the Passerine Birds of New York. *Annals N.Y. Acad. Sci.* (1900), **13**:73–360.

Elder, William H. The Oil Gland of Birds. *Wilson Bull.* (1954), **66**:6–31.

Fox, Denis L. *Animal Biochromes and Structural Colors.* New York: Cambridge U.P., 1953.

Hess, Gertrud. *The Bird: Its Life and Structure.* Translated by Phyllis Barclay-Smith. New York: Greenberg, 1938.

Humphrey, Philip S., and Kenneth C. Parkes. An Approach to the Study of Molts and Plumages. *Auk* (1959), **76**:1–31.

Huxley, J. S. Threat and Warning Coloration in Birds with a General Discussion on the Biological Functions of Color. *Proc. 8th Internatl. Ornith. Cong.* (Oxford, 1938), 430–455.

Lillie, F. R., *et al.* Physiology of Development of Feathers. I–VII (A series of 7 papers by Lillie and Juhn, and Lillie and Wang). *Physiol. Zool.* (1932–1944), 5–17.

Pettingill, Olin S., Jr. A *Laboratory and Field Manual of Ornithology.* Minneapolis, Minn.: Burgess, 1956. Parts on topography, feathers and feather tracts, plumage and plumage coloration.

Rawles, Mary E. The Integumentary System. Chapt. VI in A. J. Marshall's *Biology and Comparative Physiology of Birds.* New York: Academic, 1960.

Thayer, G. H. *Concealing Coloration in the Animal Kingdom.* New York: Macmillan, 1909.

Van Tyne, Josselyn, and Andrew J. Berger. *Fundamentals of Ornithology.* New York: Wiley, 1959. Chapt. 3.

Wetherbee, David K. Natal Plumages and Downy Pterylosis of Passerine Birds of North America. *Bull. Am. Mus. Nat. Hist.* (1957), **113**:339–436.

# 4

# INTERNAL FEATURES AND THEIR FUNCTION

The preceding chapter treated only one of the ten organ systems of a bird, but it was covered in considerable detail because the external features are of particular interest. The other organ systems, though of great importance in advanced studies in anatomy and physiology, can be dealt with more briefly, merely calling attention to the more significant functions and adaptations. These nine comprise (1) a skeletal system for support; (2) a muscular system for locomotion; (3–6) four sustentative systems—digestive, respiratory, circulatory, and excretory—which together with (7) coordinating hormones (endocrine system) take care of the internal needs of a bird; (8) a reproductive system for perpetuation; and lastly (9) a nervous system to coordinate and supervise the complicated functions of all the other parts.

## *The Skeleton*

In dealing with internal anatomy it seems logical to start with the skeleton, which provides anchorage for the muscles and houses the internal organs. Fig. 40 illustrates and identifies the principal bones of a bird. The following paragraphs point out, briefly, the use that skeletal features serve in ornithological studies and, at more length, the many serviceable adaptations exhibited by the skeleton.

As pointed out in Chapter 2, skeletal features are important in classifi-

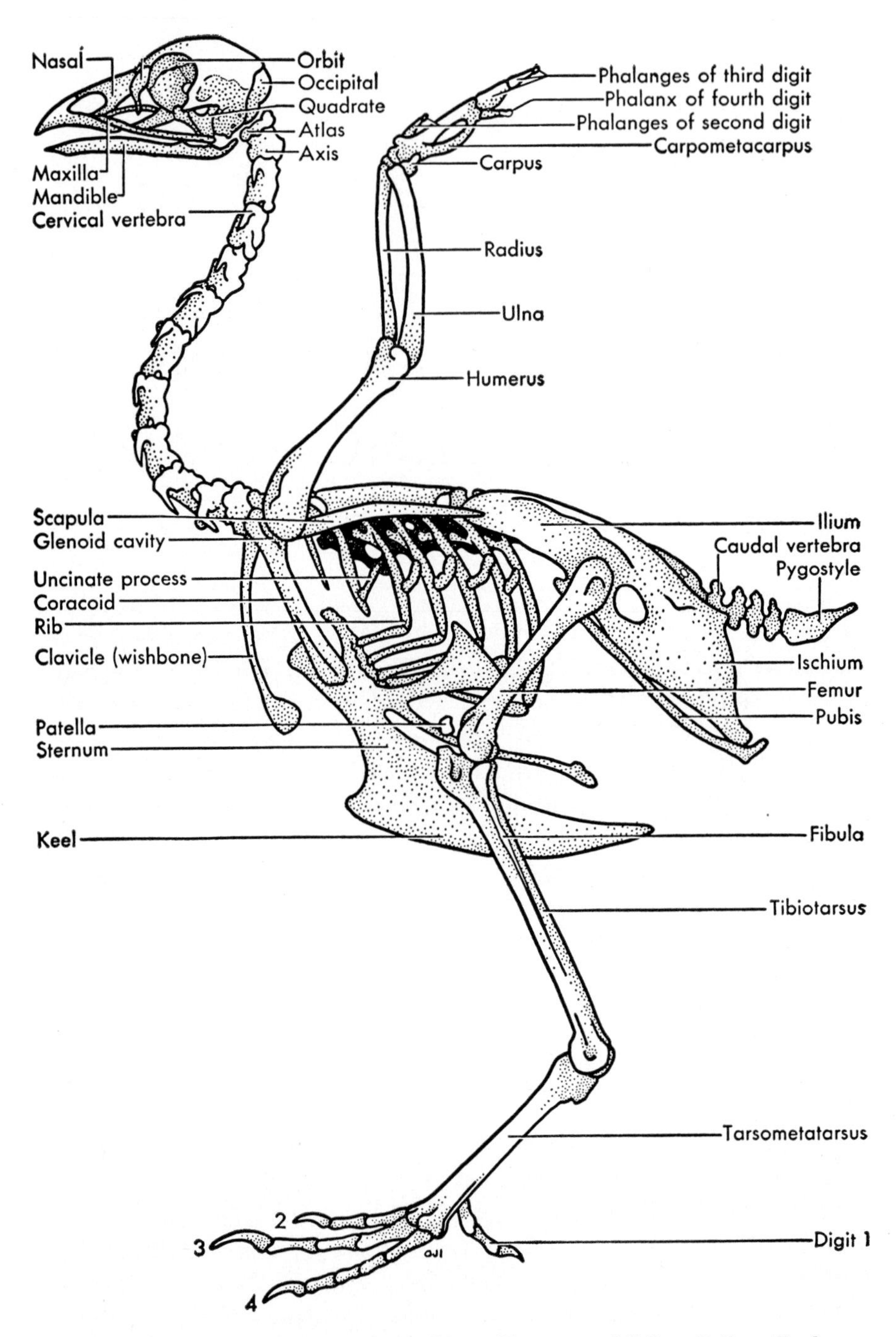


*Fig. 40. Skeleton of a domestic fowl. (From Hegner and Stiles,* College Zoology, *copyright 1951 by the Macmillan Company, New York.)*

cation. The higher categories, of ordinal rank or higher, are based largely on the structure and arrangement of bones, and skeletons are used, in conjunction with other features, in determining phylogenetic relationships. Bird skeletons are becoming an increasingly important part of museum collections.

There are pitfalls, as well as advantages, in using skeletal structures in determining relationships, for though they become modified more slowly than external features and therefore have been extensively used in systematics, even bones respond in time to habit. The formerly accepted major division of birds into a more primitive *ratite* and a more advanced *carinate* group, on the basis of raft-shaped and keeled sterna respectively, has long since been abandoned in favor of divisions based on palatal structure, a primitive (*palaeognathous*—old jaw) type and a more modern (*neognathous*—new jaw) type. Studies on the bony palate (McDowell, 1948), however, suggest that even this criterion may be no longer tenable, a feature taken cognizance of in Wetmore's latest (1960) classification (superorder Palaeognathae dropped).

The chief interest of the beginning student with skeletal features, however, is in the truly remarkable modifications they exhibit. These adaptations, mainly for flight and bipedal locomotion, may be summed up under the following headings.

## LIGHTNESS

The bones of a bird are of exceedingly light weight for their size. Corresponding mammalian bones are usually heavier and more massive. Lightness is achieved by having *pneumatic* bones, that is, filled with air spaces. The limb bones, in addition, are frequently hollow, with the upper arm (*humerus*) in many species containing an air sac extending from the lung. The bones of the skull, though thin and transparent in young birds, become double-layered with age with air spaces in between. There is great variation, however, in the pneumaticity of the bones of different species. Oceanic birds like the albatrosses (Fig. 41), which float over the waves for hours with little or no wing flapping, are the most completely aerial of all birds, with air-filled bones clear to their toes. Land soarers like vultures and hawks, which also spend much time aloft, are similarly buoyant. The bones of the highly aquatic Common Loon, however, lack this pneumaticity and the bones of the smaller land birds (where the saving in weight would be relatively small) also are much more solid.

*Fig. 41. Wandering Albatross in flight. The albatrosses, some with wingspreads exceeding 10 feet, are the most completely aerial of all birds and have light pneumatic bones and a large sail area to keep them aloft. Wilson's Petrels are shown below. (Courtesy of Amer. Mus. Nat. Hist.)*

Strength of bones is not sacrificed by having them hollow. They illustrate the "hollow-girder" principle familiar in engineering, the hollow girder being stronger for its weight than a solid one. The vultures, in addition, exhibit internal strutting in some of the long wing bones, well suited to the stresses they must bear (Fisher, 1946). The enlarged, hollow bone also permits increased surface for muscle attachment.

### REDUCTION AND FUSION

A relatively rigid skeleton is needed for flight. This is achieved by the elimination of many bones found in other vertebrates and by the fusion of others. The avian skull has lost some of the bones found in the reptilian type, and others are more or less unrecognizably fused. Loss of teeth, another weight-saving feature, also eliminated the need for a heavy lower jaw to support them, and the alternative of having a grinding gizzard permitted more rapid intake and quicker utilization of food—chewing would be uneconomical for a bird (Dilger, 1957). The elements of the thoracic region in birds are welded into a firm but slightly expansible basket composed of (1) fused vertebrae, (2) ribs with upper (vertebral) and lower (sternal) segments which connect the back with the sternum, and (3) the peculiarly avian *uncinate processes* which overlap successive ribs. The pelvic or *innominate* bones (*ilium, ischium,* and *pubis*) fuse with the lumbar and sacral vertebrae. The solidly welded portion of the vertebral column separating the two innominate bones is called the *synsacrum;* it is composed of the last thoracic, the lumbars, sacrals, and anterior caudals. The caudal vertebrae are reduced and partially fused to form the *pygostyle* which with its surrounding flesh ("pope's nose") supports the tail feathers.

The forelimbs in birds, particularly the distal parts, are greatly modified. The *ulna,* which bears the secondaries, is enlarged, but the *carpals* (wrist bones) are reduced to two. Of the five *metacarpals* typically found in the quadruped hand, the first and fifth are gone, the second is a mere remnant fused to the third, while the third and fourth are united at their ends to form the hand (*manus*) which bears the primaries. The *phalanges* or segments forming the three digits are also much reduced, varying from about four to seven in different species. One or two phalanges of the second digit form the *alula* or bastard wing, two or three phalanges form the third finger, and one or two the fourth. (Some authors number the digits and metacarpals I, II, and III instead of II, III, and IV.)

The leg bones likewise exhibit considerable fusion, particularly at the tarsal joint (ankle), where the proximal *tarsals* are completely fused with the *tibia* to form a *tibiotarsus,* and the distal tarsals are fused with the united *metatarsals* to form a single lower leg bone, the *tarsometatarsus.* Birds typically have four toes, which facilitates perching, but some species have only three, and the Ostrich only two.

## SPECIAL FEATURES

The chief exception to the prevailing tendency toward reduction and fusion in the avian skeleton is the exceedingly flexible and often greatly elongated neck, which facilitates stretching, reaching, preening, and peering, and compensates for an otherwise rigid skeleton. It also offsets to some extent the loss of manual dexterity caused by having wings instead of forepaws, and provides for rapid directional peering with eyes that are quite firmly fixed in sockets. Unlike mammals, where the number of cervical vertebrae in a giraffe or a bat is the same, in birds a long neck is due in part to an increase in cervicals, which vary from thirteen in some hawks, parrots, swifts, and a few other birds (Brodkorb, 1957) to twenty-four or twenty-five in swans. Often there is a variation of one in different individuals of the same species (Fig. 42).

Among other special features perhaps the most important is the *sternum*. In the flightless birds such as the Ostrich the sternum is flat or raft-shaped (ratite), but in all flying forms it has a median ridge or keel for the attachment of muscles. Birds with rapid or powerful wing strokes, such as hummingbirds, swallows, pigeons, and falcons, have enormously deepened or expansive keels on their sterna, whereas soaring birds like albatrosses, which depend on buoyancy and a large sail area (Fig. 41), have

*Fig. 42. Extremely long necks in these Greater Flamingos* (Phoenicopterus ruber) *in Africa are due to an increase in the number of cervicals (18 or 19) and to lengthening of the individual bones. They have 5 to 7 fewer cervicals than a swan and only 4 or 5 more than an owl. Other adaptations include long legs and partially webbed toes for wading, and a lamellate bill for straining food items out of bottom ooze which they obtain by scooping with the bill in an inverted position between the legs. (From a Kodachrome by Roger T. Peterson.)*

smaller or shallower keels and smaller flight muscles. Another interesting feature of the sternum is its prolongation posteriorly, which helps support the internal organs in rapid flight. At its anterior end the sternum joins the pillarlike *coracoids* which in turn unite with the other elements of the shoulder girdle (*clavicles* and *scapulae*) to provide the strong support needed for powerful wingbeats. The clavicle is reduced or absent in flightless birds.

### CENTRALIZATION

The parts of the skeleton, as well as the investing muscles and enclosed viscera, are organized in such a way as to shorten the body axis and centralize the distribution of weight. The head is small and light; a long neck can, if necessary, be retracted in flight, and the feathered tail is an aid rather than an incumbrance. Thus there is little or no anterior or posterior drag in flight, the body is streamlined and well balanced with the center of gravity below the supporting wings. The center of gravity, of course, is an imaginary entity and can be shifted forward, backward, or laterally by movements of the head, wings, and tail.

## The Muscular System

The muscles of a bird are likewise specialized to perform particular functions. Though the musculature of most species has not been critically studied, there are detailed works on certain species, such as the domestic fowl (Chamberlain, 1943) and raven (Shufeldt, 1890), and treatises on the muscles of particular regions, such as the jaw musculature of icterids (Beecher, 1951), the locomotor apparatus of vultures (Fisher, 1946), and the pelvic appendage in many birds (Berger, 1952; Hudson, 1937). Muscle terminology, however, is rather cumbersome, and unfortunately not always uniform; this brief section therefore merely calls attention in a nontechnical way to a few of the muscle groups that perform a function primarily peculiar to birds.

In Chapter 3 mention was made of the cutaneous muscles that serve for ruffling or fluffing out the feathers. For purposes of nomenclature the cutaneous muscles are arranged in groups corresponding for the most part to the feather tracts to which they are distributed. Their action includes such functions as shaking the water from the feathers of aquatic birds when they come ashore, or drying the feathers of land birds after a bath, fluffing out or depressing the feathers in response to temperature changes, erecting crests, pinnae, or breeding plumes in sexual displays, parting the breast feathers for exposing the brood patch in incubating birds (Fig. 112), and, perhaps most important of all, providing for the many complicated movements of the wing and tail feathers in flight.

The jaw musculature of birds in relation to feeding habits shows some interesting modifications (Beecher, 1951). In birds of prey, and in seed-eaters which actually crush seeds, the adductor muscles (*M. adductor mandibulae*) which close the jaws are strongly developed, whereas in insectivorous birds, or in birds that merely pick up and swallow seeds (pigeons), they are generally reduced. In the Common Grackle, which saws open acorns by means of a sharp keel on the roof of the mouth, the adductor muscles are powerfully developed to perform this special function (Fig. 43a). Conversely, the protractor or gaping muscles (mainly *M. depressor mandibulae*) are less massive in the seed-eaters, but strongly developed in those fruit-eaters that puncture fruit with a closed bill and then open it to extract pulp or juices. The meadowlarks likewise have well-developed protractors (Fig. 43b), for prying under grasses with closed bill and then gaping to snatch onto prey.

Better known are the large flight muscles on the breast of a bird. These consist of the usually enormous superficial pectoral muscle (*M. pectoralis major*), which has its origin along the whole ventral border of the sternal

Fig. 43. *Jaw musculature of two icterids showing adaptations for food-getting. a. Grackle, with powerful adductors for cracking acorns and grain, and reduced protractors. b. Meadowlark, with reduced adductors and powerful protractors for gaping. (From W. J. Beecher,* Auk, *68, 1951. Redrawn by Vito Cangemi.)*

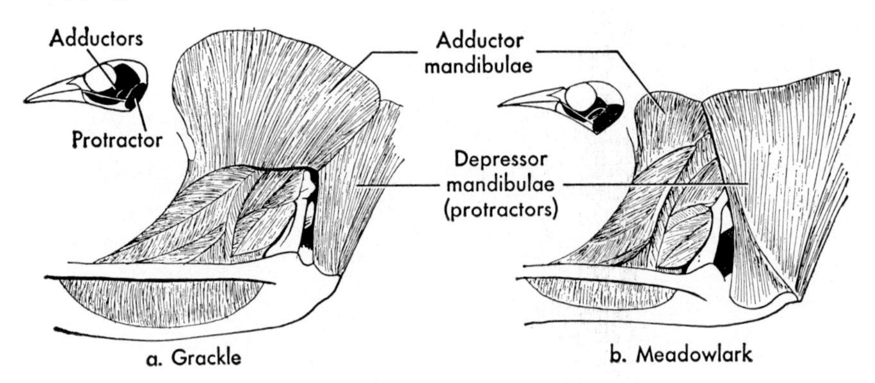

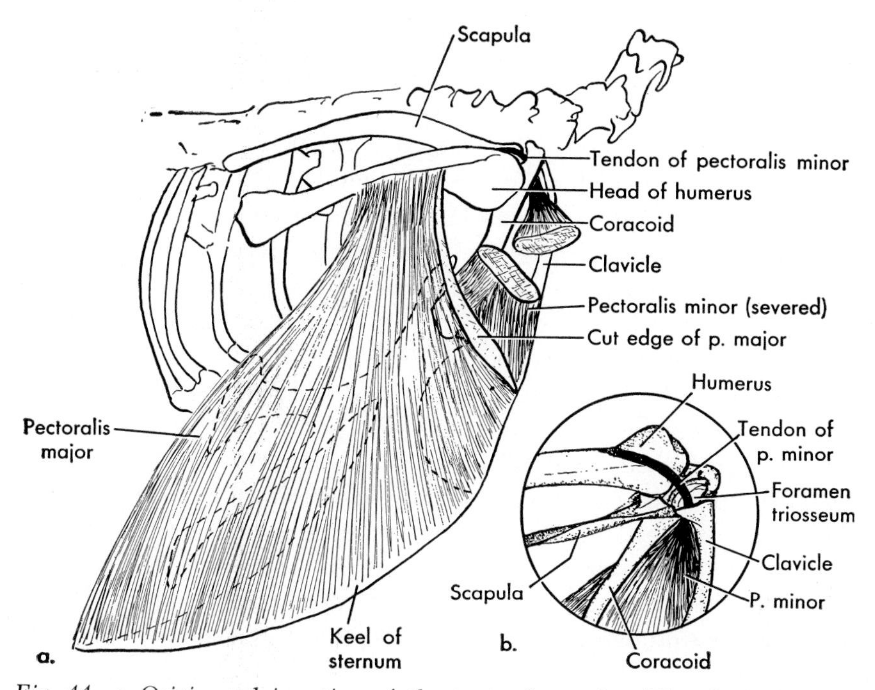


*Fig. 44. a. Origin and insertion of the pectoral muscles. The clavicular portion of pectoralis major is cut away to show the underlying p. minor. Origin of p. major along the keel of the sternum, insertion on ventrolateral aspect of the humerus, depresses the wing. b. Inset showing medial side of left shoulder elements with passage of the tendon of p. minor through the foramen and insertion on the dorsoposterior surface of the humerus to elevate the wing. (Drawings by* Vito *Cangemi.)*

crest and clavicle and inserts on the ventrolateral surface of the humerus for depressing the wing, and the deep pectoral muscle (*M. pectoralis minor* or *supracoracoideus*) which also originates on the sternum, beneath the major, and inserts on the dorsomedial aspect of the humerus. Insertion of the minor on the *upper* surface of the arm bone is achieved by passage of the tendinous portion of the muscle through an opening, the *foramen triosseum,* between the shoulder bones in a unique rope and pulley arrangement, so that contraction of a *ventral* muscle on the breast *elevates* the wing. Figure 44 illustrates this unique arrangement.

Birds with a deep keel naturally have large and powerful breast muscles, whereas soaring birds with a shallow keel have correspondingly smaller pectoral muscles. Nair (1954) points out that the smaller flight muscles in soaring birds may have two origins and two bellies, and thus act independently and alternately, preventing fatigue. In most birds the depressor muscles which control the powered downstroke are much the larger, often ten times the size of the minor which only elevates the wing, but a hummingbird's unique manner of flight also utilizes a powered upstroke so that the minor is nearly half as large as the major (Savile, 1950).

Perhaps understandably, flight of birds (pp. 112–119) is not achieved by the action of these two wing muscles alone; things are not that simple. Six different muscles supplement the action of the minor in elevating and tilting the wing, several others assist the major in depressing it, and several dozen others (not including the skin muscles to individual feathers) play a role in the complicated motions of these appendages.

The breast muscles of birds usually consist of a mixture of red and white fibers (dark meat and/or white meat), but the fowl has only white fibers, while in strong fliers the dark fibers predominate. The broad white fibers are glycogen-loaded (for quick but not sustained energy) and are relatively free of fat, whereas the narrow red fibers have abundant fat storage for sustained muscular activity. The dark muscles also have a richer blood supply (Fig. 45). A series of papers by George and coworkers in India describe these histological features in detail (see George and Naik, 1960 a and b).

The muscles of the pelvic appendage are similar in name and function to those of other land vertebrates, and only those involved in the "perching mechanism" need be mentioned here. The perching function has often been assigned to the *ambiens*, a slender muscle that arises on the pectineal process of the ilium and is continued over the kneecap into a tripartite flexor of the fore toes, but actually the ambiens plays only a

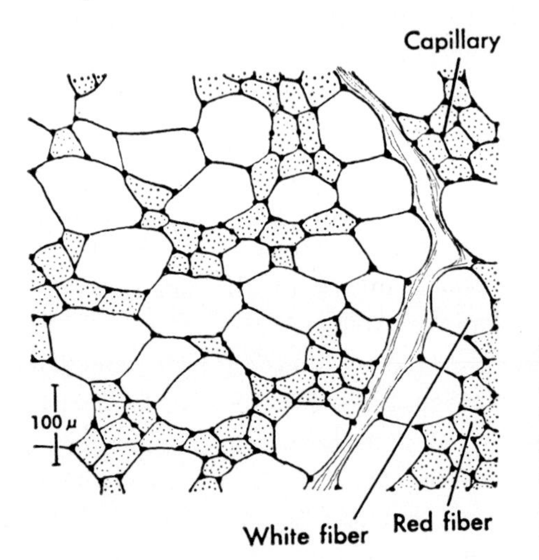


*Fig. 45. Cross section of pectoralis of Common Pigeon, showing the narrow red fibers, the broad white fibers, and the distribution of the capillaries supplying the muscles. (Drawing by R. M. Naik for J. C. George,* Auk, *77, 1960.)*

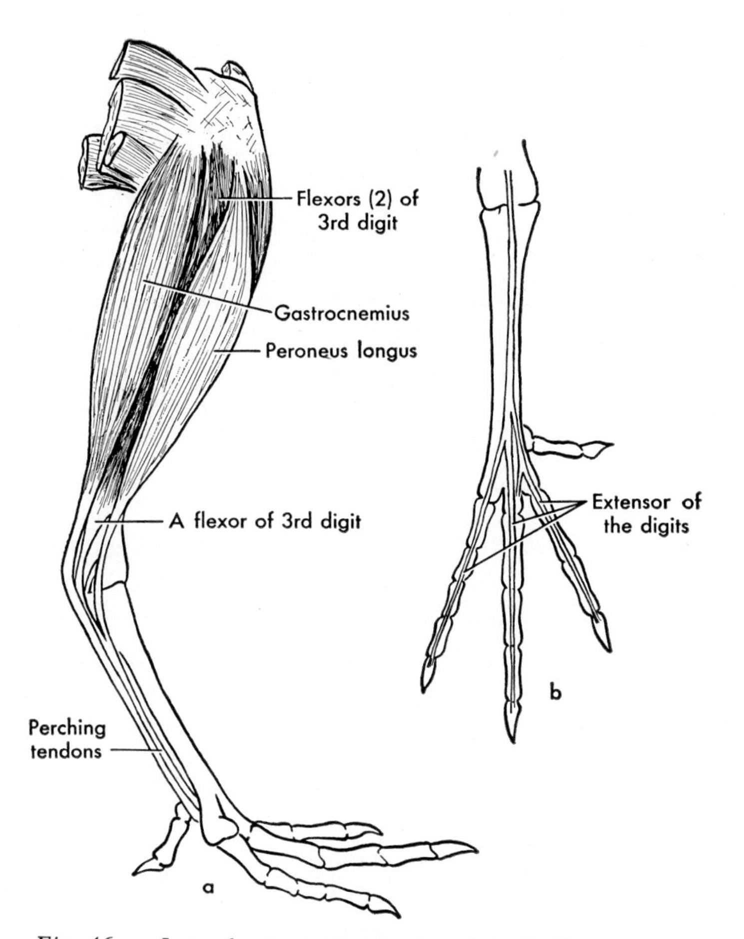


*Fig. 46. a. Lateral aspect of right leg of fowl, illustrating a part of the complex perching mechanism of the foot (underlying flexors not shown). b. Frontal (anterior) aspect of right foot, showing extensors. (From Chamberlain's* Avian Anatomy, Memoir Bull. 5, *Mich. Agric. Exp. Sta. Drawings by* Vito *Cangemi.)*

minor role in perching (mainly flexion of the second toe) and can be severed without loss of perching ability. Several leg muscles, notably the big "calf" muscle (*gastrocnemius*) and the *peroneus longus* on the anterior aspect of the crus, assist in perching, but it is chiefly the action of the flexors of the digits (eight separate but coordinated muscles, six to the fore toes, and two to the hallux or hind toe) that accomplishes the tight grip of the foot on a perch (Fig. 46a). Madura (1952) demonstrated a nerve center on the plantar surface of the foot by stimulating it with tweezers which apparently initiated the perching reflex. Several other muscles act as extensors to open the toes (Fig. 46b). It should be noted that only tendinous parts of muscles reach the toes, an important heat-conservation measure.

Fisher (1957, 1958) has described two other muscles of special significance in birds: (1) a "hatching" muscle (*M. complexus*) in the chick, which originates on the vertebral column and inserts on the dorsal surface of the head, reaches its maximum development at hatching time (twenty to twenty-one days), and then disappears; and (2) *M. depressor caudae* which depresses the tail to serve as a brake in landing. Pigeons with excised M. depressor caudae showed a 40 to 60 per cent increase in landing force due to loss in braking power.

## The Digestive System

The digestive system provides for the intake and breakdown, but not the final distribution, of food products. Because of the high rate of metabolism in birds, food requirements are great and digestion rapid, but in the interests of economy for flight, most species are highly selective in their diet, not ordinarily taking in items that cannot be promptly and fairly completely utilized. Digestive structures in birds (Fig. 47) exhibit a number of unique features; those that are peculiar to birds are briefly described and their functions explained in the following paragraphs.

The interior of a bird's mouth is comparatively featureless. There are no teeth in any modern forms, mucous glands for lubricating the hard dry *palate* or roof of the mouth are largely absent in most birds, and *salivary glands,* with a few exceptions, are poorly developed. In general, salivary glands seem to be absent or poorly developed in aquatic birds (except waterfowl), "undeveloped" in semiaquatic birds (Tucker, 1958), but with the full complement present (see Tucker for complete classification) among certain seed-eaters, insectivores, and omnivores (Farner, 1960). Use of a gluelike salivary secretion for nest building (p. 199) is well known in the swifts. Apparently, the salivary glands in the Chimney Swift have a cycle of recrudescence and regression like the gonads (Johnston, 1958). Bock (1961) points out that Gray Jays, unlike other corvids, have well-developed salivary glands, presumably enabling them to probe into bark crevices and cones to extract food items on a mucous-coated tongue.

Taste buds are scanty in birds; a few scattered over the palate or on the usually undifferentiated tongue permit some taste discrimination, but

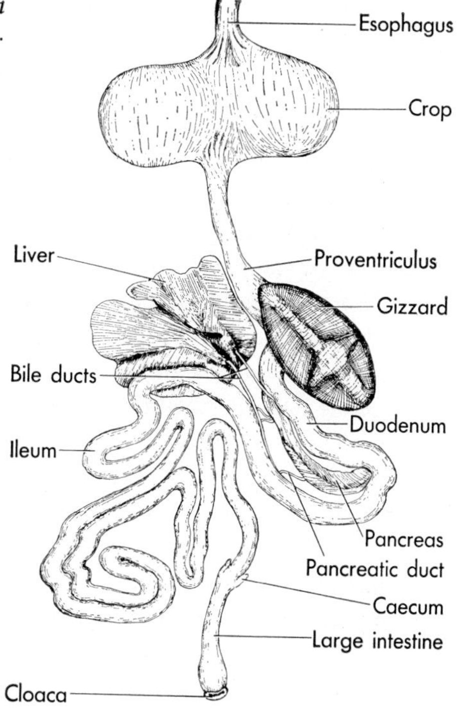


*Fig. 47. Digestive system of a Common Pigeon. (Drawing by R. M. Naik.)*

most birds are accustomed to bolt food items quickly without tasting or moistening them before swallowing. Indeed, in young birds, food is placed far back in the throat, so that taste buds, salivary glands, and even a much differentiated tongue may be superfluous.

The tongues of birds, though usually relatively undifferentiated or even degenerate in certain fish-eating species, exhibit many useful modifications, primarily for food gathering. In typical woodpeckers the tongue is barbed at the tip, to facilitate extracting grubs from bark crevices and excavations in trees, but in sapsuckers it is brushlike for licking up sap that fills the little well holes they deliberately drill into the cambium. In woodpeckers in general, but notably in the flickers, which are largely ant-eating ground-feeders, the tongue is conveniently extensible by means of the extremely prolonged *hyoids* which extend backward and curl up and over the base of the skull and forehead and attach near the nostrils. In nectar-feeders—hummingbirds, sunbirds (Nectariniidae) and various honey-creepers—the tongue is usually long and forked, and often rolled into tubes for sipping nectar, not by suction (there is no vacuum at the base of the tongue) but by a sort of capillary action. The tongues of parrots are thick and fleshy, presumably correlated with their fruit-eating habits but perhaps also aiding in modulating sounds in this notoriously articulate group of birds. The tongues of waterfowl, except for the fish-eating mergansers, are also fleshy, and fringed along the lateral margins for sifting of fine materials gathered up in bottom ooze.

The part of the digestive tube leading from the *pharynx*, or posterior part of the mouth, to the stomach is the *esophagus*, but in many birds, particularly in galliform and columbiform birds, a diverticulum known as the *crop* develops midway down the tube. This is chiefly a storage receptacle for birds that need to take in large quantities of food at a faster rate than can be taken care of immediately by the small stomach. It enables gallinaceous birds to fill their crops at a particular feeding time and then pass on the stored items a few at a time to be digested while resting or roosting. Pheasants and grouse, for example, have two main feeding periods, in the morning and in late afternoon or evening. No doubt the usually heavier evening meal helps sustain them overnight. By contrast, insectivorous birds feed much more frequently and have less need for a specialized storage place. Hummingbirds, with the highest food consumption of any animal, feed almost continuously through the day; yet even then the males cannot take in enough nourishment to sustain themselves overnight at the day-time rate of metabolism and become torpid, reducing body temperature and breathing rate until they are in a state of dormancy (Pearson, 1953). Apparently the females, in well-insulated nests, can conserve heat and not become torpid over night (Howell and Dawson, 1954).

The crop, or at least a temporarily distended esophagus (false crop), also serves as a market basket for fish-eating species that go far afield on fishing trips or transport food long distances for their young, and is used as a fruit basket for birds like the Cedar Waxwing which carries a cargo of berries to its young. Birds of prey commonly fill up with all they can hold, if it is readily available, and then may not feed again for hours or even a day or more, while the body gradually assimilates the bounteous meal. Vultures, in fact, often stuff themselves so full of carrion that they are unable to rise from the ground without disgorging (Fig. 48).

Pigeons are noted for their unique ability to produce "pigeon's milk," a caseous (cheesy) secretion resulting from degeneration of cells lining the crop, which is used to nourish the squabs until they are old enough to eat grain. The "milk" is rich in fat, 35 per cent compared to 3 to 5 per cent for cow's milk, and is produced by both sexes during the breeding season. Another unusual function of a crop is found in the Hoatzin (Fig. 58) of South America, a tree-climbing relative of the fowl, which uses the

*Fig. 48. This Turkey Vulture, like other scavengers and birds of prey, is an opportunist and gorges itself when food is available, storing the surplus in an expansible gullet. The infection conspicuous on feet and face may have been contracted from infected prey. (Photo by Allan D. Cruickshank.)*

crop as a grinding organ for crushing masses of thick tropical foliage (largely arum leaves) on which it feeds.

Other modifications of the esophagus for special purposes include (1) gular sacs in the throat of fringillids, such as the Pine Grosbeak (French, 1954), for storing seeds, and (2) a bellowslike distention in certain grouse, pigeons, and bustards which serves as a resonance chamber for producing sound during courtship (Farner, 1960).

The stomach of a bird is usually divided into two portions, an anterior small but thick-walled glandular *proventriculus* and a more posterior thick muscular *gizzard*. The former secretes gastric juice and initiates the breakdown of food before it is passed on to the gizzard, whose muscular walls, often with the aid of grit, abrade and crush hard materials for subsequent assimilation in the intestine. Insect-feeders, in general, have a well-developed though small proventriculus but also a gizzard, whereas birds subsisting on hard items usually have a powerful gizzard but a hardly noticeable proventriculus. There is great variation in the degree of development of these structures in different birds; in fact, they may vary somewhat in the *same* species at *different* seasons, depending on their seasonal food habits. Some tropical fruit-eaters have evolved a nearly straight and relatively featureless digestive tube and pass incompletely digested berries more or less continuously through the whole tract (Sutton, 1951). The grinding power of the gizzard is well illustrated by birds which feed on acorns, beechnuts, and hickory nuts (Wood Duck, Ruffed Grouse, Turkey). The hard nuts are crushed and pulverized by muscular contractions of the gizzard. Schorger (1960) found that penned Turkeys required about an hour to crush pecans, but that hickory nuts (perhaps not a part of their natural diet) required thirty to thirty-two hours.

An extensive but somewhat controversial literature exists regarding the need for grit in seed-eating birds. Undoubtedly grit aids materially in the mechanical mastication of hard materials, for gizzard stones soon become smooth and polished, but in the absence of grit gallinaceous birds at least can utilize hard seeds which abrade against each other and the hard lining of the organ (Beer and Tidyman, 1942). Grit of the right kind is also a source of valuable minerals, such as calcium and phosphorus, needed especially for bone and feather development, but sand, which is largely quartz, is almost purely abrasive with little mineral content (Dennis, 1951, 1952). Some grit is taken in accidentally in normal feeding operations by flickers in gleaning ants from an anthill or by the Robin and American Woodcock in probing for earthworms. Beach-combing shorebirds may have 10 to 60 per cent of their stomach contents composed of incidental sand (Reeder, 1951). Kilham (1960) noted Blue Jays visiting a sandpile daily in winter and consuming sand.

Digestion in birds, as in other vertebrates, is mainly consummated in the small intestine whose duodenal portion receives bile from the liver and pancreatic enzymes from the pancreas. The bile assists in the chemical preparation of food for further digestion (neutralizes acids and emulsifies fats), and the enzymes from the pancreas break down carbohydrates, fats, and proteins. The large liver has many other important functions in birds, but most of them, such as the storage of lipids and glycogen, are nondigestive (Farner, 1960). A gall bladder, for storage of bile, is present in some birds, but absent in many.

The small intestine is comparatively short though coiled in most animal-feeders, but long and extensively looped in omnivorous and herbivorous species. The intestine of the largely vegetarian Ostrich is 46 feet long, but in the insect- and nectar-feeding Ruby-throated Hummingbird it is only 2 inches long. This is associated with the greater needs for intestinal space in the herbivorous forms which in general require a greater bulk of food than the animal-feeders.

The large intestine in birds is much reduced, as digestion is relatively complete in both vegetarian- and animal-feeders, particularly the latter, and there is a minimum of nondigestible wastes. Many birds have economized further by evolving other methods of voiding indigestible items. Birds of prey, particularly the owls, form pellets (Fig. 49) of the bones, fur, and feathers of their prey in the proventriculus, and periodically eject them through the mouth rather than having them complete their passage through the digestive tract. In fruit-eaters a variety of methods is found. Evening Grosbeaks, with their powerful beaks, crack the pits of cherries and feed the kernels to their young; corvids form pellets of small seeds and spit them up; thrushes strip the flesh from berries in their crop or stomach and eject the pits; whereas Cedar Waxwings and many tropical species apparently pass even large pits through the digestive tract.

Paired *caeca,* usually rudimentary but well developed in gallinaceous birds, anatids, and the Ostrich, mark the transition between the small and large intestine. In gallinaceous birds the length of the caeca, and also of the intestines, is related to the diet, being longer in browsing forms like grouse than in seed-eating quail and pheasants, and longer in a coastal race of California Quail living on a low-grade winter diet than in a close relative living on richer seeds (Leopold, 1953). Studies on grouse in Finland indicate that the caeca, which harbor bacteria, function in the microbial decomposition of cellulose which figures prominently in the diet of these birds (Suomalainen and Arhimo, 1945).

A final function of digestion not related to any specific organ is the extraordinary ability of birds to store up reserves of fat in preparation for migration (p. 266) or other needs. Migratory birds often increase their body weight by 15 to 40 per cent by heavy feeding in advance of a long flight.

## *The Respiratory System*

The respiratory system provides for the various gaseous exchanges that take place between the outside medium and, via the lungs, the cells of the body. Fresh air (oxygen) is introduced into the lungs with each intake of breath (inspiration), and gaseous wastes (carbon dioxide and water) are

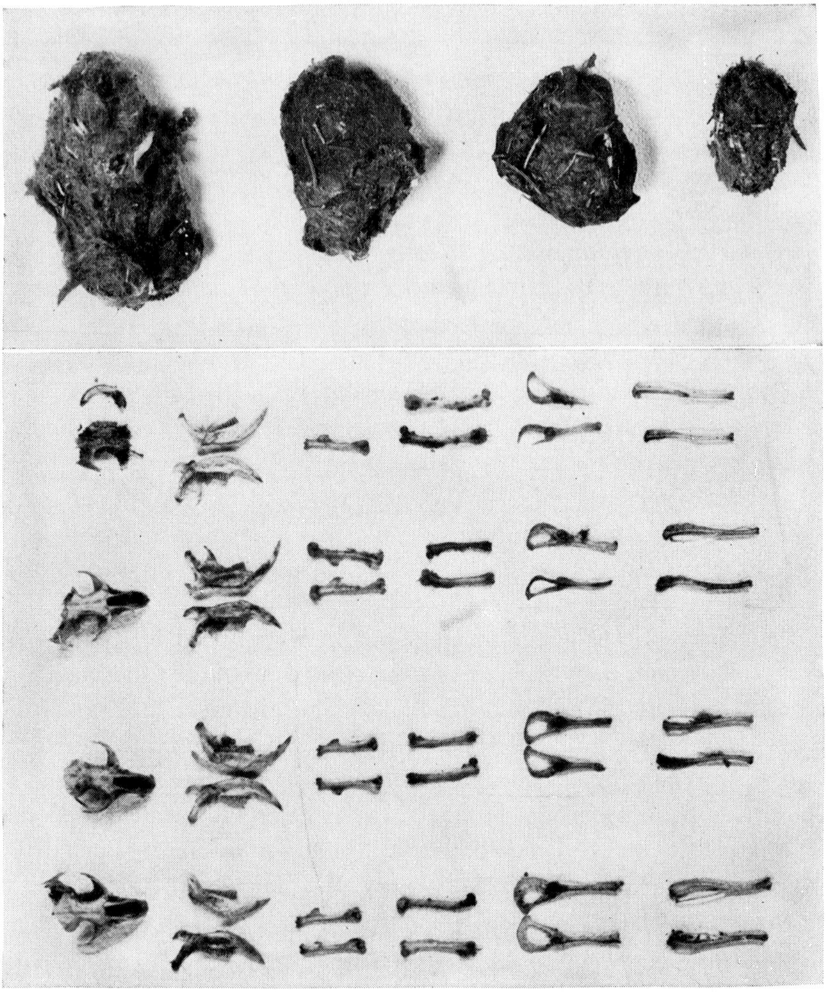

*Fig. 49. Above, sample pellets from a Barn Owl. The smallest probably includes the remains of only one mouse; the largest contained the bones of four mice as shown below—skulls, lower mandibles, humeri, femora, pelvic bones, and tibia. One humerus was missing. (Photos by Philip G. Coleman, courtesy of Mich. Agric. Exp. Sta.)*

expelled during expiration. The blood is the medium transporting fresh oxygen, in chemical combination with hemoglobin, to all the cells of the body and returning gaseous wastes to the lungs.

From the standpoint of gross anatomy the respiratory system in birds is fairly simple. The *external nares* or nostrils usually open into the base of the bill. Typically these are mere slits or small oval-shaped openings in the horny beak, but in hawks they are surrounded by a soft membrane, the *cere,* and in pigeons by a swollen sensitive *operculum.* The nostrils may be *imperforate,* with a septum completely separating them, or *perforate,* without a nasal septum, as in the vultures. Fig. 50 shows some of these variations.

Within the nasal cavity are several spongy bones (ethmoids) which for the most part lack sensory olfactory epithelium (see p. 122). Some marine birds also possess well-developed nasal or salt glands. Schmidt-Nielsen and Fange (1958) and Frings and Frings (1959) have shown that the glands function in salt excretion in gulls, pelicans, and albatrosses, enabling them to utilize salt water for drinking without suffering progressive dehydration of tissues. The liquid oozing from the nostrils has a far greater NaCl content than sea water, and more than can be taken care of by the kidneys.

The *internal nares* open directly into the pharynx from which a slit-like opening, the *glottis,* leads into the *trachea* or windpipe. The latter is usually long and flexible; it is four feet long in the Whooping Crane with two feet of it looped within a concavity in the sternum. It is composed of a series of stiffened rings, bony on the ventral surface and cartilaginous on the dorsal. At the upper extremity of the trachea is the relatively undifferentiated *larynx,* largely lacking the complicated cartilages and vocal

*Fig. 50. External nares of birds. a. Cory's Shearwater, with tubular nostrils. b. Turkey Vulture, with perforate nostrils (no nasal septum). c. Prairie Falcon, with circular nostrils in a cere. d. Common Pigeon, showing soft swollen operculum. (Drawings by Homer D. Roberts.)*

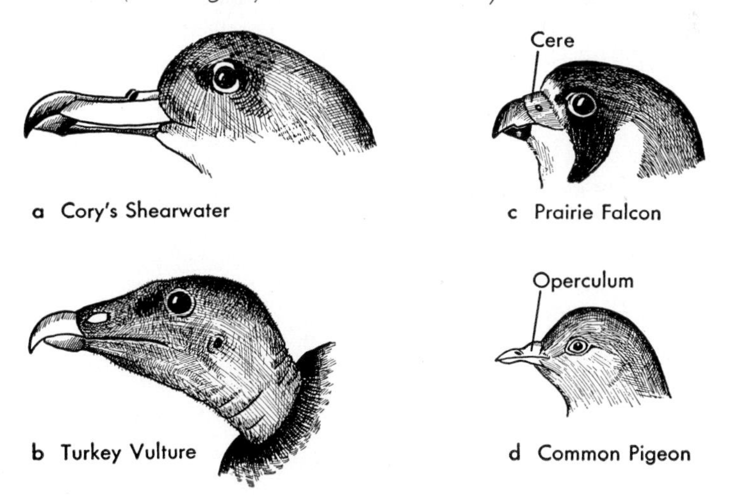

cords characteristic of mammals, but at the lower end of the trachea, at or near the juncture where it divides into short *bronchi* leading to the lungs, is a special structure, the *syrinx* or voice box.

A few birds, such as the Turkey Vulture, lack a syrinx and the structures associated with it (Miskimen, 1957); others such as storks and the ostrichlike birds lack functional syringeal muscles and can only grunt, hiss, or boom. Still other birds have a relatively undifferentiated syrinx located in the bronchi (*bronchial*) or in the trachea (*tracheal*), but in most species the syrinx is *tracheobronchial* in position (Van Tyne and Berger, 1959). The latter, usual type (Fig. 51) is composed of modified tracheal and bronchial rings, expanded to form a chamber or *tympanum*, within which sound is produced. At the bifurcation of the trachea is a bony ridge, the *pessulus*, equipped with a vibratory *semilunar membrane* which extends forward into the trachea and backward to form the membranous inner wall of the bronchi. The *tympaniform membranes* (internal and external) forming the slitlike opening out of the bronchus are controlled and regulated by *intrinsic syringeal muscles*, a single pair in the Common Pigeon, but at least three pairs in most songbirds and seven or more pairs in versatile vocalists like the Crow (Fig. 52), Catbird, and Starling (Miskimen, 1951). Air expelled from the lungs during expiration passes between the tympaniform membranes whose tension is under delicate muscular control and produces the amazing repertoire of sounds characteristic of birds.

Other structures also may assist in sound production. The semilunar

*Fig. 51. Section of syrinx of a magpie, showing internal structure. (From Walter and Sayles,* Biology of the Vertebrates, *copyright 1949 by The Macmillan Company, New York.)*

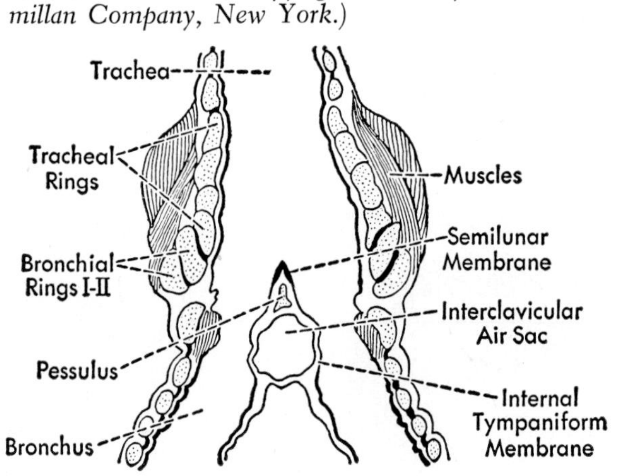

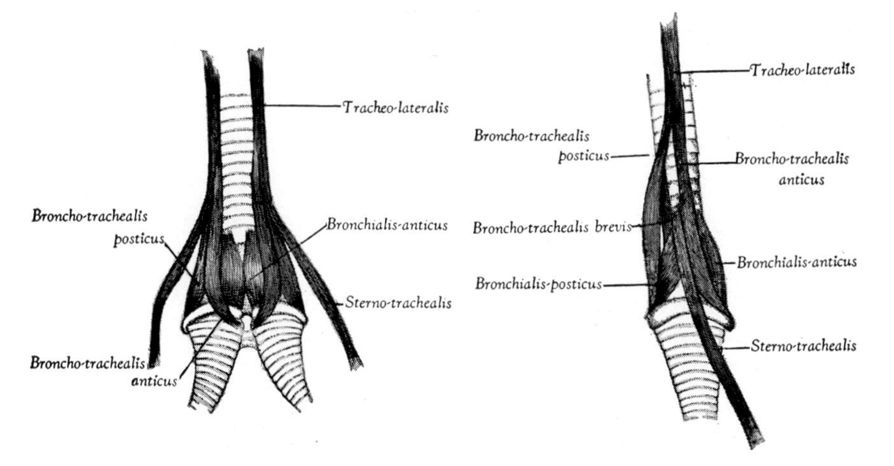


*Fig. 52. Syringeal muscles of Common Crow. Ventral view (left) and right side. (Drawings by Robert Albertin for Mildred Miskimen,* Auk, 68, *1951.)*

membrane, once thought to be the chief means of vocalization, may supplement the vibrations of the tympaniform membranes, although it can be amputated in the Starling without apparent impairment of sound (Miskimen, 1951). Male ducks have an expansive *bulla,* single or double, associated with the syrinx, which may serve as a resonance chamber, but females, which lack this structure, are often louder voiced than the males. The loud trumpeting of swans and cranes is no doubt influenced by the long tracheal loop within the sternum.

The two lungs in birds are small and compact, with little elasticity, and lie in a dorsal depression closely appressed to the thoracic vertebrae and adjoining ribs. The lungs have an intricate system of ramifying and anastomosing air passages. The primary bronchus (*mesobronchus*) into each lung gives off a series of secondary bronchi (the *dorsobronchi* and *ventrobronchi*) which in turn connect with numerous minute *parabronchi* (perhaps a thousand in each lung) which serve as the chief respiratory membranes. This is quite unlike the mammalian lung in which blind pouches (*alveoli*) provide the respiratory membranes. Thus a relatively small and inelastic lung in birds is able to supply their extraordinary oxygen demands, which are the greatest of any of the vertebrates.

Supplementing the lungs of birds is a remarkable system of air sacs which almost completely fill the body cavity. Figure 53 illustrates the nine air sacs of the Common Pigeon and shows also the lateral extensions of the *interclavicular sac* supplying the humeri, and diverticulae from the *cervical sacs* affording cushions of air between successive neck vertebrae. There is

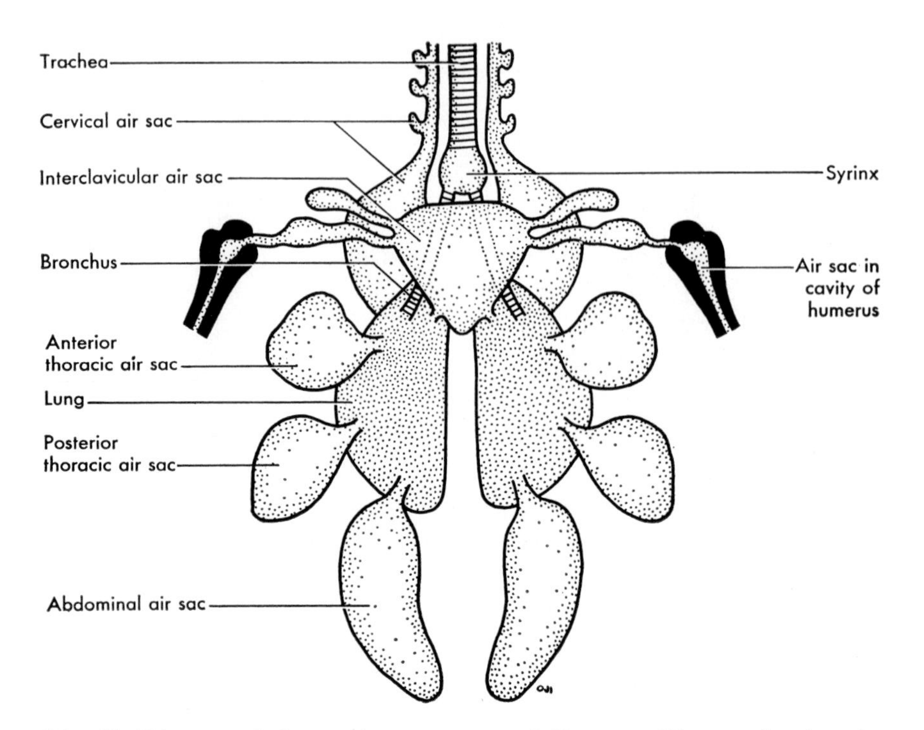


*Fig. 53. Diagram of the respiratory organs of Common Pigeon, showing the air sacs. (From Hegner and Stiles,* College Zoology, *copyright 1959 by The Macmillan Company, New York.)*

considerable variation in the degree of development of the air sacs in different species. In many birds the air sacs permeate the hollow bones, but in the Common Loon, a diver not buoyant in flight, the air sacs are simpler and reduced: there is no cervical air sac and no penetration of any of the bones by other sacs (Gier, 1952).

According to Hazelhoff (1951) fresh air during inspiration flows through the intricate parabronchial passageways in the lungs and out into air sacs, particularly into the larger posterior pairs (*abdominal* and *posterior thoracic*) which are more important in breathing. During expiration these sacs act as bellows, forcing air back through the lungs by much the same route by which it entered. Salt and Zeuthen (1960), in perhaps the latest analysis, seem to agree with this interpretation. Some authors, however, maintain that much of this inspired air passes directly through the main bronchioles into the posterior air sacs and that most of the gaseous exchange takes place in the parabronchi during expiration. Normal activities, such as flight, probably aid in breathing by muscular contractions of the thorax forcing out used air and automatically introducing new. Unlike mammals, the avian lung is completely emptied with each breath, leaving no residual air. In a pigeon in flight the air sacs also are completely emptied with each breath, but not when the bird is at rest (Hess, 1951).

Birds that sing a long uninterrupted song, like the Winter Wren, are believed to utilize reserve air in the air sacs while singing, as do water birds, like dabbling ducks, when submerged. Deep divers like a Common Loon and Oldsquaw, however, which have reduced air sacs, meet their oxygen requirements in other ways (see pp. 111–112).

The respiratory rate in birds, as might be expected, is normally rapid, but varies so much under different conditions that figures may be misleading. The breathing rate of a hibernating Poor-will in California (Jaeger, 1949) was hardly measurable; no moisture collected on a mirror held before its nostrils. The minimum rate in torpid European Swift nestlings during their fasting periods in rainy weather (p. 235) was determined at 8 times per minute, but reached a maximum of 90 coming out of torpidity. Basal rates in the Black-capped Chickadee asleep at night (Odum, 1943) varied from 65 per minute at low air temperatures (43° F.) to 95 per minute at high air temperatures (90° F.); the faster rate at higher temperatures is correlated with the necessity for heat loss (chickadees are uncomfortable at 90° in winter). Baldwin and Kendeigh (1932) found rates in House Wrens varied from a low of 28 times per minute in a bird whose body temperature had been lowered to a lethal 74° F. up to 340 times per minute at maximum body temperature. The rate at standard temperature was 92 to 112.

Blake (1958) measured respiration rates of 30 species of birds held in the hand. Except for an unexplained low in a Starling, the rates ranged from 75 times per minute (average of three trials) in a Mourning Dove to 294 in a House Wren (263 to 334 in four trials). In most birds (all passerines except the dove and a Downy Woodpecker), the rates ranged between 100 and 200 times per minute. Presumably rates would be somewhat lower in a completely relaxed bird (not in the hand) but much higher in a bird under stress, excitement, or in flight.

Thus it appears that respiration is very rapid in active birds, but that they can adjust themselves remarkably to different environmental conditions, to conserve energy during fasting, sleeping, or in cold weather.

## The Circulatory System

The circulatory system provides for the transportation of various products to and from all parts of the body. A circulating medium, the blood, in a complex system of arteries, veins, and connecting capillaries, transports (1) nutrients from the digestive system to tissues for growth and repair, (2) oxygen and carbon dioxide carried by hemoglobin to and from cells all over the body, (3) liquid wastes to the kidneys, and (4) hormones from the ductless endocrine glands for regulating growth and behavior. In addition to these well-known functions, Sturkie (1954) credits the circulatory system with an important role in (5) the regulation of water in avian tissues and (6) in temperature regulation.

Structurally, the circulatory system of birds is quite comparable to that of other higher vertebrates, and only a few of its unique features need to be described. The heart, relatively large with strong ventricular walls to withstand the strain of the extremely high heart rate, is completely four-chambered, thus showing some advance over ancestral reptiles. The right aortic arch, instead of the left as in mammals, is developed as the loop leading from the heart to the dorsal aorta. Glenny (1955) discusses in detail the phylogenetic significance of the aortic arch patterns in 123 families of birds; apparently the various arrangements of the vessels, as well as serological data, are useful in taxonomic studies.

A vessel peculiar to birds is a cross vein between the two jugulars in the neck; this prevents blocking of the flow of blood from the head when one vein is momentarily shut off by twisting the neck. Figure 54 illustrates the principal arteries and veins in the Common Pigeon. The considerable reduction, compared to reptiles, of the *renal portal system* and the increased importance of the *brachials* and *pectorals* to and from the wings and breast muscles, respectively, may be noted.

Several authors have examined heart weights of birds and pointed out interesting correlations with physiological needs and environmental conditions. In records on 1,340 birds of 291 species (64 families), Hartman (1955) found heart weights varying from 0.2 per cent of the body weight in tinamous to 2.4 per cent in hummingbirds. Relatively small hearts were characteristic of nonfliers, limited fliers (turkeys and quail), and soarers (vultures), whereas large hearts were found in shorebirds, kingfishers, swallows, warblers and vireos, and of course hummingbirds. Heart size was definitely correlated with metabolism, increasing with metabolic rates.

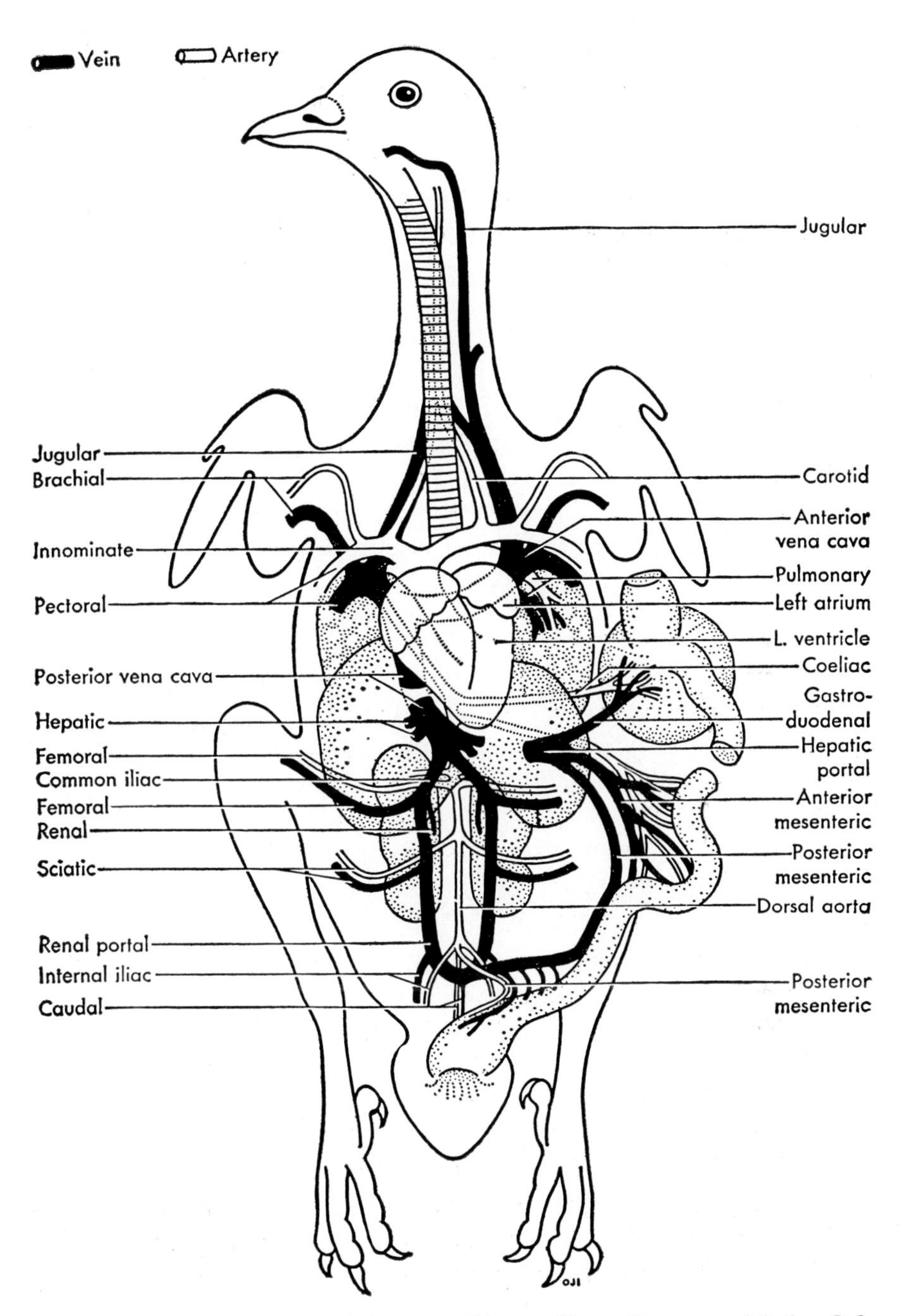


*Fig. 54. Circulatory system of Common Pigeon. (From Hegner and Stiles,* College Zoology, *copyright 1951 by The Macmillan Company, New York.)*

There was also an increase in the heart weight-body weight ratio with altitude and latitude. Norris and Williamson (1955) confirmed this increase in heart size with altitude in 12 species in the mountains of California and Nevada, and Williamson and Norris (1958) found the highest known ratio (no apparent explanation) in a Warbling Vireo.

The blood of birds, as in other vertebrates, consists of plasma, corpuscles, and various inclusions, such as salts and chemicals. Of special interest are the red corpuscles (erythrocytes) which in birds (unlike mammals) are nucleated and oval. As might be expected, the number per cubic millimeter of blood is higher in the smaller, more active forms, in order to carry more oxygen-laden hemoglobin; counts range from 1.89 million per cubic millimeter in the Ostrich to 7.6 million in a Slate-colored Junco (Nice, *et al.*, 1935). Of interest also is the pronounced increase in blood calcium and phosphorus, and also of blood lipids, in female birds during ovulation and laying (Sturkie, 1954).

### HEART RATE

The heart rate in birds is extremely rapid, but varies greatly in different species and in the same species under different conditions, such as air temperature and physical activity. It is lower in the larger, more primitive birds and higher in the smaller, more active passerines. The mean heart rate in Black-capped Chickadees, completely relaxed (asleep), varied in experimental tests (Odum, 1943) from 346 beats per minute at air temperatures of 90° F. to 674 beats at 43° F. But this rate was approximately doubled under stress, up to a maximum of 1,000 per minute. Table 4 gives some measurements of heart rates for various birds.

Such a rapidly beating heart in small birds places a severe strain on the arterial vessels. Hence, the *innominates* leading out of the heart (supplying the brachials and pectorals) are enlarged and thick-walled. In spite of this, however, when birds "die of fright" it may in some cases be due to hemorrhage from ruptured vessels placed under too heavy a strain (Walkinshaw, 1945). On the other hand, the small capillaries may become constricted during periods of inactivity, at night or during incubation; possibly stirring or stretching occasionally is required to restore circulation (Odum, 1944).

*Table 4. Some Heart Rate Readings in Birds*

| *Species* | *Beats/min. Average* | *Maximum Beats/min.* | *Authority* |
|---|---|---|---|
| Duck | 217 | — | Sturkie, 1954 |
| Buzzard | 301 | — | Simons, 1960 |
| Chicken | ♂:243–286 | — | Sturkie, 1954 |
| | ♀:279–341 | — | Sturkie, 1954 |
| Turkey | 93 | — | Sturkie, 1954 |
| Pigeon | 192–244 | — | Simons, 1960 |
| Mourning Dove (3 ad.) | 165 | 571 | Odum, 1941 |
| Hummingbird | 615 | — | Odum, 1941 |
| Crow | 342 | — | Simons, 1960 |
| Chickadee | 520 | 1000 | Odum, 1941 |
| House Wren (4 ad. & juv.) | 445 (relaxed) | — | Odum, 1941 |
| | 550–650 (♀ inc., day) | — | Odum, 1941 |
| | 670–701 (♀ inc., night) | — | Odum, 1941 |
| Robin | 570 | — | Sturkie, 1954 |
| Yellow Warbler | 480 | — | Odum, 1941 |
| House Sparrow (6 ad. & juv.) | 450 | 902 | Odum, 1941 |
| Cardinal (2 ad.) | 370 | 800 | Odum, 1941 |
| Canary | 795–1000 (max.?) | — | Sturkie, 1954 |
| Towhee (4 juv.) | 445 | 810 | Odum, 1941 |
| Song Sparrow | — | 1021 | Odum, 1941 |
| Chipping Sparrow | — | 1040 | Odum, 1941 |

BODY TEMPERATURE

Body temperatures of birds are likewise high and variable. They are slightly lower in the more primitive birds, at about 100° F. in kiwis, but may reach a maximum of about 112° F. on occasion in most passerines. There is considerable fluctuation in the temperature rhythm of most birds. In diurnal birds, it is highest during the day, rising until about midday and then gradually dropping to a minimum during the night. In nocturnal birds (kiwis, owls, and goatsuckers), the daily cycle is reversed, with the highest readings obtained at night. It also varies with other conditions, rising with muscular activity and dropping during rest periods, rising with active digestion of food (full stomach) and dropping with hunger (empty stomach), rising to adjust to high environmental temperatures and dropping when air temperatures are lower.

The fluctuating range may be as much as 8° or 10°, say from 102° to 112° F. in passerines and, experimentally, can be brought much lower and a little higher without being lethal. In tests with House Wrens, one bird recovered from an experimentally induced body temperature of 74.6° F., but about 90° F. was nearer the lethal minimum for others. The lethal maximum was between 115.1° and 118.2° F. for four individuals (Baldwin and Kendeigh, 1932). In chickens, the lethal minimum is slightly lower than in wrens for about sixteen days; thereafter, it is about the same (Sturkie, 1954). In the few birds capable of dormancy (caprimulgids, swifts, and hummingbirds), and in nestlings still incapable of temperature regulation, body temperatures may be very low at times, approaching that of the environment.

In general, however, there is not much geographical, seasonal, or sexual difference in body temperatures of birds; they are about the same in tropical species as in those of high latitudes, nearly the same in winter as in summer, and show little variation in the sexes, except for the higher ventral skin temperatures (brood patch) in females during incubation and brooding.

### TEMPERATURE REGULATION

Birds meet the many problems of adjustment to environmental conditions in an interesting variety of ways. Bartholomew and Cade (1957) found body temperatures in Sparrow Hawks very stable at night but remarkably adjustable during the day; their tolerance of elevated body temperatures during the heat of the day was thought to enable them to occupy the inhospitable deserts of the southwest. Arctic species and birds in winter have efficient methods of conserving heat, while in warm climates various means of dissipating heat are utilized. Arctic species in general are more densely feathered (Fig. 55) than are tropical species. The insulating effect of fluffed feathers in cold or depressed feathers in warm weather has already been mentioned. Sleeping birds commonly tuck the bill in their feathers in cold weather to reduce heat loss in breathing, and the breathing rate and general body metabolism are lowered. Even shivering is a temporary expedient to adapt to sudden cold, as it converts muscular energy into heat, but of course the used energy soon has to be replaced.

In warm weather the chief means of dissipating excess heat is through the air sacs which collect warm moist air from overheated tissues and expel it via the lungs. "Panting" is a means of speeding up dissipation of internal heat by an increased breathing rate and faster evaporation of moisture. The Lesser Nighthawk, incubating in full exposure to the southwestern sun, apparently utilizes the extraordinarily large oral surface of the interior of the mouth as a cooling mechanism, even fluttering the gular membrane of

*Fig. 55. The white plumage of the Willow Ptarmigan in winter affords both protective coloration and heat conservation, as the feathers are dense and fluffy, and well-developed aftershafts furnish additional insulation. This bird was trapped in Alberta for experimental release in the Upper Peninsula of Michigan and is not in good plumage. (Courtesy of Ebb Warren and G. A. Ammann.)*

the throat to hasten evaporation (Cowles and Dawson, 1951), a device also employed by Poor-wills (Brauner, 1952) and nestling pelicans. This aid to temperature regulation necessitates increased intake of water, perhaps from widely scattered sources. Desert creatures in general, however, are adapted to get along with a minimum of water by subsisting on a succulent, or a carnivorous, diet. In warm weather the exposed tarsi, and possibly the cere, of hawks (Bartholomew and Cade, 1957) serve as additional cooling devices, but this poses the problem of *preventing* heat loss through unfeathered portions of the body in cold weather. This problem is thought to be solved, in part at least, by the low thermal conductivity of such areas and in the restricted circulation to exposed extremities. The tarsi and feet of birds, for instance, contain no fleshy muscles, only tough tendons with a limited nerve and vascular supply. High temperatures are not maintained in such areas in cold weather; instead temperatures are kept just above the freezing point and blood flow is sluggish. Birds' feet appear to be impervious to thermal severities; Canada Jays have been observed to perch without immediate discomfort (30 to 40 seconds) on the rim of a hot pot and on a camp stove (5 to 8 seconds) hot enough for a drop of water to flash into steam (Norris-Elye, 1945).

In general, the larger birds have a more favorable surface-mass ratio for withstanding extremes of cold; thus northern forms are usually larger than closely related southern forms (Bergmann's rule). The Snowy Owl (Fig. 133) and the ptarmigans (Fig. 55) are better adapted, more efficiently insulated, than the smaller Snow Bunting, which nests in the Arctic but migrates out for winter. The smaller birds also expend more energy, thus requiring greater intake, in maintaining their characteristically higher metabolism. Thus there are many ways in which birds make physical and physiological adjustments to meet changing environmental conditions.

Young birds, particularly of altricial species, do not have the capacity for regulating body temperature at hatching time and have to be brooded more or less constantly at first. Thus they are essentially *poikilothermous* at birth, that is, with a body temperature corresponding to that of the surrounding medium, but with feather development the *homoiothermous* (warm-blooded) condition progresses rapidly; in the House Wren it is well established at about nine days of age (Kendeigh and Baldwin, 1928). Dawson and Evans (1960) found nestling Vesper Sparrows unable to hold their body temperature more than 3° C. above that of the environment for the first two days after hatching, but at four days they could maintain it 10° C. above air temperatures of 20° to 25° C. and at seven to nine days they could keep their own temperature levels 35° C. above environmental temperatures ranging from 10° C. to 38° C. Precocial birds are more advanced at hatching time, but their body temperature is unstable for several days. Nestling gulls, for instance, have some capacity for temperature regulation before hatching; after hatching this capacity is correlated with environmental conditions, that is, it is good in moderate weather but poor in cold weather (Bartholomew and Dawson, 1952).

## The Urogenital System

The structural features of the excretory and reproductive systems are so closely associated that they may be conveniently considered together. Figure 56 illustrates these features in the Common Pigeon. The main excretory organs are the paired kidneys, which in birds are three-lobed, with each lobe divided into smaller lobules, and lie securely imbedded in a concavity formed by the fusion of the pelvic bones with the synsacrum.

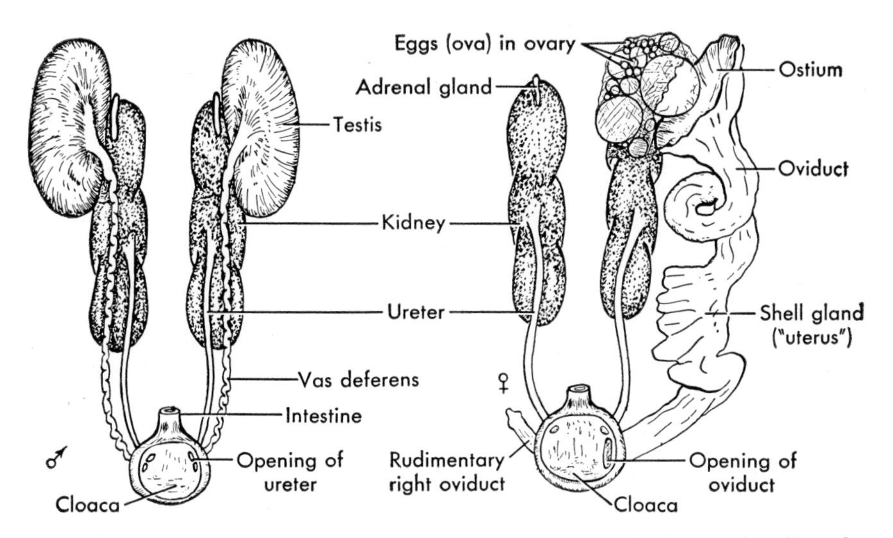


*Fig. 56. Urogenital system of Common Pigeon. Left, Male. Right, Female. (Drawings by Vito Cangemi.)*

The kidneys consist of a complicated array of circulatory vessels, capsules, and tubules which process liquid wastes brought in by the blood. Paired *ureters* then conduct the wastes to the cloaca where water not already removed in the renal tubules in the kidneys is resorbed; this and the absence of a urinary bladder (except in Ostriches) are further means of economizing on unnecessary weight. Nitrogenous wastes (largely uric acid) are thus reduced to a semisolid state and added to solids from the digestive tract, then voided from the cloaca as a whitish guano.

A special feature in the dorsal wall of the avian cloaca, which has proved useful in wildlife management work, is a blind pocket of uncertain function, the *bursa Fabricii,* which develops in young birds but disappears with age. The larger game birds, such as pheasants (Gower, 1939) and waterfowl (Hochbaum, 1942) can be fairly accurately aged by probing into and measuring the depth of the bursa during their first year of life, but this is hardly practical in the Mourning Dove and American Woodcock (Petrides, 1950). Use of special instruments facilitates this examination in smaller birds (Hanson, 1953a).

As is evident from Fig. 56l, the chief reproductive structures in the male are the paired *testes,* two oval whitish organs that lie near the anterior end of the kidneys, and the much coiled tubes, *vasa deferentia,* which conduct the sperm produced in the testes to the cloaca. In many birds the enlarged posterior portion of these tubes serves as a *seminal vesicle* for the temporary storage of sperm preceding breeding, sometimes causing a cloacal protuberance that makes sex determination possible. The testes of birds enlarge (*recrudesce*) several hundred times during the breeding season, then shrink (*regress*) after breeding. Day length (light) is the chief environmental factor inducing this remarkable change (p. 266). The small size of the gonads in fall and winter birds often makes sex determination by internal examination difficult, and has led to many unsexed or wrongly sexed specimens in museum collections.

Transfer of the sperm to the female during breeding is accomplished by direct cloacal contact during copulation, when the male mounts the back of the female momentarily so that their cloacas are closely appressed and the transfer effected quickly. There is no intromittent or copulatory organ (*penis*) in most birds, but in waterfowl and in ostrichlike birds a special erectile structure on the cloacal wall serves as a penis. Perhaps this is an additional precautionary device in ducks, which often copulate on or under the water. Copulation is frequent during the early part of the breeding season (p. 175), just prior to and during the egg-laying period, but usually wanes or ceases altogether during the later phases of the nesting cycle.

Reproductive structures in the female (Fig. 56r) are a little more elaborate, as might be expected for the production of eggs. Though there are potentially two *ovaries*, normally only the left develops. If this is lost, however, by disease or experimental ovariectomy, the right gonad may develop, usually into an ovotestis, or more rarely into a functional testis (p. 136). Raptorial birds (hawks and owls) frequently have paired ovaries, both apparently capable of producing ova (Snyder, 1948). Like the testes, the ovaries regress after the nesting season.

Eggs (*ova*) produced by the ovary are passed into the *oviduct* where they are fertilized, if fertilization occurs (hens regularly and wild birds occasionally lay unfertilized eggs). The egg follicle (mainly yolk) then receives a thick enveloping layer of albumen from glands in the middle portion of the oviduct, and then the shell is added from glands in the lower or expanded "uterine" (*shell gland*) portion of the tract. Here also pigments are added in the many birds that lay colored or speckled eggs. Recent studies have disclosed that the egg-white proteins in birds are apparently specifically distinct, that closely related species have similar but not identical egg-white proteins, and that there are usually successively greater generic, familial, and ordinal differences somewhat accurately expressing the closeness of relationship of birds—a feature that may prove useful in supplementing and checking other methods used to determine relationships (McCabe and Deutsch, 1952; Sibley, 1960).

The completed egg—yolk, albumen, shell, and pigments—is then ready for deposition (Fig. 57). Usually an egg a day (or less frequently in the larger birds) is laid until the clutch, or set of eggs, is complete. Wild birds exercise an unexplained control over egg deposition (p. 210), laying only one, two, or a dozen, as required for the clutch characteristic of the species; yet if the nest is destroyed, another clutch is produced.

The development of a chick within the egg is usually dealt with in considerable detail in embryology courses and need be summarized only briefly here. The egg, composed mainly of storage materials, contains a thin disc of protoplasm (*blastodisc* or *germinal vesicle*) on the upper surface of the yolk which is constantly kept uppermost by its lesser weight when the egg is turned, producing the characteristic twisting in the ropelike *chalaza* (Fig. 57). The egg and sperm nuclei unite soon after extrusion of the egg from the ovary, and segmentation or cleavage is initiated within the warm reproductive tract before the egg is laid, but is then arrested until incubation begins, which may be several days to a week or more after oviposition. In a few cases (Goldfinch, Song Sparrow, and Brown Thrasher) twin embryos have been reported to hatch from single eggs (Berger, 1953b).

Development proceeds rapidly with incubation. Within 24 hours in the chick, forerunners of the nervous system, digestive tract, and vascular system have appeared. Before 36 hours the heart begins beating and food is brought to the embryo by *vitelline veins* from the yolk. By 48 hours many of the organs—eye, ear, aortic arches, and lobes of the brain—are in evidence. Respiration—intake of oxygen and elimination of gaseous wastes—takes place through the porous shell. Near the end of the incubation period (about 21 days in the domestic fowl) the chick almost completely fills the shell, having utilized all of the egg white and all of the yolk except that

*Fig. 57. Structure of an egg. (From Walter and Sayles,* Biology of the Vertebrates, *copyright 1949 by The Macmillan Company, New York.)*

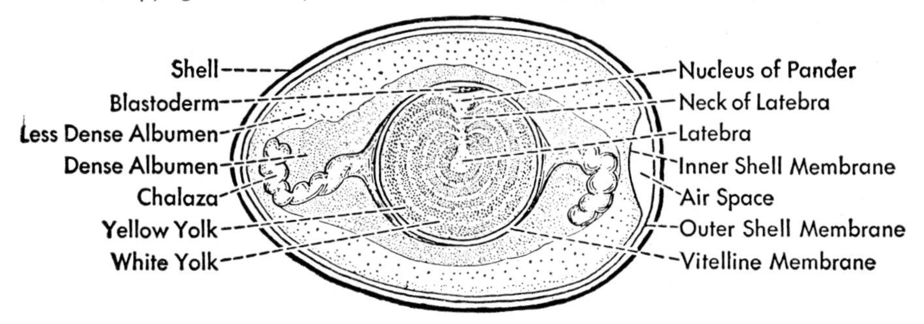

remaining in its swollen abdomen (yolk sac) for sustenance immediately after hatching. It then thrusts its beak into the air chamber of the egg for its first breath of air and gradually pips its way out of the shell by means of the egg tooth on its bill (p. 219) for its first excursion into the outside world.

## Selected References

Baldwin, S. Prentiss, and S. Charles Kendeigh. Physiology of the Temperature of Birds. *Sci. Publ. Cleveland Mus. Nat. Hist.* (1932), **3**:1–196.

Berger, Andrew J. The Comparative Functional Morphology of the Pelvic Appendage in Three Genera of Cuckoos. *Amer. Midl. Nat.* (1952), **47**:513–605.

Brodkorb, Pierce. Birds. Part Five in *Vertebrates of the United States* by Blair, Blair, Brodkorb, Cagle, and Moore. New York: McGraw, 1957.

Chamberlain, Frank W. Atlas of Avian Anatomy: Osteology, Arthrology, Myology. *Mich. State Coll. Agr. Exp. Sta., Memoir Bull.* (1943), **5**:1–213.

Farner, Donald S. Digestion and the Digestive System. Chapt. XI in A. J. Marshall's *Biology and Comparative Physiology of Birds.* New York: Academic, 1960.

Fisher, Harvey I. Adaptations and Comparative Anatomy of the Locomotor Apparatus of New World Vultures. *Amer. Mid. Nat.* (1946), **35**:545–728.

Hess, Gertrud. *The Bird: Its Life and Structure.* Translated by Phyllis Barclay-Smith. New York: Greenberg, 1951.

Hudson, George E. Studies on the Muscles of the Pelvic Appendage in Birds. *Amer. Mid. Nat.* (1937), **18**:1–108.

Hyman, Libbie H. *Comparative Vertebrate Anatomy.* Chicago: U. of Chicago, 1942.

Odum, Eugene P. Variations in the Heart Rate of Birds: A Study in Physiological Ecology. *Ecol. Mono.* (1941), **3**:299–326.

———. Some Physiological Variations in the Black-capped Chickadee. *Wilson Bull.* (1943), **55**:178–191.

Romanoff, Alexis, and Anastasia Romanoff. *The Avian Egg.* New York: Wiley, 1949.

Shufeldt, R. W. *Myology of the Raven (Corvus corax sinuatus).* London: Macmillan, 1890.

Simons, J. R. The Blood Vascular System. Chapt. IX in A. J. Marshall's *Biology and Comparative Physiology of Birds.* New York: Academic, 1960.

Sturkie, Paul D. *Avian Physiology.* Ithaca, N.Y.: Comstock, 1954.

Thompson, J. A. *The Biology of Birds.* New York: Macmillan, 1923.

Van Tyne, Josselyn, and Andrew J. Berger. *Fundamentals of Ornithology.* New York: Wiley, 1959. Chapt. 2.

Wetmore, Alexander. A Study of the Body Temperature of Birds. *Smithsonian Misc. Coll.* (1021), **72**:1–52.

# 5

# LOCOMOTION, ON LAND, WATER, AND IN THE AIR

Birds, perhaps more than ony other animal group except the insects, have mastered the art of navigation in nearly all media. Though mastery of the air is their most spectacular accomplishment, birds also climb, walk, run, jump, burrow in the ground, swim on and under water, and dive. True saltatorial forms, such as those that occur among the jumping mammals, and fossorial forms (excluding nest burrowers) are not characteristic of birds and are not discussed here, but climbing, running, navigation in the water and in the air and the adaptations associated with each will be analyzed briefly.

## *Scansorial Birds*

From fossil evidence it is believed that the first birds were arboreal and climbed trees to gain altitude before launching out on short gliding flights. The arboreal habit necessitated the development of clawed toes and a perching type of foot for roosting and for hopping from branch to branch. In *Archaeopteryx,* the first known bird, the three fingers were also separate, not fused as in modern birds, and terminated in claws. These claws on the wing, as well as the clutching foot, supposedly enabled *Archaeopteryx* to clamber among the branches of trees before taking flight.

Although quite a few modern birds—about 17 species in 4 families according to Rand (1954)—have well-developed spurs on the wings, these are mainly offensive or defensive weapons, not used for climbing. The classic example of functional claws on the wing among living birds is the Hoatzin (Fig. 58). The young of this species have well-developed claws on the second and third digits which aid them in climbing about the branches in their nest trees; if lost from the nest, they scramble back to it like quadrupeds, but in a few days the claws are shed and the young Hoatzins become bipedal.

In other scansorial birds, modifications in the pelvic appendages and tail are the chief structural features associated with climbing. These include well-developed opposable toes with sharp claws, a shortened tarsus, and (except in the nuthatches, piculets, and wrynecks) a strong tail whose stiffened shafts often terminate in sharp barbless spines. In the woodpeckers (Picidae), the zygodactylous foot (Fig. 39c) enables them to get a vicelike grip on the bark of trees. The woodhewers (Dendrocolaptidae), true creepers (Certhiidae), and nuthatches (Sittidae and allies) have the typical passerine foot structure (three toes in front and one in back), but

*Fig. 58. Odd in many ways, the Hoatzin of South America uses its crop as a gizzard and has claws on its wings when young for clambering about in trees. Even its taxonomic position among gallinaceous birds has been questioned, and it has no close relatives, being the sole member of the Opisthocomidae family. (From Hegner and Stiles,* College Zoology, *copyright 1951 by The Macmillan Company, New York.)*

long sharp claws enable them to cling to vertical surfaces. The stiff spiny tail in most species gives additional support, but largely limits climbing to ascending tree trunks and makes descending awkward. A nuthatch, by contrast, can clamber up or down or around a tree trunk without using its tail for support.

Parrots (Psittacidae) are also expert climbers and have zygodactylous feet with a reversible outer toe to aid them in maneuvers, but the strong bill also is used to pull them from one perch to another. In India large numbers of parakeets (which are economic pests) electrocute themselves by standing on one wire and grasping an adjacent wire with the bill (Dilger, 1954). Swifts (Apodidae) have small feet and are not good climbers, but use their strong curved claws and conspicuously spine-tipped tail (in some species) for support in chimneys, mine shafts, and on the sides of cliffs and caves.

## Cursorial Birds

A less generally accepted view of the origin of flying birds is that fleet-footed bipedal dinosaurs achieved flight by fast running and flapping of their free forelimbs which developed frayed scales (feathers) on their posterior margins, thus permitting gliding flight. Later some flying birds lost their power of flight and became strictly cursorial (e.g., the ostrichlike birds) or aquatic (e.g., penguins and some auks), although some authors, notably Lowe (1933, 1935), maintain that both the ostriches and the penguins were derived from flightless stock. This, however, poses a *diphyletic* (two lines of descent) rather than the more generally accepted *monophyletic* (one line of descent) theory of the origin of the flightless and flying birds.

Though the origin and subsequent evolutionary history of running birds is still somewhat nebulous, many present-day forms, flying and flightless, illustrate cursorial adaptations. These usually include an elongation of the hind limb, a reduction in the surface area of the foot coming in contact with the ground, and a reduction in the number of toes (Storer, 1960). Such features are well exemplified by the struthious birds, that is, the Ostrich, rheas, emus, and cassowaries. All are heavy-bodied, flightless forms with fluffy feathers ill-adapted for flight; show a reduction in toes; and, except for the forest-dwelling cassowaries, inhabit open areas where their speed is unimpeded. The Ostrich (Fig. 59) has been credited with a speed

*Fig. 59. The Ostrich* (Struthio camelus) *is probably the fastest running bird. It lives in relatively open parklike savannas or treeless areas of Africa where it can attain great speeds. This black male (the smaller females are gray) was photographed in Serengeti National Park, Tanganyika. (From a Kodachrome by Dale A. Zimmerman.)*

of 60 miles per hour, measuring 25 feet at a stride when full momentum is attained, but perhaps such a speed is an exaggeration. One paced by a car in an African park ran 30 miles per hour for more than 20 minutes (Grzimek, 1961), but this may not have been maximum speed. Men with horses can run down Ostriches, which run in wide circles, by taking an inside track and bringing in fresh steeds occasionally. Rheas in South America are sometimes hunted by a more picturesque method; "gauchos" on horseback pursue and surround groups of the big birds and lasso them with bolas—three-pronged ropes with weights at the ends—which trip up or entangle the helpless birds.

Somewhat transitional in nature are the neotropical tinamous (Tinamidae), which can fly, at least to a limited extent, but are primarily terrestrial and depend on running, often in dense forest cover (or among tall grasses and forbes in the upland species), for escape. Flights, when attempted, are of short duration, in a straight line, and result in some crash landings and quick exhaustion after a few take-offs.

Many other birds among the nonpasserines are true runners, as opposed to most terrestrial passerines which walk (larks, pipits, blackbirds) or hop (thrushes, sparrows). Nonmigratory galliform birds, such as pheasants and quail, take short rapid flights to escape terrestrial predators, but otherwise depend on fast running (see p. 105 for running speed) and concealment for escape. Rails, though capable of sustained flight during migration, are difficult to flush in their breeding marshes; they depend on maneuverability of their laterally compressed bodies (hence, "thin as a rail") in running through dense vegetation. Among the shorebirds, some of the sandpipers are particularly fleet-footed, apparently as an adaptation for rushing ahead of incoming waves and then back-tracking rapidly for food items left stranded by the receding waters.

Cuckoos (Cuculidae), a heterogeneous family of some 127 species, are primarily aboreal, but one aberrant subfamily group of about 13 species has taken up a terrestrial mode of life. Best known of these is the Roadrunner (Fig. 60) of our southwestern deserts. These birds have been credited with amazing speed and dexterity in pursuing swift lizards, outmaneuvering hounds, and outdistancing human pursuers (Sutton, in Bent, 1940); two actual checks with car speedometers set their speeds at 10 and about 15 miles per hour, respectively. Cottam, *et al.* (1942), timed two Roadrunners at 12 and 15 miles per hour, respectively (in soft sand and upgrade), but found two Ring-necked Pheasants (at 15 and 21 miles per hour) and a Chukar (at 18 miles per hour) equalling or exceeding the

*Fig. 60. The Roadrunner is one of the most agile and fleet-footed of terrestrial birds, can outmaneuver most predators, and captures grasshoppers, lizards, snakes, and even adult birds. (From a Kodachrome by Dale A. Zimmerman.)*

speed of the Roadrunner. Dissection of the pelvic musculature of both arboreal and terrestrial cuckoos (p. 100) indicates that while muscle formulae are similar in both groups, the Roadrunner's cursorial habit is reflected in the elongation of the hind limbs and a corresponding increase in the length of the pelvic muscles.

## Wading Birds

Some nonswimming birds have developed useful adaptations for wading in shallow water for prey not usually available on shore. Extremely long legs, counterbalanced by a long neck and long bill for making sudden thrusts or for probing, are characteristic of herons (Fig. 61), cranes, flamingos (Fig. 42) and some shorebirds. If walking on soft surfaces is neces-

*Fig. 61. Long sharp beaks, long flexible necks, long legs, and widespreading toes are among the adaptations exhibited by many wading birds for capturing prey in shallow water. Here a Common Egret is presumably stalking a fish or frog. The kink in the neck is due to the lengthened sixth cervical. (Photo by Allan D. Cruickshank.)*

sary, the toes are elongated (a handicap for running or perching), as in the case of herons, or webbed as in flamingos, to give additional support. The elongation of the toes is carried to extremes in jaçanas and gallinules which walk on floating vegetation. Among the shorebirds, curlews, yellowlegs, avocets, and stilts are particularly noted for long legs and bills for foraging in shallow waters.

## Swimming Birds

Although most land birds can probably swim for short distances under dire necessity, nearly all true swimmers show some special adaptations for aquatic existence. These usually involve an expanded foot with the toes fully webbed or lobed (Fig. 38), a dense compact waterproof plumage (except in some pelecaniform birds), and an enlarged oil gland. Some groups show additional adaptations (see below), but aquatic birds are numerous, many of them apparently independently evolved, and it is not possible to discuss them all here. Many oceanic birds, such as petrels, shearwaters, gulls and terns, are primarily aerial and merely rest or float on the water rather than doing much active swimming.

*Hesperornis* (Fig. 16), a flightless bird that inhabited the inland seas of North America in the Cretaceous, is proof that birds took to the water at a very early date. *Hesperornis* had powerfully developed hind limbs with large feet and broadly lobed toes. The legs were set far back on the body, useless for locomotion on land, and were apparently laterally disposed for sidewise strokes, features which denote early specialization for swimming both on and under water, presumably in pursuit of fish.

Among modern birds the loons and grebes are expert swimmers both on and under water. The loons in particular exhibit a streamlined body, have their legs set far back (making walking on land difficult and awkward), have their tarsi flattened and bladelike to lessen the resistance of the water when the foot is drawn forward, and show various modifications in pelvic musculature and in the skeleton for life in the water (Wilcox, 1952). They use simultaneous forward and backward strokes, closing the toes when the foot is brought forward. Grebes (Fig. 62), which have lobed rather than webbed toes, bring the foot forward in a sidewise stroke, with the top of the foot parallel with the surface of the water (Storer, 1956). Grebes also have a dense hairlike plumage which encloses little air and thus facilitates sudden submergence and underwater swimming. These and other differ-

*Fig. 62. This Western Grebe is highly specialized for aquatic life and rarely ventures out on the land. It builds a floating nest, performs spectacular displays by "dancing" on the water with its mate, and is an expert swimmer both on and under the surface. (Photo by Allan D. Cruickshank.)*

ences between the loons and grebes denote that they are not of common origin and that similarities are due to convergence (Storer, 1956).

Among the Anatidae, the geese and swans are surface swimmers and feed by "tipping up" in shallow water or grazing on land. The ducks include both tip-up types (the Anatinae of the A.O.U.) and diving forms—pochards (Fig. 63), sea ducks, mergansers. Ducks of both types usually swim with alternate strokes of the feet, and underwater swimmers use their wings to a considerable extent, but there appears to be considerable variability among different species as well as intraspecific differences under different conditions, such as depth of water, fast pursuit, or leisurely foraging. Humphrey (1958), observing the activities of a captive Common Eider in a tank, says that it used both feet and wings during submergence (for quick descent), but used only its feet when foraging on the bottom (to conserve energy) and rose to the surface by buoyancy without noticeable movements of either feet or wings. Submergence in pochards, scoters, and mergansers is accomplished without use of the wings.

*Fig. 63. This Ring-necked Duck, a diving pochard, has presumably just emerged from an underwater swim; its dense waterproof plumage enables it to shed water effectively. (Photo by Allan D. Cruickshank.)*

Swimming speeds appear not to be available for many ducks. Hochbaum (1944) gives the rate of flightless adult Canvasback as 2 to 3 miles per hour and the "skittering" speed as 8 to 10 miles per hour. Stewart (1958) timed day-old ducklings of the Wood Duck swimming at the average speed of 0.6 miles per hour and skittering at 5.8 miles per hour (for short distances). An adult male in the flightless stage skittered at the rate of 9.5 miles per hour.

A most remarkable aquatic specialization is found in the dippers or water ouzels (Cinclidae), a small family of 6 species of passerine birds that inhabit swift-flowing mountain streams in the Americas and in the northern parts of the Old World (Fig. 64). Though primarily land birds, they feed almost exclusively on aquatic organisms gleaned from streams. They plunge into and swim or walk under water, usually progressing upstream. Goodge (1959), both from observations in their natural haunts and from the analysis of motion pictures of captive birds in tanks, reports that the North American species uses its wings almost exclusively for underwater swimming, but employs a paddling motion of its unwebbed feet (webs would

*Fig. 64. This water-loving songster, the Dipper, inhabits Rocky Mountain cascades, builds its mossy nest beside a stream, and forages under water for insect prey. (Drawing by Dale A. Zimmerman.)*

be a handicap in clinging to rocks) when swimming on the surface. It dives into a stream either from the air or from the surface of the water and can emerge from the water flying.

Perhaps the most specialized of aquatic birds are the penguins (Fig. 65), which have forsaken flight entirely and eke out an existence in some of the bleakest and most inhospitable regions on earth (p. 192). The forelimbs in penguins are scale-covered flippers with no remiges. The bony elements in

*Fig. 65. King Penguins (*Aptenodytes patagonica*) of the Antarctic are most at home in the water, swimming and diving, but they shuffle around awkwardly on the land during the prolonged breeding season. Some King Penguins hold their single egg on their feet during incubation, others place it in a nest in a burrow. (From Hegner and Stiles,* College Zoology, *copyright 1959 by The Macmillan Company, New York.)*

the wing are flattened, the dense plumage covers the entire body (no apteria), and a heavy layer of fat insulates their bodies against the cold. Penguins use their flippers almost entirely for underwater swimming, and can attain speeds of 25 miles per hour (Austin, 1961). By building up momentum under water they can leap up out of the water for 6 feet or more to land on rocks or floating ice cakes. On shore they progress by an awkward upright gait, or occasionally drop onto their ventral surface and "toboggan" over the ice and snow by using their flippers and kicking with their feet. On the long inland march of certain species to distant breeding rookeries they alternate walking and tobogganing and may take several months to reach their destination (Rivolier, 1959).

## *Diving Birds*

Diving is accomplished by two methods: (1) surface diving, such as employed by penguins, loons, grebes, cormorants, and most ducks, and (2) plunging into the water from a height, as illustrated by the Gannets, Brown Pelican, kingfishers, and Osprey. Of course, some birds use both methods. Many others merely dip into the water for surface prey with or without submerging.

Land birds that dive from considerable heights include the Osprey and many kingfishers. The former hovers over the water, then folds its wings and plunges down with great speed, but breaks before hitting the water and grasps fish with specially equipped talons (Fig. 39), often without submerging completely. The kingfishers, by contrast, dive head first into the water, either from a perch or a hovering position. Fish are speared (punctured) with the beak closed, then taken to a convenient perch to disengage and swallow. Red oil droplets in the eyes of kingfishers are believed to function in underwater vision (see p. 129).

The Gannet of the North Atlantic is one of the most remarkable divers. It plunges headlong from heights up to 150 feet and hits the water with a tremendous impact which carries it deep beneath the surface. Subcutaneous air cells act as shock absorbers to cushion the blow. Brown Pelicans (Fig. 66) use a similar technique, but curiously turn under water and emerge facing the opposite direction from which they entered, or sometimes merely bounce back from the water without submerging completely.

Deep divers such as the Common Loon and Oldsquaw, which have been recorded at depths up to 200 feet, face the problem of reducing their

*Fig. 66. The Brown Pelican, though grotesque in appearance when perched, is a skillful aerialist and expert diver, plunging into the water for fish. Often, however, the pelicans congregate on wharves and pilings and wait for fishermen to toss them handouts. (Photo by Allan D. Cruickshank.)*

buoyancy before submergence (Schorger, 1947). It is now thought that they expel the air from their air sacs as well as that trapped in the plumage and draw on oxygen converted from the oxyhemoglobin and oxymyoglobin stored in the muscles. Such divers also are capable of high carbon dioxide tolerance and of reducing the flow of blood to the muscles while under water. Voluntary submergence in water birds is usually of short duration, commonly less than three minutes, but domestic ducks have been held under water in experimental tests up to a maximum of sixteen minutes before asphyxiation, or twenty-seven minutes when the trachea was tied off. Presumably in such cases, both air from the air sacs and "converted" oxygen are utilized.

## *Bird Flight*

In preceding sections reference has been made repeatedly to various features of a bird's physical equipment for flight: (1) the body is streamlined, thus offering the least resistance to air; (2) feathers as a body covering in most birds are constructed and arranged to aid flight rather than hinder it; (3) the avian skeleton appears to be largely remodeled from the original vertebrate plan to facilitate flying; (4) the internal organs are well centralized, with certain structures reduced and others eliminated; (5) respiration, unique in itself, is supplemented by a remarkable system of air sacs; (6) rapid metabolism provides for high intake, quick consumption, and economic utilization of fuel; and (7) a marvelously designed wing, equipped with special flight muscles, has been developed as an instrument of propulsion through air.

### GLIDING FLIGHT

Three different types of flight are commonly recognized, although all three kinds may be used at different times by the same bird. The first and simplest of these is gliding flight (Fig. 67l), presumably worked out by the earliest birds, which climbed trees and launched out on set wings to coast as far as the prevailing conditions of air and height of take-off permitted. We see a similar performance in many birds today, as when a pheasant works up considerable initial velocity by rapid wing flapping and then goes into a long glide. Air conditions, wind direction, and speed of take-off determine how far the bird can go before gravity brings it down. Shorebirds coming in for a landing, ducks descending over water, swallows and swifts in the air, are among the birds commonly seen to utilize gliding flight.

### FLAPPING FLIGHT

The most common type of flying is ordinary flapping or cruising flight (Fig. 67r), perhaps originally developed by arboreal or cursorial reptiles and birds to increase the distance or effectiveness of the glide. Flapping flight, as the name implies, consists of up-and-down motions of the wings, but they are so skillfully executed that the effort of keeping the bird aloft is minimized and forward velocity achieved at the same time.

Keeping the bird aloft involves economy on the upstroke in several

*Fig. 67. Left. Gliding flight, illustrated by a Gambel's Quail. Right. Flapping flight of Arctic Tern. (Drawings by Dale A. Zimmerman.)*

ways: (1) the convexity (camber) of the upper surface of the wing in most birds permits ready air flow off the feathers when the wing is raised; (2) separation of the tips of the primaries (a device known as "slotting"), which in some birds are notched or emarginate, allows free passage of air through them and reduces turbulence at the trailing edge of the wing; (3) the wing is partially folded at the wrist and elbow and drawn back in toward the body, thus reducing friction; and finally (4) the upstroke is often accomplished by a quick flip, especially at the end of the stroke, the air itself helping to throw the wing backward and upward. Conversely the effective power of the downstroke is usually increased by (1) the concavity of the under surface of the wing which thus grips more air, (2) holding the flight feathers firmly together (closing the slots), (3) extending the fully expanded wing, and (4) relatively slow (compared to upstroke) and powerful motion downward. The vacuum created on top of the wing by the downstroke provides additional lift. We have already seen (p. 75) that the pectoralis major muscle is especially well developed in strong fliers, less so in soarers, although Nair (1954) has pointed out that the latter may use a double set of muscles alternately to minimize fatigue. Conversely, the deep pectoral (supracoracoideus), except in swifts and hummingbirds, is relatively small.

Up-and-down motions of the wings serve to keep the bird aloft, but this does not explain forward progress. Of course, as motion pictures show, the movements of the wings are not strictly up and down, but upward and backward, then powerfully downward and forward. On the downward-forward motion, the leading edge of the wing is depressed, thus displacing air backward, so that the bird is virtually pushing itself forward on air beneath and behind the wings. Then, as the wing is pulled posteriorly at the end of the stroke, further forward motion is imparted to the body.

Though this is the pattern of strokes characteristic of most birds, there are many variations. The aerial gymnastics of the swifts involve many different wing motions—banking and veering and stalling with one wing in a jerky sort of flight that gives the optical illusion of alternate wing beats (Savile, 1950). Hummingbirds and swifts, as previously mentioned, utilize a powered upstroke as well as downstroke, the former in a whir of wings that beat from fifty-five to seventy-five or more times per second compared to the slow flapping of a vulture at one stroke per second. Then of course the flight feathers, particularly the first primary, as well as the various parts of the wing (alula, manus, forearm, and so on) can be moved more or less independently, thus allowing for all sorts of adjustments in position, balance, and maneuvers in correlation with wind and air conditions. Other variables are that the requirements for the take-off may be quite different than those for leisurely flying, that a sudden burst of speed imposes new demands, and that landing involves new techniques and the use of other muscles.

### SOARING

Soaring (Fig. 68) is a highly specialized flying skill which employs alternate flapping and gliding, but, in its highest development, utilizes updrafts

*Fig. 68. Frigate-birds (man-o'-war birds) have long, narrow wings (high-aspect ratio), providing a large sail area. An extremely light, pneumatic skeleton gives them additional buoyancy and they remain aloft for long periods, often without visible movements of the wings. (Photo by Allan D. Cruickshank.)*

and air currents so expertly that flapping is often dispensed with for long periods. Soaring is characteristic of birds with a large sail area per body weight (Poole, 1938), but two quite different wing types seem to be equally effective for this kind of flight: those with long, narrow wings like albatrosses and frigate-birds (high-aspect ratio) and those with short, broad wings like hawks (low-aspect). Both types require a large supporting sail area; the broad tail fans of the hawks help materially in this respect. Oceanic birds may drift along on nearly motionless wings for long periods, riding on turbulent air currents at certain levels or on updrafts created by ships. Jameson (1958), however, maintains that updrafts at sea are entirely inadequate for keeping an albatross aloft; this is achieved by skillful use of *variations* in wind speed at different levels, the surface winds being slowed down by friction against the waves. He credits the Wandering Albatross with an "instinctive knowledge of meteorology, aerodynamics and applied mechanics. . . ."

Land birds in mountainous regions make use of updrafts from adjacent valleys; hawks at Hawk Mountain, Pennsylvania, move long distances along a famed migration route by taking advantage of updrafts from precipitous Appalachian slopes. An Osprey has been observed to attain the amazing speed, while still coasting, of eighty miles per hour (Broun and Goodwin, 1943). Hawks can also be observed circling on sunny spring days over warming patches of meadows, taking advantage of the rising air associated with the earth's radiation. Again a hawk may execute wide circles by riding down wind to pick up velocity, then turning and riding up wind until it begins to lose altitude, when it will again ride down wind to regain speed for the up-wind segment of the circle.

Savile (1957), elaborating on the traditional division into low- and high-aspect ratios (wing length-breadth ratios) recognizes four different though often overlapping wing types: (1) the elliptical wing with low-aspect ratio, characteristic of birds living in restricted spaces (gallinaceous birds, doves, woodpeckers, most passerines); (2) a high-speed wing, with moderately high-aspect ratio, characteristic of birds with narrow tapered wings for fast flight in open spaces (falcons, swifts, hummingbirds, swallows); (3) high-aspect ratio wing found in oceanic birds (albatrosses, frigate-birds); and (4) the high-lift or slotted soaring wing, with moderate aspect ratio, pronounced slotting and camber, found in hawks and owls operating in wooded areas.

### TAIL, WIND, AND SPEED OF FLIGHT

The tail of a bird is an important instrument in flight. Though a bird temporarily deprived of its tail is not necessarily flightless, its progress is more labored and its balance in the air more precarious. The tail serves a variety of balancing and steering functions, and in long-tailed birds is a decided asset in aerial maneuvers. Closing and tilting of the tail fan adjusts a bird to surrounding air conditions. In horizontal flight, spreading the tail fan would give additional lift toward the rear, the center of gravity would shift anteriorly, and the head of the bird dip for downward descent; conversely, closing the tail fan would shift the center of gravity backward and the bird would rise. Turns may be initiated by tilting the tail sidewise, but of course merely turning the head in the desired direction and stalling with one wing also help execute a turn. Tails can be used as an air brake coming in for a landing, as is observable in ducks descending on a pond or a bird alighting upon a perch. We have already seen (p. 78) that severing the M. depressor caudae in pigeons causes a loss in braking power (Fisher, 1958). The broad tail fan of a Ruffed Grouse is useful in dodging obstacles in the forest. The short tail of the Chimney Swift is offset by the versatility of its wings. Ducks are somewhat handicapped by an extremely short tail, and straight, fast flights without quick turns are characteristic of this group of birds.

Wind as a factor in modifying flight is important. Birds have two speeds, an air speed due to their progress irrespective of the accelerating or retarding effect of the wind and a ground speed which is measured in terms of actual progress through space. That is, a duck flying with an air speed of 40 miles per hour in a tail wind of 10 miles per hour would have a ground speed of 50 miles per hour; conversely, in flying into the same wind the bird's ground speed or actual progress would be slowed down to 30 miles per hour.

Many measured flight speeds are now available for many different birds. Cooke (1937) tabulated the early records for more than 100 species and Cottam, *et al.* (1942), measured (or listed) flight speeds for 91 birds of 57 species. Cruising speeds among the latter varied from a low of 12 miles per hour in a Burrowing Owl and 18 miles per hour in two herons to a high of 55 miles per hour in a Redhead when pressed.

Most passerine species normally fly at about 15 to 25 miles per hour, but can usually accelerate this to about 35 miles per hour for short distances when pursued. Swallows and Starlings, among passerines, are somewhat faster; Starlings attain speeds of 40 to 48 miles per hour. Many of the larger nonpasserine birds are capable of higher speeds; records for ducks and geese range from 40 to 60 miles per hour, and a Canvasback and Oldsquaw have been clocked at about 72 (Speirs, 1945), but aviators claim that they can run down most ducks when their planes are traveling 65 miles per hour. Some of the shorebirds are also fast fliers, with speeds ranging from 40 to 60 miles per hour. McCabe (1942) estimated the flight speed of two flocks of sandpipers (which *passed* his plane) at 110 miles per hour. Pittman (1953) clocked the flight speed of a Common Loon at about 90 miles per hour as it went into a shallow dive in front of a plane.

The swifts and falcons are believed to be the fastest flying birds. E. C. Stuart Baker's oft-quoted record of a swift in Asia achieving a speed of 171.4 to 200 miles per hour has been questioned by Wing (1956), but Lincoln (1939) estimated that a large neotropical swift (*Streptoprocne zonaris*) might approach that speed (150 miles per hour estimated). Two records listed by Cooke (1937) for the Duck Hawk or Peregrine Falcon gave a speed of 165 to 180 miles per hour for one and 175 for another, both apparently attained in the sudden downward plunge or "stoop."

Birds fly readily into or with the wind; the view that a bird oriented with the wind is handicapped by having its feathers ruffled applies only to a perched bird, as (obviously) a bird in flight is traveling faster than the wind (its own speed *plus* that of the wind) and feels no effect of it other than in increased speed. A bird on the ground or in a tree, however, nearly always faces into the wind, not only to avoid ruffled feathers, but also to facilitate the take-off. Many birds cannot rise in a tail wind but have to face into it. A flock of sparrows on a highway, when approached by a car traveling with the wind, may be observed to fly *toward* the car momentarily before swerving out of its path. Large-winged birds like vultures and albatrosses, so graceful in soaring flight once they are launched, are very awkward on the take-off and have to get a running start into the wind before they can rise. South American natives have capitalized on this in capturing condors in baited enclosures, from which the birds can not escape because of the lack of an adequate runway.

Cross winds affect a bird's flight more seriously. To maintain a straight course in a strong cross wind, a bird has to head slightly into the wind, as an experienced boatman heads his vessel upstream to cross a river in a straight line. It is not clear whether a bird in sustained flight, as over a body of water, consciously pursues a straight course by constantly tacking slightly into the wind, or allows itself to be blown out of its direct course and then regains its position by flying into the wind. Limited observations suggest that both methods may be used: Starlings and other birds are often observed, over short courses at least, to fly sideways, and migrating birds have been observed to come ashore *into* the wind, though a direct line of flight would have brought them in on a cross wind.

## Selected References

Aymar, Gordon. *Bird Flight.* New York: Dodd, 1935.

Cooke, May Thatcher. Flight Speed of Birds. *U.S. Dept. Agric. Circ. No. 428.* (1937).

Cottam, Clarence, Williams, Cecil S., and Clarence A. Sooter. Flight and Running Speeds of Birds. *Wilson Bull.* (1942) **34**:121–131.

Fisher, Harvey I. Adaptations and Comparative Anatomy of the Locomotor Apparatus of New World Vultures. *Amer. Midl. Nat.* (1946), **35**:545–727.

Jameson, William. *The Wandering Albatross.* London: Rupert Hart-Davis, 1958.

Savile, D.B.O. Adaptive Evolution in the Avian Wing. *Evolution* (1957), **11**: 212–224.

Storer, John, H. The Flight of Birds. *Cranbrook Inst. Sci. Bull.* No. 28 (1948).

Storer, Robert W. Adaptive Radiation in Birds. Chapt. II in A. J. Marshall's *Biology and Comparative Physiology of Birds.* New York: Academic, 1960.

Van Tyne, Josselyn, and Andrew J. Berger. *Fundamentals of Ornithology.* New York: Wiley, 1959. Chapt. 8 on Flight.

# 6

# THE SENSE ORGANS AND ENDOCRINE GLANDS

Sense organs (*receptors*) are responsible for perceiving sensations (*stimuli*) in the outside environment and transmitting them through nerve cells (*neurons*) to the brain. Details of the nervous system *per se* are not considered here, but the brain and sense organs in birds are explained, primarily from a functional, rather than morphological, point of view. A brief account of the endocrine glands, whose secretions (*hormones*), play so vital a role in development and behavior, is included.

The avian brain (Fig. 69) is similar in structure and function to that of other vertebrates. The *olfactory lobes* are small, in correlation with the poorly developed sense of smell in birds; the *optic lobes* are large, in keeping with the well-known visual acuity of the avian eye; and the expansive *cerebrum*, though showing considerable advance over lower vertebrates, is relatively smooth and lacks the deep fissures characteristic of the mammalian brain. This apparently results in the highly stereotyped, yet selectively efficient, behavior patterns characteristic of birds. The *cerebellum*, which is responsible for precise control over movements, is well developed. The whole brain is packed into a comparatively small space in the cranium, crowded posteriorly by the extremely large orbits whose medial margins are separated only by a thin interorbital plate. Posterior crowding is carried to the extreme in some of the shorebirds; in a snipe the cerebral axis is actually vertical or at right angles to the bill, compared to the horizontal position of the brain in a smaller-eyed cormorant (Portmann and Stingelin, 1961), and in the American Woodcock (Cobb,

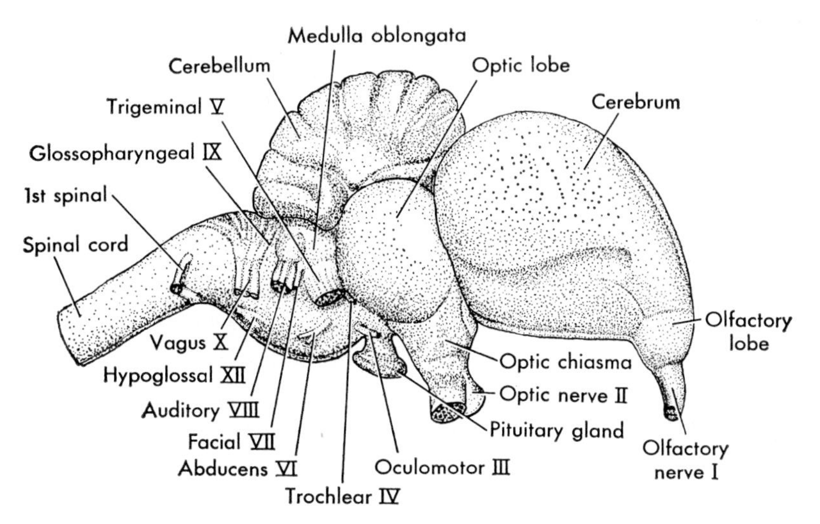


*Fig. 69. Brain of Common Pigeon. (Drawing by R. M. Naik.)*

1959) the brain is tilted 117° so that the floor of the cerebellum faces upward!

The avian brain reaches its highest development in the corvids, a group displaying unusual adaptive resourcefulness, but it is also exceptionally large in the parrots, owls, and woodpeckers. The importance of the *pituitary*, a glandular structure suspended from the floor of the brain, is discussed under endocrine glands.

## *The Sense Organs*

### TACTILE ORGANS

Tactile senses are not well developed in birds; this is largely prevented by the nearly complete investment of the body with feathers. There are sensory nerve endings in the bill, however, which so often is used as an exploratory instrument, particularly in ducks, whose beaks are equipped with sensitive sifting plates for sorting food particles out of bottom debris. The swollen operculum of pigeons (Fig. 50d) is believed to play an important stimulatory role in love-making. Rictal bristles about the bill and other protruding feather structures, while in themselves without nerve endings, have sensory cells in the feather follicle at their base, and thus can perform a tactile function when they come in contact with another object. The tongue in many birds also has tactile receptors, apart from the taste buds. The presence of sensory corpuscles on the tibia is thought to enable birds to perceive vibrations while perching (Pumphrey, 1961).

### SMELL

The sense of smell is apparently of little importance to birds. Structural proof of this lies in the poor development of the *turbinal* bones in the nasal passages, which are usually relatively bare instead of being covered with sensory epithelium as in mammals. The external nares (Fig. 50) in most birds open into a horny beak and lack the sensitive muzzle so useful for deer, for example, in testing the wind or for a carnivore in following a trail. In the adults of some pelecaniform birds (e.g., gannets, boobies, cormorants) the external nares are practically obliterated. In some sea birds, as pointed out in Chapter 4, glands in the nasal cavity function in the extraction of salt from sea water but have little or nothing to do with smell.

Dissection of the olfactory apparatus—turbinals, olfactory tract, and lobes—of representative avian types reveals the poorest development in the more advanced terrestrial birds and somewhat better development in aquatic species, suggesting phylogenetic degeneration perhaps correlated with increased specialization of other senses, such as vision. Only the primitive kiwis (Fig. 13), of birds examined, possess good olfactory equipment. This is in keeping with their known habits, for kiwis, unlike most other birds, have poor vision, and feed chiefly at night, groping about in the semidarkness and sniffing the ground for concealed prey. Tests conducted with earthworms buried in buckets of sand have disclosed the kiwi's uncanny ability to ferret out hidden worms, probably by smelling them, as it ignored buckets containing no worms. However, the experiments did not rule out the possibility that hearing was involved.

Tests with vultures have been somewhat contradictory, but seem to indicate that they are unable to detect concealed carrion by smell and use visual clues in locating it. Seeing the dead animals from afar, watching other carrion-feeders gravitate toward a carcass, or even detecting sarcophagous insects buzzing about in the vicinity of carrion are among the visual clues believed to be utilized by vultures in locating food. However, there may be some species differences, as Lewis (1928) states that Turkey Vultures have better olfactory equipment than Black Vultures and that this is more useful to them in warm weather than in cold. Walter (1943), after seemingly exhaustive tests, concluded that none of his avian subjects had any appreciable sense of smell, but Frings and Boyd (1952) and Hamrum

(1953) concluded from feeding experiments that Bobwhites were guided in their selection of food by olfactory stimulation.

### TASTE

Taste discrimination, which so often is correlated in part at least with smell, is also an uncertain entity in birds. We have seen from the scarcity of taste buds in the mouth (p. 78) that the structural basis for tasting is relatively poor and we know from general observations that most birds bolt down hurriedly the apparently hereditary foods that they are accustomed to eat without much experimental sampling for palatability. The more adaptable birds, particularly those with somewhat omnivorous diets, do experiment at times with new or questionable foods. Birds at feeding stations are commonly observed to sample, then accept or reject, unfamiliar items, although it is not certain just what part taste plays in their selections. Bené (1947) believed that hummingbirds at feeding vials could discriminate between different concentrations of sweets and ignored, after one taste, those below a certain standard. In the wild they feed at selected flowers, although factors other than taste—color, flower structure, and the nectar supply—may influence their choice.

Insectivorous birds may have a greater need for taste than seed-eaters, as there are some distasteful insects. Experiments show apparent taste discrimination in some subjects and not much in others. A young Gray-cheeked Thrush kept in captivity for a year (Wallace, 1939) became very choosey about his diet. He had decided fruit preferences, preferred steak to hamburg, and would not eat the latter if it was stale. When very young he learned that certain sawfly larvae (*Pristiphora geniculata*) were distasteful; he would eat them only when nothing else was offered, then shook them violently and gulped them down quickly, blinking his eyes and erecting the feathers on top of his head as the worms passed down. Nestlings, when fed these worms by their parents, commonly spit them out.

Carrion-feeders must have little or no sense of taste, at least the "ripeness" of a carcass seems to perturb them not at all. Many birds (several hundred neotropical species) appear to relish ants, possibly having an alkalizing digestive substance to neutralize the formic acid in the insects, yet some species will not eat them. Birds in captivity do considerable choosing when variety is offered, and even seem somewhat conscious of a balanced diet, but how much selectivity is governed by taste is uncertain. The young thrush referred to above was apparently able to distinguish poisonous insects, for when rose chafers (*Macrodactylus*) were given him (by mistake) they were sampled, then rejected; possibly one or two were actually swallowed and found not to "set right." Young pheasants in rearing pens sometimes die of rose-chafer poisoning, but adults will not eat the insects.

Thus some birds seem to have a fairly discriminating sense of taste, others little or none, while most birds have a high capacity for selectivity which may be governed in part by taste.

## VISION

The eye of a bird is a remarkable structure with great visual acuity, as is vital for creatures so dependent on keen sight for existence. Having mastered the most difficult medium in which an animal can live—the air—the need for sharp and discriminating vision is readily apparent.

Figure 70 shows the main features of the avian eye. Structurally a bird's eye is quite comparable to the human eye, but differs in relative size, shape, and degree of development of various parts. It is notably large, for in some hawks and owls it is fully as large as the human eye, though largely concealed by lids. Rather than being strictly spherical, as in most mammals, it is flattened in most songbirds and in swans, is somewhat globose with a bulging *cornea* and *lens* in the diurnal birds of prey, and is nearly tubular in the owls (Fig. 70). A ring of bony *sclerotic plates* holds the eye in place (in most birds), and imparts a forward bulge to the cornea. A special muscle (Crampton's) controls the curvature of the cornea, and other mus-

*Fig. 70. Structure and shape of birds' eyes. a. Flattened type found in swans and most songbirds. b. Globose, with bulging cornea, as in diurnal birds of prey. c. Tubular, as in owls. (Drawings by Vito Cangemi, adapted from Wall's* Vertebrate Eye, *Cranbrook Inst. of Science, after Soemmering.)*

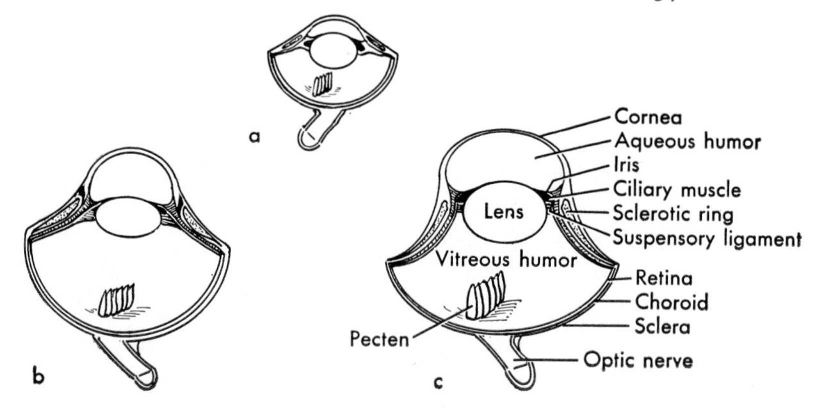

cles change the shape of the relatively soft lens, thus effecting a double means of quick accommodation, or instantaneous focus from far to near. In diving birds, Crampton's muscle is degenerate, suggesting that the shape of the cornea is not important in underwater vision, but other structures permit extreme flattening of the lens for close views under water (Pumphrey, 1961).

The *retina* of a bird, the image-forming tissue completely lining the posterior cavity of the eye, is elaborately developed. It is nearly twice as thick as in the human eye and densely packed with minute visual cells, the *rods* and *cones*, the former light-sensitive cells operating chiefly at low-light intensities (for night vision), the latter operating at high-light intensities for color discrimination and for forming sharp images. In centers of concentration these visual cells may be very abundant, as many as 1,000,000 per square millimeter in some falconiform birds. All diurnal birds and most nocturnal birds have at least one sensitive spot or *fovea* on the retina for focusing sharply on an object, and many birds have two. One of these, the central fovea, is near the center of the retina for sharpened lateral (monocular) views; the other, the temporal fovea, is toward the posterior margin of the chamber for looking forward (binocularly). The former is sometimes called the "search" fovea for picking up items from the ground or foliage, the other the "pursuit" fovea for pursuing flying insects or moving prey, or, in the case of kingfishers, for underwater vision (Milne and Milne, 1950; Shepard, 1951; Smith, 1945).

Most birds, obviously, depend mainly on *monocular* vision, that is, each eye is used independently for lateral views. Owls, however, have their eyes directed forward and are believed to use *binocular* vision only. There is great variation, however, in the actual position of the eyes, and most birds, other than owls, are capable of both monocular and binocular vision. Songbirds, pigeons, and waterfowl, for example, with laterally directed eyes used chiefly for scanning foliage, the ground, or the water, have a wide angle of monocular vision, nearly half a circle on each side, but only a narrow zone, ranging roughly from 10° to 25°, of binocular vision ahead (Fig. 71a). Hawks, however, with eyes set more nearly forward, have a smaller range of monocular vision and cannot see backward without turning the head, but have a considerably wider field of binocular vision (35° to 50°) in front (Fig. 71b). Owls, as already mentioned, see only forward, but over the widest binocular field found in birds (Fig. 71c). Their restricted field of view to the side is compensated for by swift movements of the head which can be turned completely backward.

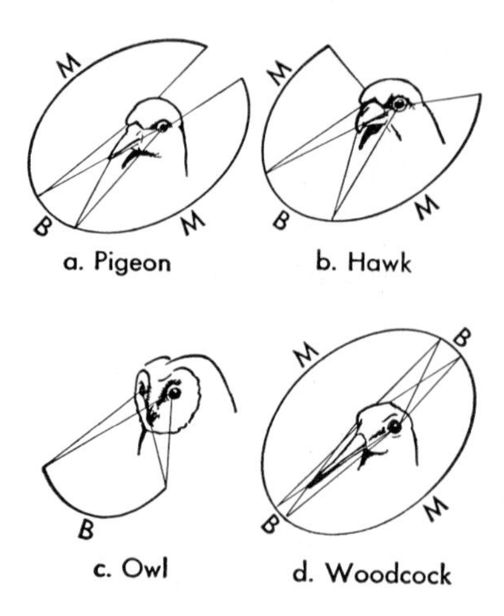


*Fig. 71. Range of monocular and binocular vision. a. In pigeon. b. In hawk. c. In owl. d. In woodcock. (Drawings by Edward Bradbury, reproduced by permission from Stuart Smith,* How to Study Birds, *copyright 1945 by Wm. Collins Sons and Company, Ltd., London.)*

The American Woodcock is noted for its curious backward-directed eyes, and apparently is capable of binocular vision *both* forward and backward (or upward when its bill is plunged in the ground) as well as having a monocular view over nearly half a circle on each side (Fig. 71d). The bitterns, to cite another peculiarity, have "low-slung" eyes, and in "freezing" they can point the beak upward and look forward binocularly for danger (Fig. 72).

*Fig. 72. Three Least Bitterns "freeze" in the nest and look forward binocularly for danger, a feat made possible by their exceptionally low-slung eyes. (Courtesy of Edward M. Brigham, Jr.)*

Monocular vision, however, is not without certain disadvantages. It gives a poor conception of distance until the eye is brought to bear directly upon an object. Hence we see a bird cock its head to focus with one eye upon an object before snatching it. Offsetting these disadvantages, however, are the advantages of long-range vision, extraordinarily quick accommodation from telescopic to miscroscopic views, a wide field of vision in all directions, and in nocturnal birds a specialized ability to make use of dim light. According to some authors, the visual acuity of some hawks, on the basis of retinal structure of rods and cones, is judged to be eight times that of man, and an owl's capacity of seeing in dim light is about ten times that of the human eye. But Pumphrey (1961) warns against trying to compare vision in birds with man and, except for quickness of accommodation and the ability to survey a large field rapidly, doubts the alleged superiority of avian vision.

Two additional structures of somewhat uncertain function in the avian eye are the *nictitating membrane*, a semitransparent third eyelid which can be drawn posteriorly over the surface of the eye, and the *pecten*, a vascular comblike structure jutting out from the retina into the posterior cavity. The nictitating membrane is thought to serve mainly for cleansing the eyeball, but it may also function as a protective device when birds are facing or flying against the wind, to cut down on the glare of sunlight for nocturnal birds during the day, and to shield the eyes of aquatic birds under water. The pecten is a highly vascular body undoubtedly associated with the nutrition of the hard-worked avian eye; some thirty other possible functions assigned to it are largely speculative, although Menner's theory that it casts a shadow on the retina when a distant object appears, thus facilitating detection of movement, has received considerable support (Pumphrey, 1961).

Various eye defects, or anomalies in development, have been frequently described in poultry and pigeons, but rarely in wild birds, presumably because the defects prove lethal. Wetherbee (1958), in the artificial incubation of more than 2,000 eggs of over 100 species of wild birds, found only two teratological specimens: one Common Grackle had no right eye, and a Mockingbird embryo had fused optic capsules (*synophthalmia*). Wallace (1956) reported a young Robin, successfully fledged, in which one eye had no lens and the other was only one-fourth its normal size (*microphthalmia*) with the eyelid sealed shut. Such anomalies would appear to make self-feeding impossible for most birds, but Lorenz (pers. comm.) says that cases of microphthalmia have appeared in his captive ducks in Germany and that the young are capable of limited self-feeding, presumably by contact with food (tactile sense) rather than vision.

Several substantial lines of evidence denote good color vision in birds. Structural proof rests in the abundance of cones in the retina, which are in part for perception of colors. The colorful plumages of birds strongly suggest the role these play in species and sex recognition. Some early experiments testing color vision in poultry and pigeons by using colored grains (dyed or flooded with spectral light) showed that the birds invariably ate the grains at the red-orange-yellow end of the spectrum, but hesitated at or ignored those at the blue end, a result that was interpreted as "blue-blindness." Tests by the Fish and Wildlife Service (Kalmbach and Welch, 1946) with colored poisons seemed to offer considerable promise for rodent control because color-blind rodents would eat green poison baits, whereas House Sparrows and blackbirds would not. But other species may react differently; pheasants take any color of repellents used to protect planted corn (Dambach and Leedy, 1948) and nuthatches at feeding stations provided with dyed seeds merely leave the greens and blues till other colors have been removed. Avoidance of the greens conceivably might be related to the fact that green grains and unripe fruits are not ordinarily eaten in the wild (Dennis, 1951, 1952) and that blue grains are practically nonexistent.

Some ingenious experiments in England, testing the succession in removal of plasticene models of differently colored feces from the nests of two closely related motacillids (the Meadow-pipit and Yellow Wagtail), suggest that birds with yellow in their plumage may be more conscious of yellow than are brown-plumaged birds (Smith, 1945). Bowerbirds in Australia, which decorate their bowers with petals of flowers, often, but not invariably, choose colors that occur in the plumage of the females they wish to attract. The preference of Ruby-throated Hummingbirds for red flowers and for red and yellow feeding cups (Fig. 73) used at feeding stations to attract them is borne out by many observations, yet tests with western species are not so conclusive (Bené, 1947).

Another feature of the avian eye that may influence color perception is the presence of oil droplets, primarily of red, orange, and yellow, in the retina (Smith, 1945). Though the exact function of the droplets is uncertain, it has been suggested that they act as filters, much as a camera filter, increasing a bird's perception of red, orange, and yellow, but making blues more dull or colorless. Species differ in the amount as well as in the color and distribution of these droplets; pigeons, for instance, have the yellow

*Fig. 73. The apparent preference of the Ruby-throated Hummingbird for red has been capitalized on by distributors of feeding vials who sell more red cups than any other color. Note that the rapid whir of the wings (55–75 beats per second) has been stopped by the fast action of the camera. (Photo by Winthrop N. Davey and James R. Davey, courtesy of* Jack-Pine Warbler.*)*

droplets concentrated in the lower part of the retina, supposedly for sky vision or toning down blue. Kingfishers have an abundance of red droplets (60 per cent compared to about 10 per cent in hawks and 20 in songbirds), which may offset the glare of water and increase visibility of objects below the surface. The percentage of red droplets is also high in early-rising passerines, and is believed to be an aid in hunting at early hours, but late-rising hawks and swallows have mainly yellow droplets.

Sensitivity to reds has led to the suggestion that birds may be able to detect infrared rays, invisible of course to the human eye, and that by this means nestling Wood Ducks, like turtles, can find their way to the nearest water (infrared reflection being different over water). A similar suggestion that infrared rays emanating from an animal's warm body might aid owls in detecting prey in the dark has been quite conclusively disproved by experiment (Dice, 1945). Pumphrey (1961) doubts the ability of birds to "make use of extraspectral frequencies at either end of the spectrum."

A final feature associated at least indirectly with vision is the importance of light which regulates so many of the activities of birds. Most birds have definite awakening times, definite periods of morning song, and usually exact times of cessation of singing and of going to roost at night. Robins are among the earliest birds to awaken in the morning, whereas Blue Jays and Common Crows are relatively late risers. Thrushes, though not nocturnal, are noted for their punctual vesper performances, and Whip-poor-wills start calling in the evening with clocklike regularity. Herons in a rookery have specific morning and evening periods of arrival and departure, well synchronized with the rising and setting of the sun (Seibert, 1951). All of these activities are governed, in considerable part at least, by light intensities of which birds are very conscious.

## HEARING

Birds have always been credited with acute and discriminating hearing ability. The belief that owls hunt largely by ear and that the Robin and American Woodcock listen for subterranean prey, as well as the logical presumption that the great variety of vocal performances uttered by birds have real meaning to the birds themselves, are among the lines of evidence cited in support of this view.

Basically, the ear of a bird is quite comparable to the hearing organ in other vertebrates, but there are some pertinent structural differences. There is no external *pinna*, as found in mammals, for collecting sound waves. Instead, the external ear opening is covered over by a special group of feathers, the *auriculars*, which are delicately and loosely constructed, thus not interfering with reception of sound, and which can actually be lifted slightly when a bird is listening intently (Blake, 1950). The various ear tufts and "horns" of certain owls (Fig. 134) and Horned Larks are probably only incidental to hearing. Owls do, however, have enormous external ear openings beneath the auricular feathers; in some they are asymmetrical, that is, one cavity is larger than the other, probably for the better localization of the direction of sound.

Within the ear cavity is the vibratory *tympanum* or eardrum which receives and transmits sound to the fluid-filled inner ear (cochlea) by means of a rodlike bone, the *columella,* which replaces the three ear bones (incus, malleus, and stapes) of the human ear. Allen (1925) suggested that this more direct transmission of sound waves (tympanum through columella to coclear nerve to brain) might be responsible for the observed ability of birds in aviaries in France during World War I to detect distant sounds of battle inaudible to human ears. He also suggested that this remarkable, and now well-authenticated, sensitivity to distant explosions (Pumphrey, 1961) might be due to the quivering of perches, a fact later verified by studies of the sensory end organs in the legs which apparently perceive earth-transmitted sound waves.

In some pioneer work on auditory responses of birds at Cornell University, Brand and Kellogg (1939a) determined the hearing range, expressed in cycles per second, of Common Pigeons, Starlings and House Sparrows and compared them with man. Subsequent work with other birds at Cornell and in Europe (Schwartzkoff, 1955) extended both the upper and lower limits of hearing. Schwartzkoff indicated that cochlear potentials as high as 30,000 cycles per second might be reached in certain birds when greater intensities of sound than those normally encountered were used. This is considerably beyond the 20,000 cycle limit he set for man. Table 5 gives the range of hearing obtained for birds tested at Cornell and a few of those obtained in Europe.

***Table 5. Hearing Range of Selected Birds (in cycles/second)***

| *Species* | *Lower Limit* | *Upper Limit* | *Author* |
|---|---|---|---|
| Mallard | <300 | <8,000 | Trainer (in Schwartzkoff) |
| Canvasback | 190 | 5,200 | Edwards, 1943 |
| Sparrow Hawk | <300 | <10,000 | Trainer (in Schwartzkoff) |
| Pigeon | 200 | 7,500 | Brand and Kellogg, 1939a |
| Great Horned Owl | 60 | 7,000 | Edwards, 1943 |
| Long-eared Owl (Europe) | <100 | 18,000 * | Schwartzkoff, 1955 |
| Horned Lark | 350 | 7,600 | Edwards, 1943 |
| Magpie (Europe) | <100 | 21,000 * | Schwartzkoff, 1955 |
| Common Crow | <300 | <8,000 | Trainer (in Schwartzkoff) |
| Starling | 700 | 15,000 | Brand and Kellogg, 1939a |
| House Sparrow | 675 | 11,500 | Brand and Kellogg, 1939a |
| Canary | 1,100 | 10,000 | Brand and Kellogg, 1939b |
| Red Crossbill (Europe) | — | 20,000 * | Knect (in Schwartzkoff) |
| Snow Bunting | 400 | 7,200 | Edwards, 1943 |
| Man | 16 | 20,000 | (Schwartzkoff, 1955) |

* It is possible that supersensitive instruments used in the tests in Europe account for the higher values at upper levels (Frings and Slocum, 1958).

Tests of the songs of passerine birds (Brand, 1938) show that they range from about 1,100 cycles a second to 10,000, which indicate, as might be expected, that birds sing songs well within the range of their own hearing as well as within the acoustic capacity of most other birds. It seems probable, however, that birds with a low range of hearing cannot hear the high frequency notes of warblers, kinglets, or the highest notes of the

Starling, and that the low-pitched voices of other birds may not be audible to birds whose hearing is defective at the low end of the scale.

Some authors, however, believe that the larger predatory birds cannot hear the high-pitched alarm notes of small songbirds; hence the latter can sound an alarm without exposing themselves to danger. Hailman (1959) suggests that the high notes may not actually be inaudible to the predator but merely difficult to localize as to source, a significant safety factor for the prey. It is also thought that young chicks can hear the low clucking notes of their mother but *not* the high peeps of their siblings, which would be a needless distraction.

Owls have long been credited with a sensitive ear which aids them in hunting, and recent information indicates that this ability may be even more fantastic than formerly supposed. Dice (1945) tested the ability of four species of owls in finding prey (under laboratory conditions) in low-light intensities and concluded that light in natural habitats "must often fall below the minimum at which the birds (owls) can see their prey." Later, Payne and Drury (1958) demonstrated that Barn Owls could locate prey almost unfailingly in *total darkness* by hearing alone (Fig. 74). Mice

*Fig. 74. Barn Owls can locate moving prey almost unerringly in total darkness by hearing alone. Vision is useful to them in dim light, but mice rustling in the leaves or grass are detected by sound. (Photo by A. D. Moore, courtesy of the* Jack-Pine Warbler.)

released in a darkened room were pounced upon—as soon as the rustling of the mouse ceased (not during its movements) the owl dropped on it and was successful in thirteen out of seventeen strikes. The possibility that odor or heat (infrared) were involved was ruled out by dragging a paper "mouse" along the floor; it was attacked like the living mice. When one ear of the owl was plugged, it missed its prey by 18 inches, probably indicating the value of asymmetrical ears in localizing sounds exactly.

Another remarkable acoustic ability developed in a few birds is echolocation. It has long been known from experiments with bats, that the delicate ears of these mammals pick up supersonic sounds reflected back to them from obstacles in their path, enabling them to dodge through a maze of wires in the dark. Recently, similar investigations on oilbirds (*Steatornis*), which inhabit deep caves in northern South America, show that they use a type of echolocation to find their way to and from their nests and diurnal roosting places; their calls (not supersonic) are reflected back from walls and other obstacles and picked up in the sensitive ears of the birds (Griffin, 1953). Possibly swifts nesting in subterranean caves in the East Indies use this same device.

## *Endocrine Glands*

Though the endocrine glands are commonly regarded as constituting a separate system, their products, the hormones, are definitely associated and interrelated with all the other systems. These hormone-bearing secretions of the ductless glands are distributed by the blood to all parts of the body where they act as excitors or inhibitors in regulating and coordinating various life processes such as growth, development, and behavior. Minute amounts produce profound effects; too much or too little of the secretions results in abnormalities. Extracts of many of the endocrines are now widely used in experimental work, and some hormones have been prepared synthetically. This brief account of avian hormones points out some of their interesting influences on bird life.

The following tabulation lists the more important endocrine glands in birds, the hormones they produce, and some of their functions.

Pituitary ("master" gland)—controls and regulates secretions of other glands.
- Anterior Lobe—secretes following hormones:
  - Thyrotropin (TSH)—stimulates and influences secretions of the thyroid.
  - Adrenocorticotropin (ACTH)—acts on adrenals, both cortex and medulla.

Gonadotropin—controls growth of gonads and their secretions.
Prolactin—stimulates production of "pigeon's milk," parental behavior.
Posterior Lobe—produces several hormones related to physiological activities (blood pressure, urine flow, egg expulsion).
Thyroid—produces thyroxin, for feather development, pigmentation, molting.
Parathyroid—produces parathormone, for calcium and phosphorus regulation.
Adrenals—produces (1) adrenalin from medulla, for blood pressure, digestive processes; (2) cortin from cortex, for carbohydrate metabolism.
Gonads—produces (1) androgens (testosterone) from testes, secondary sexual characters; (2) estrogens (estradiol) from ovaries, female functions.

From the list of the glands and their secretions, the importance of the *anterior pituitary* is immediately apparent. It stimulates and regulates the activities of the other endocrine organs, which are discussed below. In addition it produces a lactogenic hormone (*prolactin*) which stimulates the production of "pigeon's milk" in pigeons by a sloughing off (desquamation) of cells in the walls of the crop. Prolactin also regulates broodiness, influences various aspects of parental behavior, and, in the presence of estrogen, is responsible for the full development of the brood patch (see p. 210) in incubating birds. The absence of broodiness and the failure of brood-patch development in such parasitic birds as certain cuckoos and cowbirds are thought to be due to hereditary failure in prolactin secretion (Höhn, 1961), although Selander (1960b) suggests that the abdominal skin in Brown-headed Cowbirds may be insensitive to hormones.

The *posterior pituitary*, less studied in birds, apparently influences a variety of physiological functions (regulates blood pressure; may cause premature expulsion of eggs, even of soft-shelled eggs; and reduces urine volume, probably by increasing resorption in the kidney [Höhn, 1961]).

Another very fundamental endocrine gland in birds is the *thyroid*, which is responsible for the proper growth and development of many structures. Via the pituitary, its secretions (chiefly *thyroxin*) control the growth and development of the gonads; deficiencies (*hypothyroidism*) retard and inhibit development of the gonads and males remain immature. An excess (*hyperthyroidism*) accelerates molting, increases barbule formation in feathers, and causes heavy pigmentation, especially deposition of melanins, whereas a deficiency has the opposite effect (inhibits molting, produces barbless, fluffy feathers, and causes loss of pigmentation). The thyroid is also important in the maintenance of proper metabolism and in temperature regulation. Wilson and Farner (1960) found an annual cycle of thyroid activity in migratory White-crowned Sparrows (Fig. 75) in eastern

*Fig. 75. White-crowned Sparrows, and related* Zonotrichia, *are extensively used in experimental studies on migratory restlessness, fat deposition, thyroid activity, and the effects of light on the gonads. (Photo by Dale A. Zimmerman.)*

Washington, apparently correlated with temperature, but the cycle did not apply to a sedentary race in California nor to other passerine birds.

The *parathyroids* in birds are closely associated physically with the thyroid. Their secretion (*parathormone*) regulates the calcium and phosphorus level in the blood and aids in bone formation. Amputation of the parathyroids produces convulsions and death (Sturkie, 1954).

The avian *adrenals,* small yellow or orange-colored glands situated on the anterior-ventral surface of the kidneys, consist of poorly defined and intermingled cortical and medullary tissue, quite unlike the well-defined outer *cortex* and inner *medulla* in mammals. Their secretions and functions seem somewhat debatable too, but several cortisonelike secretions from the cortical tissue influence various metabolic processes, perhaps including emotional stress. *Adrenalin,* or an adrenalinlike substance, from the medullary portion also helps regulate metabolism and can raise blood pressure in chickens by constricting the walls of blood vessels. Emotions like anger and excitability, known to be related to adrenalin flow in mammals, probably occur in birds but their relation to a specific hormone is uncertain.

The avian hormones most studied have been those associated with sex. The gonads, in addition to producing sex cells, also produce hormones, primarily an androgen (*testosterone*) and an estrogen (*estradiol*) which, in coordination with other hormones, control the development of the sex organs and the secondary sexual characteristics (male plumage, spurs, and comb) and profoundly influence sexual behavior. In domestic fowl and many other birds, male hormones are also present in the females, for if deprived of ovaries by disease or castration, females develop male characteristics; in rare cases sex reversal goes all the way so that in the common fowl, at least, egg-producing hens have been known to change completely into functional cocks. Sexual plumage reversals are also known in the Ostrich, herons, ducks, pheasants, the English Robin, and some fringillids. Yet in the House Sparrow (and presumably other species), the plumage of the sexes is genetic and neither gonadectomy nor administration of hormones alters it. Apparently in species subject to plumage reversal, a female hormone normally suppresses the influence of the male hormone, and when the effect of the former is removed the latter asserts itself. Castration in the male, however, usually produces only minor effects, if any, on the male plumage, though the development of some secondary sexual characters is arrested and male behavior largely nullified.

Thus administration of testosterone to females, in some cases at least, produces profound effects—hens become cocks and female Canaries sing—but attempts to feminize males with estrogen are only partially successful and sometimes in fact only serve to stimulate further development of male characters. Bill color changes in the breeding season are usually due to hormones; the horn-colored bill of the male House Sparrow becomes blue-black due to increased testosterone, but that of the female remains the same due to the suppressive effect of estrogen.

## *Selected References*

Allen, G. M. *Birds and Their Attributes.* Francestown, N.H.: Marshall Jones, 1925. Chapt. X.

Höhn, E. Otto. Endocrine Glands, Thymus and Pineal Body. Chapt. XVI in A. J. Marshall's *Biology and Comparative Physiology of Birds.* New York: Academic, 1961.

Hyman, Libbie H. *Comparative Vertebrate Anatomy.* Chicago: U. of Chicago, 1942.

Pettingill, Olin S., Jr. A *Laboratory and Field Manual of Ornithology.* Minneapolis, Minn.: Burgess, 1956. Pp. 38–89 on anatomy and physiology.

Portmann, Adolf. Sensory Organs: Skin, Taste, and Olfaction. Chapt. XIV in A. J. Marshall's *Biology and Comparative Physiology of Birds.* New York: Academic, 1961.

———, and Werner Stingelin. The Central Nervous System. Chapt. XIII in

A. J. Marshall's *Biology and Comparative Physiology of Birds*. New York: Academic, 1961.

Pumphrey, R. J. Sensory Organs: Vision and Hearing. Chapt. XV and XVI in A. J. Marshall's *Biology and Comparative Physiology of Birds*. New York: Academic, 1961.

Smith, Stuart. *How to Study Birds*. London: Collins, 1945. Chapt. 8 and 9.

Sturkie, Paul D. *Avian Physiology*. Ithaca: Comstock, 1954. Chapt. 14, 17–21.

Turner, C. Donnell. *General Endocrinology*. Philadelphia: Saunders, 1949. Pp. 90, 97–99, 129, 306, 340–341, 352, 373 for application to birds.

Walls, Gordon L. The Vertebrate Eye and Its Adaptive Radiation. *Cranbrook Inst. Sci. Bull.* 19 (Bloomfield Hills, Mich., 1942).

Walter, W. G. Some Experiments on the Sense of Smell in Birds. *Arch. Nierland. Physiol.* (1943), 27:1–72.

# 7

# BIRD BEHAVIOR

The past decade has witnessed a greatly renewed emphasis on studies of animal behavior and the consequent development, as in all new sciences or new approaches, of a new and somewhat confusing terminology. Commendable, but not always successful, attempts are being made to get away from earlier anthropomorphic interpretations of animal behavior and to explain phenomena on a more scientific neuromuscular basis. Thus, Emlen (1955) defines behavior as the "overt expression of the coordinated life processes of the animal." Recent books by Lorenz (1952), Scott (1958), Thorpe (1956), and Tinbergen (1951, 1953), and shorter works by many others, explore modern concepts in great detail.

## *Definitions and Concepts*

Many authors explain behavior by a *stimulus-response* theory. The stimuli, which may be internal (hunger, emotions, hormone balance) or external (environmental or social), act as *releasers* which produce some sort of a response, or attempt to adapt to the new condition produced by the stimulus. That the response may be quite variable or unpredictable is sometimes facetiously summed up by the "Harvard law" which states: "When stimulation is repeatedly applied under conditions in which environmental factors are precisely controlled the animal will react exactly as it pleases." Sometimes responses are divided somewhat arbitrarily into an *appetitive* (or exploratory) phase and a *consummatory* phase, the former including such reactions as a lost chick seeking its mother or a bird seeking food, the latter including the reactions of the chick after finding its mother or of a bird finding food.

*Imprinting* is a process of learning in which young birds, often within a few hours of hatching in precocial birds, get impressions that may remain with them throughout life. Thus young birds learn to recognize their parents or foster parents, or become attached to the one of the first objects they notice after birth. Incubator chicks often "adopt" the man who feeds or takes care of them, even to the extent of attempting to "mate" with him and refusing to accept mates of their own species. Hess (1959), in a study of imprinting in 5,700 birds, observed distinct species differences and classified his subjects from excellent to poor. Canada Geese and Mallards were examples of "excellent" imprinters and Wood Ducks "poor." Apparently imprinting has to come early, for the capacity for it is lost within a few days of hatching.

Imprint learning differs from *trial-and-error* learning, which starts later in life and teaches the young bird to distinguish edible from inedible substances, how to fly, or how to sing. For although feeding, flying, and singing are to some extent inborn characteristics, they can be modified or perfected by trial-and-error learning.

*Habituation* is a term sometimes applied to the process of learning what *not* to do. This often involves, among other things, enemy recognition. A bird startled by a harmless butterfly or a dangerous predator soon learns that one is harmless and that the other is not. Starlings become "habituated" to artificial sounds (p. 337) designed to frighten them from a roost and cease to react negatively to such disturbances (Fig. 76). Habituation has survival value as it teaches the bird what to fear or avoid and what to ignore or accept—it is "uneconomical" for a bird to be alarmed by a harmless object. There can be no trial-and-error in case of the predator, if the bird is to survive.

In experimental work, animal subjects are often "conditioned" to respond in particular ways (*conditioned reflexes*). Pavlov's (1927) classic experiments with dogs which salivated at the sound of a buzzer whether food was provided or not, are oft-cited examples of this, but since then many experimental animals have been conditioned to respond, or not to respond, to various visual or auditory signals. Scott (1958) considers "conditioned reflex" an unfortunate (but well-established) term "since behavior is affected by change in conditions rather than by conditions."

*Fig. 76. The Starling, introduced from Europe, is among the most adaptable of birds and quickly adjusts to new situations. Sometimes it can be dispersed from roosts by playing sound recordings of Starling alarm notes, but it soon learns that such sounds are harmless and ceases to react to them. The white flecks indicate winter plumage. (Photo by Allan D. Cruickshank.)*

# *Breeding Behavior*

Many interesting traits of behavior develop, or are most readily observed, during the breeding season. Several of these merit more explanation than is accorded them in the chapters on the annual cycle (Chapters 8 to 10) and are described below.

## AGONISTIC BEHAVIOR

A conspicuous feature in the early phases of the breeding cycle is the development of a hostile attitude between certain individuals, particularly rival males (Fig. 77). Birds which fed or associated together more or less peacefully during fall and winter (but see sections on flocking and dominance) become antagonistic during the breeding season. Males in particular tend to isolate themselves and to defend plots of ground known as territories (p. 161). Increase in a male hormone at the onset of the breeding season is believed to be largely responsible for this aggressiveness (Emlen, 1952b).

During the breeding season, males resort to a great variety of displays, sing almost constantly, and when necessary, attack and expel intruders

*Fig. 77. Herring Gull in agonistic or threatening display. (Photo by Allan D. Cruickshank.)*

from their small domain. Both displays and song help to minimize the need for fighting, however, and thus conserve the bird's energy for other purposes. Displays and their apparent significance have been described in detail for ducks (Ramsey, 1956; Johnsgard, 1960), Coots (Gullion, 1952), Red-winged Blackbirds (Nero, 1956), and for many other species. Some of these are mentioned more specifically in connection with various phases of the nesting cycle (Chapters 8 to 10).

Birds vary greatly in aggressiveness, and perhaps in the need for it. English Robins studied by Lack (1943) were particularly aggressive; both males and females attacked dummies set up in their territories. The red breast seemed to be the provocative stimulus, as juvenile robins or adult robins whose breasts were painted brown usually were not attacked, whereas a tuft of red feathers mounted on a perch was attacked. One particularly aggressive female continued to fight the empty space after the feathers were removed and three birds deserted their nests because they could not drive dummies out of their territory. On the other hand, some species do not defend territories even while nesting, and still others seem to lack the aggressiveness characteristic of so many birds.

One apparently irrelevant outcome of agonistic behavior is *image-fighting* in which birds attack their own reflection in a window or other reflecting surface. Sometimes such an aimless pursuit is abandoned after a few trials, or engaged in only at infrequent intervals, but in some cases the attackers literally exhaust themselves in the futile attempt to drive a potential rival from their territory.

Most aggressive actions are intraspecific, but many interspecific hostilities develop, not only among closely related species which might be competitors for food or other requirements but also against potential or actual enemies. Potential nest robbers and predators are often surrounded and threatened by their would-be victims, whether the latter are being molested or not (Fig. 78). This is known as *mobbing* behavior, and is well illustrated by the long-standing enmity between crows (or jays) and owls. Altmann (1956) experimented with stuffed owls set up in various situations and studied the reactions of 39 species that might have reacted. Nineteen species paid no attention to the dummies, 13 attacked only after seeing others do so, the others mobbed the owls fairly regularly, although not all

*Fig. 78. Young owls at their daytime roosts are prime targets for mobbing by other birds, especially by crows and jays. Here the camera seemed to catch the spirit of the April woods in this young Great Horned Owl. (Photo by Leon Alger, Jr., courtesy of the* Jack-Pine Warbler.*)*

members of a given species did so. Understandably, mobbing was more persistent during the breeding season.

NESTING BEHAVIOR

The various nesting activities of birds (Chapters 8 to 10) provide many interesting illustrations of both innate and acquired behavior. Nest-site selection, choice of nesting materials, and nest-building techniques are fundamentally fixed species characteristics, but many birds adapt to new or changing situations. Many birds now take advantage of man-made facilities, nesting in chimneys or mine shafts (Chimney Swifts), in or on buildings (Starlings, Robins, swallows, phoebes), or accepting artificial nest boxes (Fig. 79). Sometimes substitute nest sites run into unforeseen difficulties, as in the frequent cases where Robins construct nests on moving or movable vehicles. Birds likewise often accept artificial nesting materials—string, paper, rags, tinsel—though such selections appear to have no real value

*Fig. 79. Cliff Swallows still utilize natural nesting situations, such as cliffs and caves, but more often they adopt man-made structures, plastering their globular nests under the eaves of barns. They are colonial nesters and highly gregarious at all times. Note the stages of nest building. (Photo by John T. Emlen, Jr., courtesy of the* Auk, *71, 1954.)*

other than availability. Oriole nests of colored yarn or a nest of bright tinsel might be disadvantageous because of conspicuousness.

Filching nesting material from unguarded neighboring nests is a fairly common trait among some colonial birds. "Pebble-stealing" is traditional in Adelie Penguin colonies. The adults spend a week or more preparing nest sites, methodically collecting stones to mark the nest location, and even showing marked preferences for size and color of pebbles. In general, the females arrange the stones which the males transport, but many of the stones are stolen from under the hens when their backs are turned. Alert females viciously attack intruders, but unaggressive birds have most of their stones pilfered. Goldfinches are good examples of noncolonial birds which commonly dismantle their own or other nests, active or inactive, to get suitable nesting material quickly.

Birds also have some capacity to retrieve eggs that have rolled out of or been experimentally moved from ground nests. Gulls and terns will roll eggs from short distances back to their nests. Common Murres, which build no nest and lay a single egg, can recognize their own egg when it is transferred to another location and will roll it back to its original position from a distance of one to five yards (Johnson, 1941).

*Brood parasitism* is an intriguing and somewhat baffling nesting specialization that has developed in a few groups of birds. Cuckoos and honeyguides in the Old World and several species of cowbirds in the Americas regularly lay their eggs in the nests of other birds, usually selecting species smaller than themselves. Such eggs are almost invariably accepted and hatched by the foster parent, often at a considerable sacrifice, since their own young may perish. In the case of the Brown-headed Cowbird only a few species, chiefly those with conspicuously different eggs, ever throw out the impostor's eggs. A few others, notably Yellow Warblers, sometimes ingeniously bury a cowbird's eggs by building a second story on the nest, although it would be much simpler to throw out the eggs. Five-story nests of the Yellow Warbler, with a cowbird egg or eggs (and sometimes warbler eggs) in each story, have been found (Fig. 80).

An Old World cuckoo (*Cuculus canorus*) has developed brood parasitism to such a high degree that it lays eggs of a color that matches those of the host species, even to the extent of laying a reddish egg which simulates the reddish egg of a host warbler (Sylviidae) in Japan. In addition, the young have a saddle-shaped depression on their backs by means of which they shoulder their nest mates and heave them out of the nest. Honeyguides lay their eggs in nests of woodpeckers and barbets in cavities and

*Fig. 80. Three-story nest of Yellow Warbler. The bottom compartment contained one cowbird egg, the second story had two cowbird eggs and a warbler egg. (Courtesy of Walter P. Nickell.)*

cannot eject the young; instead they have a murderous hook (which disappears soon after hatching) on the bill which they use to butcher their nest mates.

*Injury-feigning* or *distraction display*, a reaction in which a flushed parent bird appears to try to divert the attention of a visitor away from its nest by fluttering half helplessly just out of reach (Fig. 81), is a trait of nesting behavior whose interpretation has long been a controversial issue. The earlier naturalists credited the bird with a deliberate and conscious attempt to protect its nest by simulating injury to lead a predator astray, but later ornithologists suggested that it might be purely automatic, a partial paralysis of the locomotor apparatus brought about by two conflicting emotions, a fear for itself and an impelling desire to protect its nest (Friedmann, 1934). Perhaps the truth is somewhere between the two extremes. Armstrong (1953) calls it a "displacement activity," that is, substituting a new behavior pattern for brooding when prevented from doing the latter.

Injury-feigning is more common, as might be expected, among ground-nesting birds of open spaces, particularly shorebirds, and is rare among treetop nesters and colonial birds, where it would serve little practical purpose. Most flightless birds would jeopardize their own lives as well as maintenance of the species by injury-feigning, but in others it would have survival value by elimination of those not doing it well.

Some predatory birds with staggered hatching (p. 221) sometimes resort

*Fig. 81. Piping Plover employing distraction display. Note the scarcity of nesting material and the protectively colored eggs. (Photo by Bertha Daubendiek, courtesy of* Jack-Pine Warbler.)

to *cannibalism,* the older nestlings in a nest attacking and eating one or more of their weaker nest sibs; or, if the latter die, they may be fed to the survivors by their parents. Cannibalism is common in Marsh Hawks (Fig. 117), Barn Owls, Short-eared Owls, perhaps other birds of prey, and some sea birds. Ingram (1959) believes that this practice has survival value in species with large clutches of eggs; sacrificing the younger members of the family for the benefit of the older ensures maximum fledging in relation to the available food supply.

## *Behavior and Feeding Habits*

The feeding habits of birds afford some striking examples of behavioral adaptability as well as lack of it. The latter is illustrated by specialized feeders accustomed to live on a restricted diet, and apparently unable to change. Probably the few surviving Everglade Kites in Florida will perish rather than turn to a new source of food, if the snail supply is exhausted by draining the Everglades. Griscom (1945) relates that Brant wintering on the Atlantic coast were threatened with extinction (90 per cent perished) when a blight nearly wiped out the eel grass on which they subsisted. Partial recovery of the eel grass and the adaptiveness of a few Brant in learning to eat other foods by watching other anatids apparently saved them.

By contrast some other birds are quite resourceful at exploiting new food supplies. Many birds now utilize highway kills or other food supplies formerly not available. Mockingbirds and Catbirds will glean insects, still warm, off radiators of parked cars. A Sparrow Hawk, perhaps in an unusual display of learning, has been reported to watch pigeons feeding on bread crusts in a park, and then, after some trial and error, descend to the ground and feed with the pigeons (Warburton, 1952). Sawyer (1959) describes another case of Sparrow Hawk resourcefulness; the hawk perched on the antlers of a bull elk (the only perch available) and caught mice flushed by the elk as it foraged in haystacks in Yellowstone National Park.

Many birds now take advantage of farming practices: swallows follow mowers for flushed insects, blackbirds and Franklin's Gulls follow the plow, and cowbirds and anis follow cattle. Rand (1953a) has shown that Groove-billed Anis are more successful in making catches when using cattle as beaters for insects than when feeding alone. Dawn (1959) observed Cattle Egrets (Fig. 82) feeding ahead of grazing cattle but becoming inactive when the cattle rested. Sometimes the egrets got restless and appeared to prod resting cattle into doing more grazing to stir up more food. Similarly ant-tanagers in the tropics follow army ants, not to feed on the moving ant hordes, but to capture other insects flushed by the ants (Willis, 1960).

Crows are remarkably resourceful. They have learned to catch fish at fishing holes in winter, to dig up newly planted corn in spring, and to haul young mice out of their nests in season; there are even well-authenticated cases of cooperative hunting, perhaps planned out in advance. Perhaps the most ingenious of these exploits is described by Homberg (1957) for Hooded Crows and a raven in Scandinavia. The corvids learned to pull up fishermen's lines for the bait by running back over the ice with the line in the beak, then walking forward on the line, repeating the process until the bait was out on the ice.

A similar display of resourcefulness has been described by Smith (1945) for titmice in England. Several individuals learned to reef up a dangling string with a peanut tied on the end by standing on the loops of string as it was hauled up with the bill. Starlings and English Robins never learned

*Fig. 82. In this country Cattle Egrets commonly follow cattle, using them as beaters for insects, but in Africa they associate with native ruminants, as shown here by this egret with a rhinoceros. (Photo by Dale A. Zimmerman.)*

the trick. Equally "imaginative" is an example of Green Herons in Florida fishing with bread (Lovell, 1958). The herons retrieved bread crusts from the shore, placed them in the water and caught fish that came to nibble on the bread. In one case a heron actually moved the bread from an unsuccessful fishing site to a new location where several fish could be seen breaking the surface. Gulls and Common Crows sometimes carry hard-shelled molluscs into the air and drop them on rocks or pavement to crack the hard shells, and buzzards in Europe are said to use the same strategy with turtles. In fact Pliny relates that a Greek poet (Aeschylus) lost his life when a buzzard (the Lammergeier) mistook the poet's bald head for a rock and dropped a turtle on it.

Because of unforeseen circumstances, tapping new food resources does not always pay dividends. Hawks long ago discovered that a farmer's chickens were a new source of food, but from this learning have reaped chiefly disaster, as have fish-eating birds attempting to utilize the abundant supply of food at hatcheries. Even greater ingenuity was shown by the Kea in New Zealand when it learned to pick through the hide and into the groins of living sheep for kidney fat, a discovery that nearly proved its undoing, since sheep herders have almost exterminated the giant parrots. In the days of plume hunting, egrets soon learned to flee in panic from their nesting rookeries at the first blast of a gun, but resourceful crows merely waited nearby to plunder the nests while the egrets were gone.

Storage of food materials by birds has never reached the degree of development that it has among certain mammals (squirrels, pikas, beavers), but some birds show interesting specializations in this respect. Woodpeckers, jays, nutcrackers, titmice, nuthatches, and shrikes are among those that practice the habit quite regularly. Presumably many of the stored items are never relocated, or are stolen by other animals, but some birds show a phenomenal place memory for recovering cached items. Chettleworth (1952) watched thirty to forty jays in England bury 200,000 acorns, carrying some of them three-fourths of a mile; apparently they remembered the burial sites. Clark's Nutcrackers in the Rockies will dig through snow up to 8 inches deep to recover items buried several months previously (Cahalane, 1944). Some of the recovery ability shown by birds may be due to the habit of searching typical hiding places rather than remembering where a particular item was stored.

Sometimes woodpeckers employ special techniques for storing nuts. The Red-headed Woodpeckers along the Potomac seal in their winter stores (Kilham, 1958a), not only wedging them so tightly into the bark of trees that they are difficult to dislodge but actually sealing them in with damp splinters of wood so that they are well concealed as well as relatively inaccessible. Further protection is accorded their supplies by scattering them rather widely. By contrast the stores of the Acorn Woodpecker are more exposed; the acorns are tucked into a little cavity drilled for that purpose and are often concentrated in a single tree. Dawson (Dennis, 1957) described a case of California (Acorn) Woodpeckers storing 50,000 acorns in a single pine; recovery of acorns from tree rings dating back to 802 A.D. indicates that the habit is very old.

At winter feeding stations, carrying away and storing seeds becomes a game of hide-and-seek. Dennis (1957) credits chickadees, but not nuthatches, with great craftiness in hiding their stores; they "pretend" to hide a seed in a particular place, then move it to another less conspicuous site. Brown Creepers are not hoarders (they are chiefly insectivorous), but in their methodical search over the bark of trees they often relocate items stored by other birds.

Joseph Grinnell long ago pointed out an indirect useful result of the burying of nuts by birds in the western mountains. He noted that birds often carried nuts and seeds *up* the mountain for burial and that unrecovered items sprouted into seedling trees; otherwise there would be no nut trees at high altitudes, since subsequent generations would always be *below* the parent tree. He called such birds "up-hill planters."

Shrikes (Fig. 83) have the well-known habit of impaling surplus prey (grasshoppers, mice, small birds) on thorns of trees and barbed-wire fences. Perhaps this is not so much deliberate storage for future needs as a habit of using thorns for temporary anchorage to aid in dissecting the prey (shrikes have relatively weak feet) and then abandoning leftover items. Hawks and owls frequently accumulate surplus items at their nests, a practice perhaps carried to the extreme in Barn Owls which have been recorded with eighty mice stockpiled in the nest with six eggs, and seventy-three mice in a nest with four young (Wallace, 1948). A neotropical thrush (*Catharus*) kept by the author for several months stored up food items in various corners of the room in which he had his freedom; when we

*Fig. 83. Loggerhead Shrikes are predatory on grasshoppers and small vertebrates and have strong, hooked beaks for dissecting prey. Surplus prey is often impaled on thorns, either for anchorage or for storage for future needs. (Photo by Allan D. Cruickshank.)*

cleaned house we found his little stockpiles hidden behind furniture. Tordoff (1955) noted similar behavior in a captive Sparrow Hawk, but also observed it in a wild bird. Such a habit could prove useful, particularly in winter.

## Other Activities

Several other traits of behavior, not necessarily related to breeding or feeding, have been described for birds. Often the explanation for such habits is conjectural, and considerable literature has built up around several poorly understood behavioral phenomena. One of these is a habit popularly called "*anting.*" Many birds, particularly passerines, have a curious habit of picking up ants (or sometimes such ant substitutes as moth balls, soap suds, and burning cigarette stubs) and rubbing them over their feathers, especially the underside of the primaries, often falling over and rolling on the ground in an effort to get at less accessible parts of their anatomy. Early reports of this inexplicable behavior were regarded as fabrications, but it has now been verified by so many observers in so many species that its actual occurrence is unquestionable.

Recently Whitaker (1957a) reviewed the whole situation and did some additional experimental work on an Orchard Oriole. Her eleven-page bibliography and list of 148 species of birds known to ant indicate the extent of the literature on the subject. She divided anting birds into *active* and *passive* types, the former being those that select ants and apply them to their body, and the latter those that merely allow ants to invade their plumage. Apparently only ants that have a repugnatorial fluid (formic acid) which can be sprayed or exuded from the body are acceptable to active anters. Heated, dead, or frozen ants which had lost their taste and odor were not used. This lends support to one of the supposed functions of anting, namely that the ants have a thermogenic property which gives a pleasurable sensation to the bird through contact with the skin. It is thought that sun-bathing and the habit some birds have of exposing themselves to heated pavement or other warm surfaces (Hauser, 1957; Lanyon, 1958; Whitaker, 1960) may have a similar function. More recently, however, it has been learned (from an earlier Russian work) that secretions from ants are toxic to feather mites and thus may serve to rid the plumage of such ectoparasites.

Goodman (1960) describes the possible connection between anting and accidental fires. Firemen attribute some fires in old buildings to Starlings and House Sparrows carrying smouldering cigarettes or matches to their trashy nests, a habit better known for Rooks in Europe. It is conceivable that some forest fires are started by birds toying with unextinguished cigarettes along roadsides and transporting them to more distant and more flammable situations.

*Wing flashing* in Mockingbirds and its possible function has been a subject of recent debate. The most obvious function, suggested by the earlier observers, is that the white wing patches exposed by flashing wings of foraging Mockingbirds startled insect prey into revealing themselves, or illuminated the more sluggish forms. Several recent authors, however, have pointed out that some birds without wing patches also resort to wing flashing and that securing prey might not be the explanation of the habit. Selander and Hunter (1960) thought that it might be an agonistic or threat display (it was used against dummy owls) perhaps related to territory defense, but Hailman (1960) favors the food-gathering theory as the primary function, since in his observations 256 of 258 observed wing flashes were followed by foraging. Both Selander and Hunter (1960) and Hailman (1960) give a fairly complete bibliography for those who wish to explore this subject further.

*Foot quivering* is a similarly perplexing phenomenon. Dilger (1956) interpreted it as a form of hostile behavior in thrushes, perhaps a low motivation of attack and escape drives in balance, for he had not observed it in foraging birds. Brackbill (1960), however, noted that eight out of nine Hermit Thrushes engaged in foot quivering while foraging on his lawn. Wallace (1939) thought that the similar "dancing" of a captive Gray-cheeked Thrush on rustling surfaces, such as paper, was related to auditory or musical effects of the sound produced (the thrush cocked its head and appeared to listen while tapping its feet on paper).

*Foot stirring* and *foot paddling* in herons and sandpipers (see Meyerriecks, 1959a and b), however, seems definitely related to feeding, for such actions are invariably followed by captures of prey. Interestingly enough, Meyerriecks notes that only the yellow-toed species of egrets (the Snowy Egret in North America and Little Egret of Europe) use foot-stirring motions in searching for prey.

*Head scratching,* whose obvious function is relief from or reaction to ectoparasites or other irritation, is of interest because of the methods employed and their possible phylogenetic significance. Two methods are used: *indirect,* with the foot placed over the wing while scratching; and *direct,* with the foot under the wing. Brown (1959) points out that Wrentits (Chamaeidae) in California use the less common direct method which supports their postulated relationship to Old World babblers (Timaliidae) which also use this method. Nice and Schantz (1959), however, point out that the habit is less stereotyped and rigid than formerly supposed and that many species, especially warblers, use both methods.

## Social Organization

Some of the social relations among birds are evident in other parts of the text, but several features need additional comment here. One of the most prominent of these is *gregariousness* or *flocking* behavior. Late summer flocking is a striking feature of the postnesting season. Species that were segregated on inviolate territories during the breeding season often become gregarious again, indicating that sociability is of a fundamental nature. Some flocks are built up primarily of a single species; others are mixed aggregations of species brought together by similar food or habitat requirements. Game birds assemble into coveys (groups) usually composed of a single species, but waterfowl collect in suitable feeding areas with several to a dozen or more species somewhat intermingled (Fig. 84). After the breeding season, Starlings congregate in large flocks, scattering to forage by day but reassembling at night. Such roosts may be entirely of Starlings, or have components of Common Grackles and Red-winged Blackbirds. Great flocks of swallows, usually of several species, congregate on telephone wires, but associated with them may be flycatchers, bluebirds, various sparrows, and sometimes warblers. The social nature of swallow flocks is indicated by their perching habits; there may be uninhabited miles of wires, but newcomers alight in the center of the flock, if space permits, rather than on the periphery (Emlen, 1952a). Flocking gives birds certain advantages both in foraging for food and in escaping predators. Individuals within the flock may detect new sources of food or sound an alarm when an enemy appears. Avian predators, for instance, commonly pick off stragglers that have strayed from the group, but ignore the flock as a whole.

Close social bonds, particularly observable in late summer and fall, continue through winter in gregarious species. Winter roosts of Common Crows, Starlings, blackbirds, and Robins, in some cases numbering millions of birds at a single roost, are perhaps too well known to need further comment. Often social ties extend into the breeding season in colonial

*Fig. 84. Ducks assemble in large flocks during migration, usually with several to a dozen species somewhat intermingled, yet group associations of species within the larger flock are often maintained. (Photo by Allan D. Cruickshank.)*

birds (Fig. 85), but here, in spite of severe space limitations, small defended territories prevail. That the close social organization is fundamental in colonial nesters is indicated by the fact that breeding birds crowded to peripheral nesting sites are often unsuccessful, whereas sites near the center are sought by the dominant birds.

Bird flocks exhibit a definite social organization in which *dominance* or *peck-right* plays a fundamental role. Dominance is sometimes distinguished from peck-right, since the former may be incomplete. The dominant bird merely may win the majority of conflicts, whereas peck-right implies more complete subjugation of subordinate birds. A third type, *supersedence,* is merely a replacement at a feeding table, such as a satiated goldfinch being replaced by another on a thistle head. In a simple linear peck order, in a flock of ten birds, No. 1 may peck the remaining nine birds, while No. 2 pecks only the eight below him—and so on down the line to No. 10, a completely subordinate bird pecked by all and pecking back at none. The peck order is determined by fights which may be short and

*Fig. 85. Weaverbirds (Ploceidae) are often highly gregarious, even in the nesting season. Here a nesting colony of Spotted-backed Weavers* (Ploceus cucullatus), *with 1200 nests estimated in one tree, is found in Kruger National Park in South Africa. The leaves were plucked from the trees by the birds. (Photo by John T. Emlen, Jr.)*

quickly settled without future conflicts; or two birds, close together in the hierarchy, may be at one another constantly, frequently changing rank. Usually birds low in the hierarchy lack aggressiveness and do little fighting, yet sometimes such a bird may suddenly assert himself, probably due to a hormonal change, and fight his way up through the ranks or even displace the head bird in a single conflict, thus finding himself in a new and glorified position. Injection of testosterone into a weakling may cause him to become dominant. Further complications arise when a bird low in the peck order toadies to one high in the series and thus receives some immunity from other birds by basking in the shadow of its protector. Eventually some stability within the flock is attained; this decreases the need for fighting and permits more time for other activities, which is probably one of the chief functions of dominance.

Not all peck orders are of the linear type. Some are triangles in which A pecks B, and B pecks C, but C pecks A and not B. In geese the family is the unit—one family, usually the largest, dominating other families by sheer superiority of numbers (Hansen, 1953b).

Formerly most observations on dominance were made on domesticated birds (poultry, pigeons, and canaries), but recently such studies have been extended to native birds in confinement, semiconfinement, or in the wild. Useful studies of this type have been published by Hamerstrom (1942) on winter flocks of chickadees, Collias and Taber (1951) on pheasants, Tordoff (1954) on crossbills, Sabine (1959) on juncos, Dilger (1960) on redpolls, and Thompson (1960) on House Finches. A linear peck order, with some triangles developing within certain flocks, seems to prevail among these birds. In some species males are dominant over females (Thompson, *op. cit.*, gives a list), in others the females dominate their mates. Changes in the peck order may take place at the onset of the breeding season owing to male aggressiveness.

Dominance of one species over another is characteristic among closely associated species. Sharp (1957) found pheasants dominant over Prairie Chickens, but not over Sharp-tailed Grouse. Fighting techniques seemed to determine the relationship. Pheasants fought with spurs and had an advantage over the shorter-legged, shorter-spurred Prairie Chickens, but Sharp-tails ducked under the pheasants when the latter jumped, and plucked at their tail and under tail coverts. A pheasant thus treated beat a hasty retreat and never renewed the attack. Sharp-tails were also dominant over Prairie Chickens but quite tolerant of them.

On the other hand, a rather loose social hierarchy, without definite dominance, seems to prevail in some aggregations of birds. Norris (1960) found five races of Savannah Sparrows intermingled on their wintering grounds in South Carolina without apparent social or ecological segregation; certain individuals were dominant over others, but many showed no signs of hostility at all.

## *Selected References*


Armstrong, Edward A. *Bird Display and Behavior.* New York: Oxford U.P., 1947.

Collias, Nicholas E. The Development of Social Behavior in Birds. *Auk* (1952), **69**:127–159.

Emlen, John T., Jr. The Study of Behavior in Birds. Chapt. 5 in *Recent Studies in Avian Biology,* ed. A. Wolfson. Urbana, Ill.: U. of Ill., 1955.

Griscom, Ludlow. *Modern Bird Study.* Cambridge, Mass.: Harvard U.P., 1945. Chapt. II and III.

Lack, David. *The Life of the Robin.* London: Witherby, 1943.

Lorenz, Konrad Z. Der Kumpan in der Umvelt des Vogels. *Jour. für. Ornith.* (1935), **83**:137–213; 289–413. For English summary, see *Auk,* **54**:245–273.

———. *King Solomon's Ring.* New York: Crowell, 1952.

Pavlov, I. P. *Conditioned Reflexes.* New York: Oxford U.P., 1927.

Scott, John Paul. *Animal Behavior.* Chicago: U. of Chicago, 1958.

Smith, Stuart. *How to Study Birds.* London: Collins, 1945. Chapt. 5.

Thorpe, W. H. The Learning Ability of Birds. *Ibis* (1951), **93**:1–52; 252–296.
———. *Learning and Instinct in Animals.* London: Meuthen, 1956.
Tinbergen, N. Social Releasers and the Experimental Method Required for their Study. *Wilson Bull.* (1948), **60**:6–51.
———. *The Study of Instinct.* Oxford: Oxford Press, 1951.
———. *The Herring Gull's World.* London: Collins, 1953.
Whitaker, Lovie M. A Résumé of Anting, with Particular Reference to a Captive Orchard Oriole. *Wilson Bull.* (1957a), **69**:195–262.

# 8

# THE ANNUAL CYCLE:

## *Arrival, Territory, Courtship, Mating, and Song*

This series of three chapters on the annual cycle describes the various activities of birds through the four seasons: their arrival in spring, their nesting season activities and late summer behavior, the fall journey, and a brief account of their winter habits. This first phase in the series covers the various preliminaries that lead to nesting.

### *Spring Arrival*

The coming of the birds in the spring has long been regarded as one of the foremost harbingers of the season. Most migratory birds in the northern hemisphere respond to the lengthening days of spring by advancing northward and nonmigratory species exhibit preliminary indications of breeding. Some of the initial responses, indeed, may appear premature. A resident Cardinal may burst into full song on a deceptively sunny day in midwinter, and invariably a transient Robin or two will put in a premature appearance, only to be forced into temporary seclusion by a brief return of winter conditions.

The factors that initiate migration and subsequent breeding are poorly known. In brief, an internal rhythm, under hormonal control but often modified to keep in tune with prevailing environmental conditions, governs the breeding and migrational cycles of birds. The arrival of birds on their nesting grounds, described below, is only one phase of this cycle. Day length appears to be the chief external factor stimulating hormone flow and recrudescence of the gonads, but favorable or unfavorable weather conditions as well as the availability of proper food and suitable nesting sites can apparently modify the inherent internal rhythm. Chapter 11 on migration analyzes some of these factors more fully.

The span of spring migration over the central and northern states covers the period from February to June, usually with each species accustomed to appearing at a given time, so that its coming can often be quite accurately predicted. The early comers are less punctual in their time of return, for they may have to adjust their arrival schedule to local weather conditions. The first comers in the northern states may show up during the first mild spell of early spring, whether it be in late February or in March. But April migrants, which in general wintered farther south, are less influenced by the local weather picture and are more punctual in their time of return. May migrants, many of which wintered in South America, have even more precise arrival dates, often appearing year after year on practically the same day. When one keeps careful arrival records over the years, however, many variables are found to enter into and confuse this picture of precision; even the much publicized Cliff Swallows at Capistrano in California are not as punctual as reports make out.

Thus, though the urge to migrate is probably initiated internally, there is considerable correlation between the northward movement of birds and vernal conditions. Waterfowl often linger along the southern fringe of frozen waters, then surge northward as rapidly as thawing lakes and streams permit. Sometimes, birds advance too rapidly and then may have to hold back for a spell, reverse their migration, or suffer disaster. Many birds are victims of storms during their early spring migration, and others get blown off course by unfavorable winds. Bagg (1955) cites the case of Indigo Buntings apparently being airborne on a storm track from Yucatan to Maine and arriving nearly a month ahead of schedule.

A feature of spring migrations of which bird watchers are well aware is that birds often appear in waves. That is, they may make a fairly long flight under favorable weather conditions (southerly winds, warm temperatures, low barometric pressure), then, meeting a cold front to the north, may be stalled for days before a change in weather favors another flight (Bagg, *et al.*, 1950). From the bird watcher's standpoint this might produce good birding both during the passage of the warm front, with night migrants feeding and resting by day, and also when the migrants are arrested by meeting a cold front. Birds also accumulate fat reserves before a long flight, then when these are exhausted they stop to replenish the supply before undertaking another stage of the journey. The net result of these various factors is that migrants appear in waves which are only partly predictable. (See Saunders, 1959, for precision and irregularities in arrival schedules over a long period of time.)

Though some birds make long flights, as across the Gulf of Mexico or over long stretches of the Atlantic or Pacific, the daily rate of progress for most land birds is rather slow. Lincoln (1950) gives the average speed of all species travelling up the Mississippi Valley as only 23 miles per day, but of course this includes rest stops and interruptions. Many species, and many individuals, would achieve much faster rates. Typically, a bird might cover several hundred miles in a single flight, then wait a few days before renewing its journey, thus slowing down the daily rate of progress. Some birds proceed rather leisurely on the first laps of their journey, then speed up on the final stages. The Blackpoll Warbler (Fig. 86), which winters in

*Fig. 86. Isochronal lines show the rate of advance of the Blackpoll Warbler during spring migration. Starting out at a leisurely pace of about 30 miles per day, it speeds up to more than 200 miles per day before the trip is finished. (From drawing by Robert W. Hines, Fish and Wildlife Service.)*

South America and nests in the sub-Arctic conifer belt, averages about 30 miles per day through the states, but speeds up to about 200 miles a day over the more northern stretches. Actually there are few records of measured flights of banded birds from one station to another, and the few records available are not necessarily typical.

A frequently overlooked feature of spring migration is that all the individuals of a species do not arrive at the same time. In a study of the Red-winged Blackbird at Ithaca, New York, Allen (1914) found the different status groups arriving at greatly different times from late February to early June, thus covering practically the whole span of spring migration. The vagrants arrived first, in late February and early March, followed by the migrant and resident adult males throughout March, migrant and resident females through most of April, and immature birds throughout May and into early June. It is interesting to note that some forty years later the arrival schedule of Red-wings was restudied in Wisconsin (Beer and Tibbitts, 1950) and found to be quite similar to that ascertained in New York. Immature birds, in particular, may be irregular and late in their time of appearance, since their gonads may not be fully developed early in the season and the stimulus to migrate and breed may be largely lacking.

It should be pointed out that this description of spring arrivals applies principally to land birds in the northern hemisphere. In the southern hemisphere, where migration is less pronounced because of smaller land masses, the seasons are reversed, and tropical and oceanic birds are influenced by different external factors (pp. 259, 260, 268).

## *Territories*

The first objective of a male bird arriving on its breeding grounds is to select a suitable plot of land, the territory, that will provide a home for himself and prospective family during the nesting season. In a general way a territory may be defined as "any defended area," to which Tinbergen (1936) adds the concept of "sexual fighting" on a "restricted area." Lack and Lack (1933) define it as an "isolated area defended by one individual of a species or by a breeding pair against intruders of the same species and in which the owner of the territory makes itself conspicuous."

The concept of territories among birds is by no means new. The food territories of the eagle and the raven were vividly described by Aristotle (about 350 B.C.). That birds defended nesting areas was realized as early as 1622, restated in 1632, but not definitely christened the "territory" until 1903 (Fisher, 1951). One of the earliest descriptions of a defended nest site is that of François Legaut, who, in 1691, wrote an extensive, though perhaps somewhat fanciful, account of territorial defense in the Solitaire which lived on the island of Rodriquez, near Madagascar (Hann, 1945). Audubon's description of territorialism in the Eastern Meadowlark in 1835 is perhaps the earliest American reference of this sort (Allen, 1951). But the importance of territories to birds was largely overlooked until the publication of Howard's classic work, *Territory in Bird Life*, in 1920, gave new impetus to the topic. Since then, the concept of the territory has been subjected to much criticism, redefinition, and continued study.

There are, of course, many variations in territorial arrangements, but certain well-defined patterns can be described. Perhaps the most common of these is a territory which serves as a mating, nesting, and feeding area. In most migratory species, the males arrive from several days to several weeks before the females, and have established territories by the time their prospective mates appear. Perhaps the first male to arrive is an old-timer, seeking to reclaim his previous year's holdings. If he finds his territory already occupied by a newcomer, which is not likely, as older birds are apt to be the first to return, he may evict the intruder. Then he proceeds to advertise his holding by almost constant song, or by some type of display, or both. This serves as a warning that the territory is occupied. Other males, or even females at this stage of the cycle, that venture to trespass are expelled. Aggressive species, particularly under conditions of crowding, do much fighting or at least chasing off of intruders, but in most species the song or display is adequate advertisement and minimizes the need for fighting. Sometimes a particularly pugnacious invader can drive out the original owner, but ordinarily the first bird definitely established on a plot is invincible.

Figure 87 represents a considerably simplified, entirely hypothetical partitioning of a five-acre field by territory-holding birds, and the accompanying legend explains the sequence and manner in which the five occupants might adjust themselves.

Songbirds usually adopt one or many singing posts in or about the periphery of their territory and make themselves conspicuous to their neighbors. Nonsinging birds resort to a variety of performances (p. 171) that serve as a substitute for song. Boundaries are sometimes sharply fixed, but perhaps more often are rather fluid lines wandered over first by one male and then another.

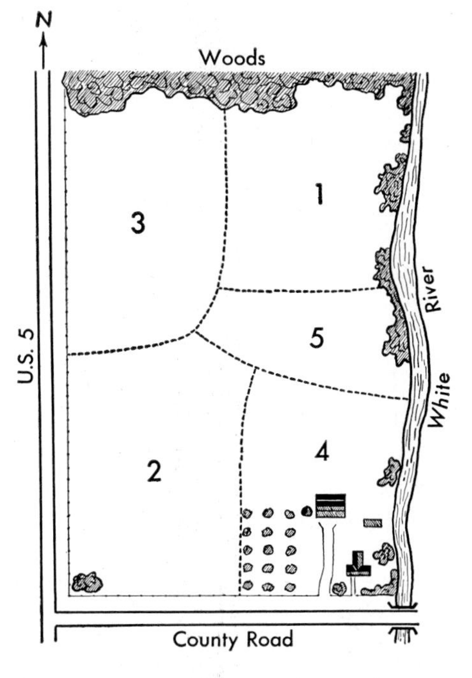


*Fig. 87. Theoretical division of a five-acre meadow into territories.*

*No. 1, the first comer, tentatively stakes out ambitious claims in the northeast corner, including most of territory 5 and part of 3.*

*No. 2, the second comer, settles largely unopposed in the opposite corner. Both birds sing and display almost constantly in their respective areas.*

*No. 3 has frequent boundary clashes with both 1 and 2, but satisfies himself mainly with singing posts along the highway.*

*No. 4 takes over the unoccupied orchard-farmhouse site, meeting opposition only in the west tier of orchard trees which No. 2 also uses for singing posts.*

*No. 5, a late comer, manages after considerable fighting to carve out a small territory, stealing a little land from each other occupant, but mainly from No. 1, which had already started another phase of the breeding cycle and was less vigilant in defending his claims.*

Ordinarily, territorial fights occur only among members of the same species; other species are not strictly competitive, and interspecific controversies only occasionally arise. That is, a pair of Eastern Meadowlarks, Bobolinks, and Field Sparrows may occupy the same acre of ground for nesting, but not, ordinarily, two pairs of Eastern Meadowlarks, Bobolinks, or Field Sparrows. Species vary greatly in this respect, however; the Song Sparrow, for instance, is particularly aggressive toward other species and tries to keep them off his territory (Nice, 1937). Coots are pugnacious to the extent of attacking other vertebrates as well as birds (Gullion, 1953b); indeed, Ryder (1959) found Coots in Utah attacking 11 species of ducks, 18 other species of birds, a fish, a turtle, a weasel, and a muskrat—a list that could be extended by including Californian and European records.

Some closely related species have interspecific problems. The House Wren and Bewick's Wren have long been regarded as arch enemies, though sometimes they are found living in close proximity without apparent animosity (Stamm, 1951a). In the mountains of Tennessee the Black-capped and Carolina Chickadees are competitive in the breeding season; the Black-caps keep the Carolinas from occupying the higher altitudes (Tanner, 1952). Ring-billed and Herring Gulls usually maintain a strict segregation in their nesting colonies. On the other hand, there are many instances of different species nesting close together; in one case, a Robin, a kingbird, an Orchard Oriole, and a Warbling Vireo nested simultaneously in the same tree and all succeeded in rearing young (Stamm, 1951b). Often closely related species have different habitat requirements; the Western and Eastern Meadowlarks, nearly identical in appearance, are usually effectively segregated by the Western's preference for drier sites (Lanyon, 1957). The Brown and Spotted (Rufous-sided) Towhees in California have different foraging habits, the latter scratching more vigorously, rather than merely pecking, in more open spaces (Davis, 1957). Cox (1960) found that Mourning Warbler territories in Minnesota overlapped with 11 other species of warblers, but conflicts developed with only two.

Obviously the size, shape, and distributional patterns of territories will vary greatly with the different species, their specific requirements, the density of populations, and the configuration of the land occupied. Many birds require about an acre of ground for nesting purposes, but some get along with considerably less and others control several acres or more. A House Wren may confine most of its activities to a small garden or yard, perhaps a half acre or so in extent. Some woodland warblers in areas of concentration may be spaced at several pairs per acre (Fig. 88). In a spruce budworm outbreak in a coniferous forest in Ontario, Kendeigh (1947) found an unusual density ("supersaturation") of Tennessee, Cape May, and Bay-breasted Warblers, some of the latter having territories of considerably less than half an acre. A pair of Song Sparrows has been found nesting successfully on each of two islands in Minnesota only 0.04

*Fig. 88. Where a variety of insect food is readily available, woodland warblers may be concentrated on small territories. This female Black-and-White Warbler forages mainly over the trunks and branches of trees and is not strictly competitive with other species of warblers in the same woods. (Photo by Allan D. Cruickshank.)*

acres in size (Beer, *et al.*, 1956), though it is not certain that they secured all their food from so small a space. However, lake-shore territories nearby averaged 0.47 acres (Suthers, 1960) and mainland territories in Ohio averaged 0.67 (Nice, 1943).

A pair of large predatory birds, on the other hand, may range over many square miles, up to a recorded maximum of fifty-nine square miles in the Golden Eagle in California (Dixon, 1937), though not all of the occupied territory (hunting space) is defended. Other predatory birds, like the Red-shouldered Hawks in flood plains and along rivers (Stewart, 1949) and Marsh Hawks in certain marshes (Hecht, 1951), may congregate on small territories where favorable nest sites are available but range more widely for food. The Mourning Dove may stake out rather ambitious claims at the beginning of the season, but defend only the immediate area of the nest site after nesting is underway. Coots in California, on the other hand, start out with a small winter core area which they enlarge in the spring (Gullion, 1953b).

Territories may conform to the lay of the land. Typically they are somewhat oval-shaped, if the habitat permits, but a kingfisher may control fishing rights to a linear mile or so of a stream and have little interest in land away from the bank. The Dipper (Fig. 64) in western mountains and the Louisiana Waterthrush in the east may have similar interests in linear strips of water courses. A pair of Common Loons may control an entire small lake, regardless of contours, but larger lakes may accommodate more than one pair (Munro, 1945).

Territories are ordinarily breeding season phenomena, established in the spring and deserted at the close of the nesting season, but some nonmigratory species remain on or near their holdings over winter. Male Song Sparrows in Ohio remain on or near, or at least periodically visit, their nesting territory at all seasons, but do not defend it as vigorously in winter, and often seek more sheltered swamps during cold spells (Nice, 1937, 1943). Many nonmigratory birds—woodpeckers, Mockingbirds, Cactus Wrens, Wrentits, Loggerhead Shrikes in the southwest, and English Robins—set up defended winter territories which may or may not coincide or overlap with the nesting territory. Often the sexes are segregated in such winter arrangements, but in spring the barriers break down and erstwhile rivals become mates on a single territory.

MODIFIED TERRITORIES

A common modification of the standardized territory outlined above is one that is used primarily for mating and nesting but not exclusively for feeding. Many birds, even of the noncolonial types (see next paragraph), do at least part of their feeding outside the defended area. This, as already noted, is particularly characteristic of predatory birds. Other birds of this type, with separate, usually undefended, feeding grounds, include Black-capped Chickadees, Cedar Waxwings, Tree Swallows, and Barn Swallows.

A more obvious and striking modification of the territory is found in the often severely restricted nesting quarters of colonial birds. Cliff-dwelling sea birds, for example, may be so crowded on a nesting ledge that each bird has only a square foot or two for a nest (Fig. 89). Often, indeed, the space occupied is determined by the length of reach of the owner's sharp

*Fig. 89. Available ledges on Bonaventure, historic bird rock in the Gulf of St. Lawrence, are densely packed with nesting Gannets. Cushionlike, subcutaneous cells act as shock absorbers when the birds plunge from 100-foot heights for fish. (Photo by Allan D. Cruickshank.)*

bill. A colony of Common Murres in Oregon is said to have a density of 22,000 pairs per acre. Table 8 (p. 308) gives some other notable nesting densities of alcids. Each bird in a sea-bird colony has a defended nest site—a true territory, albeit a small one—but the whole colony gathers its food out at sea usually on neutral feeding grounds. Gulls and terns often, but not invariably, have closely packed nest sites, but allow enough room for change-over of mates during incubation and feeding. Gulls often engage in sparring matches across a boundary line, and may even attempt to pull their opponent over the line for further punishment. Bank Swallows in a bank, Cliff Swallows on a ledge or under the eaves of a barn, or herons in a rookery have their respective defended nest sites, but perform many of their activities elsewhere. Cliff Swallows from different nesting colonies may intermix in foraging, mud-gathering, and perching on wires, but return to their respective colonies after such social affairs (Emlen, 1952a).

Some marsh dwellers, like rails and Red-winged Blackbirds, have a semi-colonial arrangement of territories. Nero (1956) found Red-wing territories near Madison, Wisconsin, averaged about 1/12 of an acre, with great variability in different areas. Berger (1951a) found five nests of the Virginia Rail and four of the Sora on less than a half acre of marsh in Michigan. In the Red-winged Blackbird the male's territory, usually including several nesting females, is zealously defended from trespassing males and unwanted females, but the birds do most of their feeding in surrounding fields and do considerable singing from undefended perches scattered about the marsh (Nero and Emlen, 1951). Common Grackles, either in a marsh or in a grove of conifers, and Mourning Doves in old orchards (Fichter, 1959) sometimes reach high nesting concentrations.

Ducks, with a few exceptions, have a strikingly different arrangement. Though there are many variations, the drake commonly selects and defends a "loafing bar" where he and his mate can find isolation and freedom from other drakes, but it is mainly a trysting place. The hen usually nests elsewhere (Fig. 90), perhaps a mile or more away at a site probably unknown to the male; but daily or more often during the egg-laying period and early stages of incubation she visits the male at his loafing bar. In hummingbirds the male and female maintain separate areas; courtship and mating may take place on the male feeding territory or elsewhere, but the female has a separate nesting area (nest site defended), seldom visited or at least not used as a feeding station by the male (Pitelka, 1942).

Goldfinches exhibit further modifications (Stokes, 1950). They delay nesting until late summer, when thistledown for their nests and new seeds

*Fig. 90. This female Redhead constructed the nest, will incubate and hatch the eggs, and rear the young without help from the drake. He frequents a "loafing bar" some distance away, but will soon abandon it to go into an early eclipse. (Photo by Allan D. Cruickshank.)*

for their young are available, but they have paired much earlier. Long after the pairs have formed, the *female* selects a territory which the male, usually but not invariably, proceeds to defend vigorously, although he apparently cannot dominate for his sole use such a priceless commodity as thistledown. Cedar Waxwings at least initiate mating activities while still in flock formation, then seek out a territory together where further courtship takes place. House Sparrows, Black-capped Chickadees, and some other hole-nesting species often mate before the territory is selected, then go house hunting in earnest after the pairs are formed.

Some gallinaceous birds (Sage Grouse, prairie chickens, Sharp-tailed Grouse) and the Ruff in Europe have developed elaborate display grounds or "arenas" (pp. 172, 176) where they mate promiscuously with whatever hens visit them. The hens then repair to nest sites of their own selection which are not defended or even known to the males. The territory in this case serves as a social gathering place for the males in winter and early spring before the females visit them, and as a place of union for the sexes later.

Apparently some birds are essentially nonterritorial. Sharp-tailed Sparrows studied by Woolfenden (1956) were semicolonial, and the polygamous males did not defend a nest site or territory. Brewer's Blackbirds, also polygamous when surplus females are available, attend and protect their females, but not the nest or a territory (Williams, 1952).

To summarize, then, territories appear to be divisible into about four main breeding types and the nonbreeding winter territories: (1) territories which provide for all the requirements of breeding and nesting—courtship, pair formation, nesting and feeding the young (most species); (2) territories, usually more restricted, which provide for all breeding requirements except food (predatory birds, chickadees, Cedar Waxwings, noncolonial swallows); (3) more severely restricted territories of colonial and semicolonial birds which usually defend only the immediate nest site (most sea birds, gulls and terns, rails, many icterids and ploceids); (4) territories that serve mainly or exclusively for pair formation and associated events, not nesting or feeding (some grouse, some shorebirds, some bowerbirds and birds of paradise). Some birds, of course, do not fit readily into any of these categories.

### THE FUNCTION OF TERRITORY

The functions of the territory are probably apparent from the preceding account, but these may be summed up under the following headings:

1. Pair isolation, or providing a place for courtship and mating without interference.
2. Assuring an even distribution of birds over available habitats, so that their carrying capacity is not exceeded.
3. Facilitating food gathering for the young.
4. Protection from predators.

Isolation for mating purposes is essential for many birds. Among ducks, where there is often an unbalanced sex ratio with excess males threatening to break up mated pairs, it appears necessary for the drake to isolate a female from other ducks onto a private territory if subsequent breeding is to be successful. In other species the territory plays a role of considerable importance in pair formation, courtship performances, and later for undisturbed nesting. The song of the male informs a hunting female of the whereabouts of an available mate and territory; this is thought to be of particular importance in dense cover, as in the deep dark forests of the tropics, where the sharp calls and sometimes elaborate ceremonies of tropical birds aid the females in finding the males.

Territorial arrangements serve a second important function in assuring a more even distribution over available habitats, so that breeding pairs will not be overcrowded in one region and entirely absent in another. That is, if about an acre of meadow is required for a pair of field birds, this would encourage a distribution over all the available acres within the range of the species rather than in congested sections. Some think that populations are regulated by such a distribution of territories. In spite of this concept of territories evening out distribution, however, birds sometimes tend to "bunch up" in selecting breeding sites, leaving some apparently suitable spaces unoccupied. Many birds are somewhat sociable even in the nesting season. Proximity of neighbors in colonies in fact stimulates breeding; the most sought after nesting sites are toward the center of the colony, and peripheral nesters are often unsuccessful.

A third and perhaps more obvious function of the territory is to facilitate food gathering from a restricted area without intraspecific competition. Species which feed their young several hundred times a day need to gather the food hurriedly in places close at hand which have not been gleaned over by competitors. Perhaps strangely, however, even this important requirement is not always fulfilled by the territory, as many birds go outside the defended area for food, and many male birds relax their vigilance during this phase of the nesting cycle and allow other birds to feed on the territory. Perhaps the explanation for this lack of vigilance at a time when it would appear to be most urgent is due to the waning of sexual aggressiveness, or because the males are too busy feeding young to defend their territories.

A fourth suggested function of the territory is to provide some protection from predators; the occupant soon becomes thoroughly familiar with the territory and may know of quick escape routes and places of concealment.

## *Courtship and Mating*

### COURTSHIP RITUALS

The preliminary ceremonies in which the sexes engage to attract and stimulate one another are commonly referred to as *courtship,* as opposed to *mating,* which implies pair formation but not necessarily sexual union (copulation) which may come later. Courtship is not necessarily restricted to the period preceding pair formation, though in some species it is. In others it is continued throughout the breeding season and seems to be the bond that keeps the pair intact. In ducks, penguins and some other sea birds, courtship begins early, often in the winter preceding the nesting season.

Some courtship antics may appear somewhat ludicrous to us, as in the case of the feather fluffing and wheezy gurgling of the Brown-headed Cowbirds and Common Grackles, but others are spectacular exhibits of precision and beauty. Usually such performances are by the male, the female appearing to be only mildly or not at all interested. But in some birds, such as the grebes and penguins, the sexes play a nearly equal role in their elaborate courtship ceremonies. In still other species, such as the thrushes, courtship is so simple it is hardly noticeable, and nesting proceeds without apparent preliminaries.

The truly great variety of courtship rituals indulged in by birds precludes the possibility of describing many of them; a few selected examples will serve to illustrate the scope of such activities. Among the songbirds, of course, the song itself is the principal means of sex attraction. Many songbirds, however, perhaps especially those with inferior voices, supplement vocal performances with displays and posturing. Redstarts flash their salmon-colored wing and tail patches both to intimidate other males and to attract females. Kinglets, the Eastern Kingbird, and the Ovenbird are examples of those that display bright crown patches. Brilliantly plumaged males such as tanagers and orioles parade before the females as well as rival males. Meadowlarks display their bright vests when they wish to attract attention, but turn their backs for concealment. Some field birds (larks, pipits, some sandpipers), perhaps because of the absence of suitable singing posts, have evolved elaborate flight songs which make them conspicuous over their territory. In general, with many exceptions, males with weak or simple songs (most fringillids) sing from conspicuous perches, but males with elaborate songs (thrushes) may sing from concealment.

Birds which do not sing substitute other performances. Woodpeckers drum on dead limbs, and have strengthened neck muscles and thickened skull bones to withstand the pounding. The male Ruffed Grouse mounts a log or stump (Fig. 911) and fans the air with his wings, slowly at first, then with increased tempo, producing a reverberating "thunder" which carries long distances. Among the shorebirds the Common Snipe and American Woodcock in particular have developed spectacular aerial displays. The latter performs every evening during the breeding season, rising on whistling wings some 300 feet above the ground, circling, maneuvering,

*Fig. 91. Left, male Ruffed Grouse mounts a log and "thunders" a proclamation of territorial ownership by fanning the air with his wings. Right, a prairie chicken issues a challenge by "booming." (Photos by Mich. Dept. of Conservation.)*

and "chippering" loudly before plunging into its precipitous descent. The related European Ruff stages its dances and sham battles in group formation on a carefully selected "hill"; the ruffs circling the necks have even evolved into different colors on different individuals. Prairie chickens congregate on hereditary dancing grounds, where the males strut and dance, inflating their colorful neck pouches to produce their characteristic "booming" (Fig. 91r). Sham battles are staged, but seldom with any physical injury to the participants, suggesting that the ceremonies at the outset at least are primarily social or to determine dominance. The similar ceremonies of the Sage Grouse in the west are even more highly evolved, with a complex hierarchy of master cocks, subcocks, and guard cocks each with his special role to play (Scott, 1942).

Perhaps the most elaborate of all courtship ceremonies are those of the birds of paradise in New Guinea and the bowerbirds in Australia. The latter (Fig. 92) carefully prepare "bowers" of twigs or leaves which they decorate with bright petals of flowers, or, in recent years, trinkets lost by G.I.'s. In these artistic pavilions they dance and display throughout the breeding season. Birds of paradise (Fig. 93) possess incredibly fantastic and often brilliantly colored plumage decorations—ruffs, capes, false wings, and wiry plumes protruding from various parts of the body (Ripley, 1950). They display, turn somersaults, and dangle upside down in all their finery before the females. But like some of the bowerbirds, they are so preoccupied with these performances that the males of most species take little or no part in subsequent family affairs. The apparent functions of such elaborate displays are to proclaim and maintain a territory (Type 4) and to provide a place for mating.

*Fig. 92. This Fawn-breasted Bowerbird* (Chlamydera cerviniventris) *seems to have assembled largely natural objects at its bower, but often other items— silverware, jewelry, bottle tops, shells, coins, etc., are confiscated to decorate the site. (Courtesy of the Amer. Mus. Nat. Hist.)*

Displays and their apparent significance have been described for many species. Some recent examples are McAllister (1958) for Eared Grebes, Johnsgard (1955, 1960) for ducks, Gullion (1952) for American Coot, Slud (1957) for manakins (Pipridae), and Nero (1956) for Red-winged Blackbirds.

## PAIR FORMATION

The processes involved in mate selection are not well understood, but courtship ceremonies generally culminate in the establishment of mated pairs on territories. Of course the territory is usually the place of union; that is one of its functions. Characteristically the male attacks or threatens any bird, male or female, which enters his domain. Attacked females usually retreat, transients not returning, but would-be residents may remain in or near the area until the male modifies his tactics from aggressive threat to invitatory displays. Sexual flights, with the male in pursuit of the female,

*Fig. 93. Lesser Birds of Paradise* (Paradisaea minor), *like other paradiseids, dance and display their fantastic plumes throughout the breeding season, but take little interest in domestic affairs. (Courtesy of N.Y. Zool. Soc.)*

are of common occurrence. The female is not territory conscious at this stage and may wander from one area to another, but the song of the male may call her back. Some territory-holding males appear to recognize the difference between transient males and potential rivals (residents), and attack only the latter, and also appear at times to distinguish transient (nonbreeding) females from the more receptive resident females, showing interest only in the latter.

Pair formation takes place early—often in the winter flock—among ducks, in the American Goldfinch, and in certain sea birds. Richdale (1951b), after years of careful observation on penguins, states that in most species the new pairs are formed and old pairs reunited in the winter before they return to the nesting colonies, but that some pairs may be formed at any time of the year. In the Yellow-eyed Penguin some individuals show definite affinities for a particular mate; one female waited six years for the "male of her choice," and "divorces" and "flirtations" played an important part in the determination of pairs.

## SEX RECOGNITION

Sex recognition poses some interesting problems for birds. For though it is a simple matter among birds in which the sexes have strikingly different plumages, in many birds there are only slight visual differences or none at all. Experiment shows that birds use visual clues, at least in part, where such clues are possible. The male and female Yellow-shafted Flicker, for example, differ chiefly in the black malar stripe or "mustache" possessed by the male. If a black mustache is experimentally painted onto a female, the male mistakes her for another male and attacks her (Noble, 1936). Such errors in recognition are usually soon rectified by characteristic reaction, however, for an altered female still reacts as a female and is thus identified by the male.

When plumages are identical in the two sexes, birds apparently depend on behavior characteristics to identify each other. Once mated, most males soon learn to recognize their mates readily at a distance, and pay little or no attention to other females. Richdale (1951b) believes that penguins readily recognize the opposite sex at all times without any experimental preliminaries, but of course certain birds in a penguin colony have been associated since birth.

## COPULATION

Sexual union or copulation usually follows pair formation, that is, though there are many variations, the usual sequence of events is a preliminary period of courtship in which selection of mates is determined, often followed by more rituals after the pair is formed before actual coition takes place. Although the male may take the lead in preliminaries, the female may initiate copulation by an invitatory call, song, display, or posture. The female Yellow-shafted Flicker, for instance, has an invitatory call without which the male will not react (Noble, 1936). In Sparrow Hawks (Childs and Mossman, 1952), Cactus Wrens (Anderson and Anderson, 1959), Cardinals (Laskey, 1944), and tinamous (Pearson and Pearson, 1955) copulation has been observed to follow the invitation of the female by call, song, or posturing. In some cases, as noted in the tinamous and Sparrow Hawk (Hartman, 1959), the male may fail to respond to the invitation.

Copulation is usually repeated at frequent intervals during the breeding season, mainly before and during the egg-laying period in order that the eggs may be fertile, but there is great variation. Ducks, Sparrow Hawks, Cactus Wrens, and House Sparrows may start such activities in winter, long before the eggs are laid, and continue throughout the breeding season, but Swallowtanagers (Tersinidae) studied by Schaefer (1953) in Venezuela delayed copulation until after the nest was built. Female Snow Buntings observed by Tinbergen (1939) in Greenland were not receptive during the egg-laying period.

Frequency, and regularity, of copulation vary also. Haverschmidt (1946) states that a pair of Little Owls (*Athene noctua*) in his garden came and perched on a branch near the nest tree at about six o'clock each evening and that the male mounted the female from one to four times (perhaps not always effectively) each evening during March, April and early May. The eggs were laid in late April. Coition in a pair of captive Sparrow Hawks (Hartman, 1959) reached a peak in mid-March (fourteen times between 7 and 7:36 A.M., six more times before noon, and once in the afternoon), but dwindled to once or twice a day thereafter, then ceased altogether. Berger (1957) observed 11 copulations in rapid succession in a pair of House Sparrows; sexual activities began in March long before the eggs were laid and continued after egg laying. In some cases, prolonging such activities may be necessary to assure fertility of later clutches of eggs. Unlike domestic hens which have been known to lay fertile eggs three weeks after separation from the rooster, and domestic turkeys which have laid fertile eggs 73 days after separation from the tom, Elder and Weller (1954) found some Mallard eggs infertile after 6 days. They speculated that the function of excess unmated ducks might be to insure fertility of second clutches, if the first clutch failed after desertion by the original drake which might already be molting (p. 167).

Among "arena" birds (some grouse, the Ruff, bowerbirds, and so on) there is no regular pair formation, and copulation is usually promiscuous. Hen prairie chickens visit the dancing grounds of the males, pair temporarily with the male of their choice, then withdraw to their respective nesting sites unaccompanied by the males. Similarly in the Sage Grouse, the females visit the ceremonial grounds and are served mainly by the more virile master cocks; one master cock has been known to serve twenty-one hens in a single morning, but the subcocks and guard cocks are relegated to subordinate roles (Scott, 1942). Oystercatchers (Fig. 94), at least in the European species (Makkink, 1942), are promiscuous during group court-

*Fig. 94. In oystercatchers (Haematopodidae) preliminary courtship activities are often communal affairs, but later the pairs settle down to a monogamous relationship. As their name implies, oystercatchers feed on shellfish, prying the valves open with their powerful beaks. Note the broken shells about the nest. (Photo by Allan D. Cruickshank.)*

ship preliminaries but become monogamous as soon as permanent nesting pairs are established. Meanly (1955) observed promiscuity in Little Blue Heron colonies in Arkansas during the nesting season; males frequently visited neighboring females on their nests and were accepted by them.

## Types of Pairing Bonds

It is probably apparent by now that monogamy for one breeding season is the prevailing relationship between the sexes, but that other types of pairing bonds exist. The several kinds known to occur in birds and examples of each are outlined below.

Monogamy (paired to a single mate, may be of short or long duration):

1. Pair for life—swans, geese, eagles(?), Wrentits, probably parrots.
2. Retain, or reunite with, mate for more than one season—probably most sea birds, Paridae, Corvidae.

3. Pair for one breeding season—ducks, most passerines, and the smaller nonpasserines.
4. Pair for single brood (change mates between broods)—House Wrens (commonly), bluebirds, and other hole-nesters sometimes.
5. Shorter term than one brood-oropendolas, woodcock(?), hummingbirds(?), some sandpipers, some weaverbirds.

Polygamy (paired to two or more mates at the same time, either sex):

1. Polygyny (male with two or more mates)—Ostrich, pheasants and many other gallinaceous birds, many icterids (meadowlarks; Red-winged, Brewer's, and Yellow-headed Blackbirds), Marsh Hawks, Bittern (of Europe), Winter Wren.
2. Polyandry (female with two or more mates)—some tinamous, bustardquail, phalaropes(?), sometimes cuckoos and cowbirds, longspurs.

Promiscuity—Little Blue Herons; probably most grouse, bowerbirds and birds of paradise (in part); cuckoos and cowbirds (in part), Boat-tailed Grackles; Sharp-tailed Sparrows.

### MONOGAMY AND ITS VARIATIONS

PAIRING FOR LIFE. It has long been supposed that many of the larger birds—sea birds, cranes, falconiform and strigiform birds—mate for life, but conclusive evidence in most cases is lacking. Mating for life usually means until one of the pair dies, when the other may take a new mate, but there are many known cases, particularly among captive swans and geese (Fig. 95), where the surviving bird never remated. Perhaps the idea of such birds never remating has been overemphasized, however, as there are known examples, particularly among captive geese, of voluntary changes during the life of the individuals as well as remating after the death of one partner.

Richdale (1942) thinks the Royal Albatross remains mated for life, basing his belief on the fraternization of the pair out at sea during the nonbreeding season. Parrots, at least in captivity, remain paired for long periods, a condition also believed to apply to the wild species. Among the smaller birds the Wrentits are known to form permanent pairs and some corvids (Jackdaw, magpies, Carrion Crow, ravens) as well as Paridae either form long lasting bonds or else reunite in successive seasons. A Carrion Crow has been known to have the same mate for ten years, and mate changes in magpies appear to be due chiefly to replacements.

*Fig. 95. Canada Geese are noted for the permanence of their pairing bonds. The gander guards the female and nest, and the whole family stays together until the following spring, when the young are driven away. (Courtesy of Miles D. Pirnie.)*

RETENTION OF MATE FOR MORE THAN ONE SEASON. Perhaps a more common pairing bond than actually mating for life is the frequent retention of or reunion with the same mate in successive seasons. Richdale (1951b), in his careful ten-year study of Yellow-eyed Penguins, found that they retained the same mates in successive seasons in 82 per cent of the possible cases, as compared to 18 per cent of separations or "divorces." Known pairs were intact for seven, nine, and eleven years. He believes that other penguins and most albatrosses and petrels follow a similar pattern. Associations between some gulls and terns are often of long duration. Perhaps the non-migratory Paridae as well as nuthatches and creepers are of this nature, as it is not known whether they remain paired over winter or merely so closely associated that remating in the spring is facilitated. Winter territory-holders —Mockingbirds, Loggerhead Shrikes, and English Robins—frequently reunite for the breeding season. The frequent remating of migratory birds, however, is probably purely fortuitous, aided by the return of both sexes to their former nesting area. Brackbill (1952), for instance, found only one (12 per cent) of 8 pairs of returning Robins remating, compared to 8 out of 30 (27 per cent) in Mrs. Nice's Song Sparrows and 11 out of 26 (42 per cent) in Kendeigh's House Wrens. He attributed reunion in the Robin to the faithfulness of both members of the pair to their previous year's territory and lack of reunion to unfaithfulness to territory.

PAIRING FOR ONE SEASON. In general, the way of life among birds favors seasonal monogamy as the most convenient and practical plan. Territory-holding birds pair with a single female and remain together during the nesting season, then separate and go their respective ways. When they return in the spring, males commonly attempt to reclaim their former territory, but the females are more inclined to scatter. Mrs. Nice found that female Song Sparrows in Ohio often returned to their former territories, but usually found the male already mated to a female that did not migrate. Most ducks belong in this category of monogamy for one season, for though the males desert the nesting hens early in the season, they do not remate.

CHANGE OF MATES BETWEEN BROODS. Some birds, such as the House Wren and sometimes Eastern Bluebirds and other hole-nesting species, change mates between broods, perhaps as a matter of convenience, as one parent, often the male, may take charge of the first brood while the other remates with another partner for a second brood. In the Cedar Waxwing, however, Putnam (1949) shows that overlapping of broods favors continuity of the pairing bond. The male renews courtship before the first nest cycle is finished, and the female abandons her young for the male to finish rearing while she renests. This, incidentally, gives the male an unusually rigorous schedule; he is involved in courtship, building a second nest, and rearing young all at the same time.

SHORTER TERM THAN ONE BROOD. In some oropendolas, neotropical relatives of our orioles, in which there is an excess of females, the males have several different mates during one nesting season but only one at a time; otherwise the excess females could not nest successfully. Emlen (1957) noted similar habits in African ploceids (whydahs and bishop birds); the males courted and mated with several females but apparently had only one mate at a time. Perhaps the American Woodcock (Fig. 96) belongs in this category of short-term monogamy as the male frequently moves from one singing ground to another, perhaps leaving a female at each station. Hummingbirds, at least in North America, have a pairing bond of short duration and often have no further relationship with the female or nest (Pitelka, 1942). Like the woodcock they may perhaps be polygamous; it is not certain whether they pair with more than one female at the same station or move to new stations and new females successively.

*Fig. 96. These woodcock will never know their father. He "sang" to and consorted with their mother for a brief period in early spring and then (presumably) moved on to other singing grounds. (Courtesy of L. H. Walkinshaw.)*

POLYGAMY

POLYGYNY. Among the regularly polygynous birds the pheasants are perhaps the best known example. In captivity cock pheasants are commonly mated with five or more hens, but in nature the male's crowing grounds may not be spacious enough, or sufficient hens available, to permit so large a harem. Many other phasianids (mostly native to the Old World) are regularly polygamous, but our native grouse, though often referred to as polygamous, are perhaps more properly termed promiscuous. Ostriches and rheas are also polygamous, each male having several hens contributing to a family nest over which he takes supervision.

Some icterids, notably Red-winged and Yellow-headed Blackbirds nesting in semicolonial situations, are usually but not invariably polygynous. In the Red-wing each male controls an area including several nests which he zealously guards, but both sexes frequently leave the territory for feeding and other purposes; the females, indeed, may consort with other males while "off duty," so that the males may not be the fathers of the young they so carefully protect (Beer and Tibbitts, 1950; Nero and Emlen, 1951). In Williams' (1952) study of the Brewer's Blackbird some males were monogamous, some polygynous. Cases of polygyny increased when the number of females increased. Kluijver, *et al.* (1940), found polygyny common in Winter Wrens in Europe, and Hecht (1951) reported it for Marsh Hawks in semicolonial nest situations in Manitoba. Most monogamous species may on occasions take an extra mate; sometimes when a male disappears, his neighbor takes over the vacated territory and its female occupant in addition to his own.

In some instances where more than two adults are found attending a nest of young, however, it is not polygamy but merely an unmated bird joining in voluntarily to help out in family affairs. In the tropics these "helpers at the nest" are of common occurrence; often it is a case of one or more of the young of the previous nesting remaining with their parents and helping in the rearing of the second generation (Skutch, 1935). Extra-parental cooperation is common among Chimney Swifts (Dexter, 1952), the helpers actually sharing in incubation and brooding as well as feeding, and sometimes renewing such cooperative arrangements in successive years. A study of this peculiar relationship in Ohio disclosed twenty-two "threesomes" and six "foursomes."

Trios in the Yellow-eyed Penguin are fairly common, usually due to a bird which has lost its mate trying to join with an already mated pair (Richdale, 1951b). Bleitz (1951) reported two pairs of Pygmy Nuthatches attending a nine-egg nest (normal maximum for this species) and all four feeding the young. Lawrence (1960) cited three cases of trilateral relationships at nests of the Gray Jay in Ontario, but suggested that in one case where two females were sitting on the same nest that the male in the triumvirate may have been lost and that two females tried to carry on as a pair (the eggs never hatched). Skutch (1961), from a recent survey of the literature which supplements his own observations in Central America, lists more than 130 species known to serve as "helpers" in caring for birds other than their own young.

POLYANDRY. The polyandrous relationship, or a female with several mates, is somewhat exceptional in birds, but occurs in species in which there is a sex reversal in nesting duties, such as in tinamous, button-quails

*Fig. 97. Barred Button-quail (*Turnix suscitator*) are polyandrous. The larger, more brightly colored female lays several clutches of eggs, leaving a male in charge of each. (From Delacour,* Birds of Malaysia, *copyright 1947 by Jean Delacour, The Macmillan Company, New York.)*

(Fig. 97), and perhaps phalaropes. Polyandry in these species is not universal, since it may vary with the sex ratio. The great naturalist, William Beebe, originally pointed out that in a species of tinamou (*Crypturellus variegatus*) in British Guiana the males outnumbered the females four to one. Both Pearson and Pearson (1955) and Schaefer (1954), however, found sex ratios in tinamous in Peru and Venezuela about even, and Schaefer found cases of polygyny among the older males.

Cowbirds and Old World cuckoos are considered polyandrous by some authorities, and promiscuous by others, though apparently cowbirds are sometimes monogamous. Wynne-Edwards (1952) found an excess of males among longspurs on Baffin Island; in one case three males were attending one nest-building female. A female Hicks' Seed-eater in Panama has been recorded with two mates during the nesting season; both were seen to copulate with the nesting female and both had singing posts and fed the young (Gross, 1952). Hann (1940) reported a similar polyandrous relationship in Ovenbirds. In most other species with an excess of males (e.g., ducks and penguins) the extra males remained unmated, but are available for replacements in case a female loses her first mate.

### PROMISCUITY

In three genera of our native grouse (the prairie chickens, Sharp-tailed Grouse, and Sage Grouse) courting, mating, and copulation are communal and promiscuous affairs and there is no regular pair formation. The same or a similar relationship exists with the Ruff and Great Snipe in Europe, Pectoral Sandpipers in Alaska (Pitelka, 1959), and with a few birds of paradise. In most birds of paradise and bowerbirds, however, as well as in some grouse (Ruffed, Spruce, and Blue Grouse) the males have individual (rather than communal) performing areas, but are promiscuous in mating. McIlhenny (1937) states that in Boat-tailed Grackles in Louisiana the females visit the male flocks, which are not stationary, and mate at random with them. Promiscuity in Little Blue Herons has already been mentioned (p. 177). Woolfenden (1956) found this true also of Sharp-tailed Sparrows but not Seaside Sparrows.

### REPLACEMENT OF LOST MATES

Another factor that often prevents long-lasting bonds between birds is high mortality during nesting, which in many cases necessitates quick replacements if the season is to be successful. If a female is lost, the male renews singing and displaying and soon secures another mate. If a male is lost, the vacated territory is promptly taken over by another male.

An experiment in collecting birds on their territories in a spruce-fir forest community in northern Maine showed that the collected males were usually replaced overnight; 455 birds, mostly males, were taken where only 148 males held territories at the beginning of the study. The following year 154 pairs established territories and 528 birds were collected (Stewart and Aldrich, 1951; Hensley and Cope, 1951). Both Allen (1961) and Odum (1942) tell of a female Black-capped Chickadee that had three successive mates in one season, the males presumably having perished. Griscom (1945) describes an investigation in which male Indigo Buntings were collected to see how quickly the lost birds would be replaced. Nine males in succession were taken from a single territory; the tenth was left to help the oft-widowed female raise her young. We have noted similarly quick replacements of single birds or new pairs following "die-offs" in local spraying programs (p. 381); in one case, at least three successive pairs of Robins and several singles occupied the same territory but none succeeded in carrying nesting beyond early incubation stages.

Thus there are usually many unmated birds available for replacements. Often these are young males not ready to mate early in the season. Male Red-winged and Yellow-headed Blackbirds, for instance, are not sexually mature at the beginning of their first nesting season but mature during the season and are available to take over vacated territories and widowed females. In ducks and penguins, the excess of males has already been noted. Extra drakes may harass and break up nesting pairs, but excess males in some colonial birds are believed to have a beneficial effect on the mating efficiency of the others.

## *Songs and Calls*

Some appreciation of the scope and meaning of bird song is readily apparent from the preceding account, but a summation with supplementary comments may place the whole phenomenon in a clearer light. Obviously much of the early season singing of birds is primarily concerned with the territory. Many birds do their most ardent singing at this time, before the arrival of the females; then the territory songs may be in part replaced by or at least alternate with courtship songs. Once mates have been secured, many birds reduce singing, and some cease altogether during subsequent stages of the nesting cycle. Call notes, by contrast, are used throughout the year as a means of communication, between the sexes, between different individuals within the species, and between different species.

Obviously birds have different songs and calls for different purposes. Laskey (1944), in her study of the Cardinal in Tennessee, distinguished twenty-eight different Cardinal songs. Aretas Saunders (1951), who has spent nearly a lifetime studying bird songs, has recorded 884 variations in Song Sparrow songs. Odum (1942) lists and describes, with attempted explanation of meaning, sixteen types of songs or calls used by Black-capped Chickadees, eight related to breeding behavior, eight primarily social. The American Goldfinch, according to Stokes (1950), has an "off-territory" courtship song, a territorial flight song, and a canarylike warbling song used in flock formation. Nice (1937) describes a "signal" song used by male Song Sparrows to call their mates off the nest for feeding purposes. Hann (1937) describes an "all's well" song used by male Ovenbirds to assure the females, which sit in ovenlike nests with a view in one direction only, that a certain danger has passed. House Wrens have a "stimulation" song, used to stimulate the young to gape for food when it is brought.

Davis (1959) considers the familiar "chebec" of the male Least Flycatcher primarily a "position" call advising the female of his location. R. Smith (1959) describes three vocalizations in the Grasshopper Sparrow: (1) a "grasshopper" song used early in the season for territorial defense and threat (female doesn't respond to it); (2) a "sustained" song used to attract the female and to maintain the pair bond (female responds to it); and (3) a "trill" used by both sexes to notify each other and the young of their presence. The male does not respond to the trill of another male but challenges another "grasshopper" song.

Thus songs and calls serve a variety of purposes, and express a variety of emotions; even the somewhat anthropomorphic idea that birds sing for pleasure is perhaps not entirely out of place. In listening to the amazing repertoire of the Mockingbird one gets the impression that he is really enjoying himself. But Lack (1943) appropriately comments that if birds sing because they are happy, then female English Robins are happy only in the fall, males are more happy before acquiring a mate than after they get one, and are happiest of all when fighting.

DAILY CYCLE OF SONG

It is common knowledge that birds sing most ardently in the early morning. Birds have definite awakening hours apparently determined by light intensities. Some birds, like Robins, are notoriously early risers; others, like Common Crows, Blue Jays, Black-capped Chickadees and other birds that roost in cavities may sleep a little later. Robins break into song as soon as they awaken, then cease singing for a period of feeding; other birds may forage before singing, or, like vireos, do both simultaneously. Singing definitely wanes through the later morning hours, and reaches a minimum in early afternoon when birds, especially in northern regions where summer days are long, take rest periods. Then they may renew song in late afternoon or evening, though usually this does not equal the morning climax. Some species, like vireos and wrens, or species proclaiming territory, may sing persistently throughout the day. A vireo's leisurely method of gleaning insects from leaves and branches does not interfere with singing, for it sings between bites; a wren, unlike most birds, sings while carrying food to its young.

Many birds have special times for singing, often using a distinctive song for a particular time of day. The Eastern Kingbird has a special "matin" song used for ten to fifteen minutes before sunrise (Mayer, 1952). The Alder (Traill's) Flycatcher has a peculiar flight song, different from the daytime songs, used after sunset (McCabe, 1951). The Ovenbird and Yellowthroat also have special evening flight songs and the Tree Swallow performs long before dawn. Thrushes, the most renowned songsters among American birds, are justly famous for evening performances. Gray-cheeked Thrushes in the New England mountains have a ten-to-fifteen-minute period of flight songs, just after sunset, but seldom resort to flight singing at other times (Wallace, 1939). The Whip-poor-will and American Woodcock (Fig. 98) are noted for the punctuality of their evening performances in relation to sundown.

Persistency and frequency of song have been recorded by many observers. Perhaps the record goes to a Red-eyed Vireo in Ontario which sang 22,197 songs during a ten-hour period (de Kiriline, 1954). D. Davis (1959) counted 700 "chebecs" of a Least Flycatcher in a fifteen-minute period in the early morning, but song output declined after 5:30 A.M. J. Davis (1958) counted 3,390 songs of an unmated (mated birds sang less) Rufous-sided Towhee during an eight-hour observation period (8:15

*Fig. 98. The American Woodcock, or "timberdoodle" as it is known to many sportsmen, is noted for its punctual evening performance in relation to sundown. (Photo by Lawrence A. Ryel.)*

A.M. to 6:25 P.M.); it sang 95 per cent of the time between 8:15 A.M. and 9:15 A.M. but only 64 per cent between 5:25 P.M. and 6:25 P.M.

### SEASONAL CYCLE OF SONG

Birds likewise have a seasonal cycle of song, usually closely correlated with nesting activities. Song is at its peak early in the season, during territory establishment and pair formation, then wanes abruptly, or may cease almost entirely in some species. Some birds sing during the period of incubation, some do not; a few birds (wrens) sing while feeding young, but most do not. Curiously, Yellowthroats sing, at least by spurts, through the whole nesting cycle, *except* during courtship when song ceases (Stewart, 1953).

Any threat to a male's territory, or the loss of his mate or nest, causes him to renew or increase singing, perhaps to assert his continued claim to the territory, perhaps to stimulate the female to nest again. Feeding a brood of young has a telling effect on the males and song practically ceases at this stage. Of course, the reason may be primarily physiological, associated with regression of the gonads, but also there is little environmental incentive to sing, for the territories are now being abandoned and pairs separated. If all birds were in the same stage of the nesting cycle at the same time there would probably be little singing in summer, but interrupted nests as well as early and late nesters produce great variations. That is, while one male may be silent, feeding young, another may be singing for the beginning of his second or third brood. Some birds are all through nesting in June, but American Goldfinches may be still nesting, and singing, in September. Perhaps the record for year-round persistency in singing belongs to the Andean or Rufous-collared Sparrow (*Zonotrichia capensis*). Wallace (unpublished) observed an almost constant output of song in Colombia from 6 A.M. to 6 P.M., with occasional outbursts during the night, from September 10 to July 18, though the total output of marked individuals was not determined.

Fall singing is fairly frequent among some birds. Often the songs are mere snatches, quite unlike the full songs of spring; often, too, they are the efforts of young birds trying out their inexperienced voices. There is also a slight but temporary recrudescence of the gonads in some species in the fall which may account for autumn songs. English Robins, both male and female, establish sharply defended territories in the fall, and sing vigorously. J. Davis (1958) correlated fall singing in first-year Rufous-sided Towhees in California with a slight increase in size of the testes.

## SONG IN RELATION TO SEX

Though it is well known that singing is characteristic mainly of male birds, there is ample evidence that the females in many species sing. Though some records of apparent singing females are rightly open to suspicion on the grounds that they might be immature males (e.g., Purple Finch, American Redstart), there are many cases not open to doubt. Laskey (1944) considers female Cardinals regular singers, but they have a shorter season of song than the male. Female Gray-cheeked Thrushes have been observed singing on their nests during incubation, hatching of the eggs, and while brooding young (Wallace, 1939). In the titmice, both sexes sing, as in the softly whistled "fee-be" of the Black-capped Chickadee which is employed by both sexes, but more frequently by the male. As already mentioned, female winter territory holders (English Robins, Mockingbirds, and Loggerhead Shrikes) sing quite regularly. Antiphonal singing, or the answering songs of a male and female stationed some distance apart, is common to some birds, particularly in the dense tropics where location songs are needed to inform a bird of the whereabouts of its mate. (For a detailed discussion of the possible significance of female songs, see Van Tyne and Berger, 1959.)

## INHERITANCE OF SONG

Some controversy has existed as to whether or not young birds instinctively sing the song of their species or acquire it by imitation of adults, but now many studies indicate that both inheritance and learning are involved. Certainly a crow will caw and a duck quack whether or not it has ever heard its kind. But it is likewise true that the more elaborate songs require practice and apparently imitation before reaching perfection. Wild songbirds reared in captivity often sing initial songs that are only partially suggestive of their species. A hand-reared Gray-cheeked Thrush, which had probably never heard the songs of the adults, sang a thrushlike, but decidedly off-tune, song all winter. However, when taken back to its native haunts in the spring, it learned to sing the song characteristic of the species (Wallace, 1939). Lanyon (1957) reports that the primary (territorial) song of meadowlarks (both Eastern and Western) is learned rather than inherited, since juveniles acquire the songs of other species with which they are associated. Nice (1943) divided the song-learning process of Song Sparrows into five stages before the full adult song was perfected. Many other experiments with hand-reared birds indicate that calls and simple songs are instinctive but that the more elaborate songs require some practice and learning before perfection is attained. (Again, for a detailed discussion of this problem, see Van Tyne and Berger, 1959.)

(Selected References follow Chapter 10.)

# 9

# THE ANNUAL CYCLE:

## *Nests, Eggs, Incubation, and Hatching*

### *The Nest*

The location of a nest site and construction of a nest, or receptacle for housing the eggs, is usually the first major enterprise of newly mated birds. Typically the nest site is selected by the female on the territory defended by the male, but there are numerous exceptions. In some cases the male selects, or at least designates, suitable locations. In hole-nesting species the male may lead the female to available nesting cavities within his territory, or, as in some of the wrens, the female may take over and finish a nest already largely constructed by the male. In Prothonotary Warblers the males select the nest cavity and start carrying moss before the females arrive (Walkinshaw, 1953). In the Cedar Waxwing, nest-site selection appears to be a cooperative project, the sexes seeking a suitable place together, and sometimes forming the territory around the chosen location (Putnam, 1949).

Nest situations have many possible locations, from burrows in the ground to elaborate treetop structures. They may be on any type of ground surface, in herbaceous or shrubby plants, in a great variety of tree situations, in banks and caves, floating on or suspended over water, and in or on many man-made structures. Some of these many nest situations are indicated in the following account of nest structures.

## TYPES OF NEST STRUCTURES

The nests of birds exhibit a great variety of types and degrees of workmanship, from no prepared structure to the amazingly fantastic creations of some tropical birds. The obvious and often indispensable function of the nest is to house the eggs, but the fact that many ground-nesting birds build none and that poorly constructed nests often seem to serve as successfully as the more elaborate types, indicates that the art of nest building has, in many cases, gone far beyond purely utilitarian requirements.

Various authors (notably Herrick in 1911) have attempted to classify nests, but at best such a classification is artificial and has little or no evolutionary significance. Many tree nesters, including the Robin and Mourning Dove, sometimes nest on the ground, and ground nesters sometimes build elevated nests, often modifying the structure to fit the new location. Nickell (1958), who has collected 20,000 nests of 169 different species over a period of thirty-five years, outlines some of the engineering features involved in the various types of nests. The following paragraphs describe some of the many variations in structure and placement of nests.

NO PREPARED NEST. Among the birds which do not construct a nest are some shorebirds which lay their eggs on the bare ground and may or may not take the trouble to place a few stalks of vegetation, pebbles, or shells about the eggs. Likewise Whip-poor-wills deposit their two eggs on the forest floor (Fig. 99), on whatever litter happens to be available; and their

*Fig. 99. No prepared nest. Whip-poor-wills lay their eggs on the bare forest floor, usually with no semblance of nest materials. (Courtesy of Edward M. Brigham, Jr.)*

close relatives, the nighthawks, make similar use of gravel beds, pavements, or the flat-topped roofs of buildings. The Turkey Vulture builds no nest as such, but usually seeks the protection of a hollow log or stump. Some cliff-dwelling sea birds lay on rocky ledges with no nest materials to mark the location. Nests in holes and burrows may or may not have nesting materials in the cavity.

Several unusual situations may be cited. The Fairy Tern (Fig. 100) on islands in the Pacific precariously balances its single egg on the horizontal branch of a tree with no material to hold it in place. A species of jaçana in Africa, a "lily-trotter" with an 8″ x 6″ expanse of toes as long as the bird itself, places its four eggs on a broad lily pad or cluster of floating water weeds, only occasionally taking the trouble to pull a few supporting stems about the eggs (Miller, 1952). When the nest site submerges during incubation, the eggs are taken up under the wings. Emperor Penguins, after a long inland trek which takes several months to complete, nest in the Antarctic ice fields during the long *winter night* in temperatures ranging from 40° to 70° F. *below* zero (Rivolier, 1959). With no nesting materials available, the males stand on the ice for two months and hold their single egg on the web of the foot with a fold of skin from the abdomen enveloping the egg to keep it warm.

*Fig. 100. No prepared nest. Fairy Terns* (Gygis alba) *place their egg on a bare branch, where it is incubated and the young chick brooded without apparent losses. The young are well equipped with sharp claws for gymnastics on the branches. (Courtesy of Amer. Mus. Nat. Hist.)*

GRASS AND STICK NESTS. The next step in the evolution of nest construction is a simple structure of grass or twigs. Ground-nesting birds, like gulls and terns, which have little need for nest materials, often use only a few grasses or bits of vegetation surrounding or underlying the eggs. Some ground-nesting thrushes, warblers, and sparrows build more substantial though not necessarily elaborate nests. A further step in the development of ground structures is the arched-over grassy nest of the meadowlarks and the ovenlike grass and leaf nest of the Ovenbird, which of course have considerable protective value.

For tree nesters some material is usually an absolute requisite, yet birds like the Mourning Dove get along with a minimum. Often a dove's nest is so skimpily constructed that the eggs can be seen through the interstices from below; if it is on a prostrate log or large horizontal branch there may be only a few twigs about the eggs (Fig. 101 l). North American cuckoos, the Catbird, and Cardinal do a better job, yet often the nest is shallow and insecurely fastened to the supporting branches so that the eggs or nest may get dislodged. A crude platform of sticks seems to serve the needs of tree-nesting egrets, herons, and other rookery birds, but they may reoccupy the nest in successive seasons and add more materials.

*Fig. 101. Simple twig nests. Left, Mourning Dove nest, usually a skimpy affair in trees, was here placed on a log. (Courtesy of Edward M. Brigham, Jr.) Right, the Osprey builds a bulky nest of sticks, usually in dead trees, but often on telephone poles and power lines in the East and on rocky crags in the Western mountains. (Photo by L. H. Walkinshaw.)*

Predatory birds (Fig. 101r) commonly build even more bulky structures of sticks and leaves and may add to them from year to year, though a particular nest may serve for a crow one season, and a hawk or a Great Horned Owl the next. Bald Eagles, if unmolested, usually reoccupy and enlarge their eyrie annually until the huge structure may collapse. A nest at Vermilion, Ohio, was occupied for thirty-five years and was estimated to weigh about two tons when it finally crashed (Herrick, 1934). A Bald Eagle nest in Florida, perhaps the largest known, measured 20 feet deep and 9½ feet wide (Broley, 1947).

MUD NESTS. The use of mud as a construction material is well exemplified in the familiar mud and grass nest of the Robin. It is a fairly solid and substantial structure, which heavy rains only occasionally dissolve or strong winds dislodge. When mud is not immediately available, Robins have been known to dip dry earth into water or convey water on their feathers to the dirt. The Barn Swallow (Fig. 102l) and the Eastern Phoebe are likewise mud-daubers and take the additional precaution of nesting on buildings and bridges for protection. The nest of either species may be *statant* (supported from below) or *adherent* (plastered to a vertical surface). Cliff Swallows (Fig. 102r) build a globular adherent structure of clayey materials which eventually harden to a mortar-like consistency.

*Fig. 102. Mud nests. The Barn Swallow (left) builds a solid substantial nest largely of mud and almost invariably adopts man-made structures for additional protection from the elements. (Photo by Dale A. Zimmerman.) The Cliff Swallow (right), though often nesting under the eaves of buildings (Fig. 79), sometimes utilizes natural nesting sites on cliffs or ledges. (Photo by John T. Emlen, Jr., courtesy of the* Auk, *71, 1954.)*

NESTS OF PLANT DOWN. Among the many birds that use plant down in their nests the Yellow Warbler (Fig. 80) and American Goldfinch (Fig. 103l) are particularly noted for well-made exquisite structures composed of the down of willows, poplars, and thistles or other composites. So durable are these nests, and so securely anchored to supporting twigs, that they can often be collected for classroom use long after they have been abandoned by the birds; often they are remodeled for winter nests and storage places of deer mice (Nickell, 1951). The deeply cupped nest of the American Goldfinch is relatively waterproof; if filled with rain it holds water for twenty-four hours, causing abandonment of unattended nests, or drowning the young if they are neglected by their parents during storms (Lewis, 1952).

LICHEN-COVERED NESTS. The nest of the Ruby-throated Hummingbird (Fig. 103r), neatly constructed of bud scales and spider webbing, and attractively camouflaged with gray-green lichens, is a well-known example of a lichen-covered nest. The Blue-gray Gnatcatcher and Eastern Wood Pewee build similarly attractive and substantial structures that admirably blend with the branches on which they are placed. Nests of the Parula

*Fig. 103. Left, felted nest. The American Goldfinch builds a compact, substantial nest of felted materials that weathers the elements well. (Courtesy of Walter P. Nickell.) Right, lichen-covered nest. The Ruby-throated Hummingbird builds a decorative yet well-camouflaged nest of bud scales, lichens, and spider webbing. (Courtesy of Edward M. Brigham, Jr.)*

Warbler in the northern states are commonly tucked into a dangling tuft of lichens (*Usnea*); in the southern states similar use is made of Spanish moss (*Tillandsia*—a flowering plant) which so commonly festoons the trees in cypress swamps. Where the "moss" does not occur, the Parula Warbler is said to be absent.

FEATHER NESTS. Many birds use feathers in their nests, either plucked from their own bodies or taken from other sources. Examples of the former are the down-feather nests of ducks and geese. The females of these species grow a special nuptial down which is plucked for lining their nests. Among Arctic-nesting eider ducks, the production and use of this down is so profuse that it completely surrounds and covers the eggs when the female is absent and can be harvested commercially in large quantities (p. 314) without apparent loss of hatchability of the eggs.

PENSILE AND PENDULOUS NESTS. Vireos build a pensile nest (Fig. 104l), a neat, decorative, bark-fiber affair which is suspended from a terminal fork of a limb. Like the nest of the American Goldfinch and Yellow Warbler, vireo nests weather the elements well and can be collected for classroom use after abandonment by the owners. Pensile nests are also characteristic of kinglets, seven species of blackbirds, the Parula Warbler, and Acadian Flycatcher (Nickell, 1958). Chamberlain (1954) tested the strength or "safety factor" of Yellow-throated Vireo nests by placing weights in them. Minor tearing (rearrangement but not breakage of fibers) took place at 45 ounces and total failure at 76 ounces (4.75 pounds).

Pendulous nests are characteristic of some orioles and other icterids, many tropical flycatchers, broadbills, some sylviids, and some weaverbirds. Baltimore Orioles construct a deeply cupped cradle which swings in the breeze. It is carefully woven of long strands of grasses, bark, hair, or yarn or string which some home owners provide for the birds. Oropendolas, colonial neotropical relatives of our orioles, build a drooping basket, 3 to 6 feet deep, perhaps fifty nests to a tree, with the entrance near the top and the eggs nestled in the toe of the structure (Fig. 104r). The somewhat similar nest of the Royal Flycatcher in Central America is 3 to 5 feet deep, often dangling over a stream, but the eggs are deposited in the expanded middle portion rather than in the toe (Skutch, 1952a). Nests of the Common Tody-flycatcher (*Todirostrum cinereum*) in Colombia are similar, but only a few inches deep with a neat roofed over entrance in the upper third of the otherwise completely enclosed structure.

Broadbills (Fig. 149), a passerine family of birds found in southern Asia and Africa, build a globular grass and fiber nest suspended from a

*Fig. 104. Left, pensile nest of Warbling Vireo. Right, pendulous nest of an oropendola* (Psarocolius angustifrons). *The oropendola in the case to the right of the nest is a different species* (Psarocolius decumanus). *(Photos by Allan D. Cruickshank and Robert L. Flemming, Jr.)*

branch by a single thread, often over water; the side entrance is frequently protected by an overhanging portico. Some of the Old World weaverbirds also build a suspended nest, dangling by strands of fibers over water, but have the entrance at the *bottom*, with an ingenious platform within provided with a guard rail to prevent the eggs from falling out. The Tailorbird (an Old World sylviid) forms a leaf into a tiny drooping basket to hold the single egg.

HOLE AND BURROW NESTERS. Many species of birds throughout the world utilize holes in trees, crevices, or burrows in the ground for nesting. These provide relatively safe sites compared to nests in the open (see p. 244 for nesting success). Woodpeckers, nuthatches, and some titmice excavate holes in dead trees, stumps, or branches and lay their eggs in the cavity—in the case of woodpeckers on the bare floor of the excavation, or, in the case of the nuthatches and titmice, in a cozy fur- or feather-lined nest. The original builders usually abandon these holes after one nesting, so that they are available for bluebirds, Tree Swallows, House Wrens, and other hole nesters which are not equipped to excavate their own.

Bank dwellers, such as kingfishers and Bank Swallows, construct horizontal tunnels in sand or gravel banks and deposit their eggs at the rear of the cavity. Tunnel or burrow nesting is common among tropical birds, perhaps as a protection against snakes, and among oceanic birds like petrels and shearwaters, perhaps as a protection against nest marauders. Kiwis in New Zealand nest in underground burrows which they dig with their strong claws (Fig. 13).

Some oddities among hole nesters include the Burrowing Owl, which often adopts prairie dog holes for underground nesting; certain woodpeckers and Elf Owls which nest in cactus stubs; and many tropical species (49 species in 7 different families according to Hindwood, 1959) which tunnel into large termite nests, presumably acquiring some immunity from predators by the presence of the biting insects. Wrens get into all sorts of curious nesting situations; not the least of these was a human skull hung up at a doctor's home in Kentucky and said to have been occupied by wrens from 1888 to 1945 when the skull was moved to Indiana and re-occupied there (Hobson, 1952).

AQUATIC NEST SITES. Marsh and water birds resort to a great variety of nest sites. They may utilize muskrat houses or beaver lodges, placing their nests on top or in the walls. Canada Geese, normally ground nesters, sometimes make use of tree nests of Ospreys and herons or even washtubs or baskets placed in trees (Yocum, 1952). Least Bitterns (Fig. 72), American Coots, rails, gallinules, and Black Terns construct simple platforms composed of aquatic plants and usually placed over shallow water. Problems of flooding are often partially circumvented by anchoring the nest loosely among tall reeds so that it will adjust itself to changing water levels. Nests of the Red-winged Blackbird, however, are more firmly attached so that unequal growth of the supporting stems sometimes tilts the nest and spills the eggs or young. Marsh wrens forestall such mishaps by building an enclosed nest. The nest of the Pied-billed Grebe may not be anchored to vegetation at all, but is a large, floating, water-soaked mass of material (Fig. 105); when the incubating bird departs, the eggs are deliberately covered over with wet plants without apparent impairment of their hatchability. Flamingos (6 species on five continents) nest in colonies on mud flats, scooping up a huge cone of mud a foot or more high, which hardens like mortar. Even more curious is the nest of the Horned Coot (*Fulica cornuta*). Nesting in cold water lakes in the high Andes, at 13,000 feet or higher, it heaps up a huge mound of stones, perhaps a ton or more,

*Fig. 105. Floating, water-soaked nest of Pied-billed Grebe. The conspicuous eggs are covered with damp vegetation when the incubating bird departs. (Photo by Allan D. Cruickshank.)*

until the top is above the water. The top of the nest is lined with aquatic plants.

CAVE DWELLERS. Many swifts, some swallows, and oilbirds (Steatornithidae) in South America nest in caves, or suitable substitutes, and often in complete darkness (p. 133). The Chimney Swift builds a platform of twigs glued together with a secretion from the salivary glands (Fig. 118 l). The shallow structure is then glued to some surface, formerly in a hollow tree but now almost exclusively inside chimneys or similar shafts. More remarkable are the edible nests of swifts that inhabit subterranean caves in the East Indies. The first nests of these birds are almost entirely of salivary secretions, and are collected by the natives and by visiting Chinese for making birds'-nest soup. Replacement nests, which contain more foreign materials, make a lower-grade soup and are usually left for the birds. Equally remarkable is the nest of the Cayenne Swift (*Panyptila cayennensis*) in South America (Haverschmidt, 1958). It is a tubular, sleevelike structure, often two feet long, composed of feathery tufts of plant seeds glued together with saliva and plastered to the side of a building or tree trunk. It is open at the bottom, but has a shelf inside to hold the eggs. One pair worked steadily from September to March to build such a structure.

OTHER NESTS. The Dipper builds an interesting and somewhat unusual nest (Fig. 106). It is a spherical mass of green moss with an inner bowl of dry grasses, usually tucked into a crevice over a swift-flowing stream so that the outer walls of the nest are often kept moist and green from the spray. The nests of the Black-billed Magpie, in trees or thorny bushes,

*Fig. 106. Mossy nest of Dipper beside a Colorado stream. These water-loving songsters plunge headlong into the water and swim and walk along the bottom, foraging for insect fare.* (*Photo by* H. W. *Hann, courtesy of* Condor.)

are huge affairs several feet deep and completely domed over, often with a crown of protective thorns (Lindsdale, 1937). Abandoned magpie nests are often used by other birds for shelter in inclement weather and for breeding purposes in spring. Sociable weaverbirds in South Africa are gregarious even in the nesting season (Fig. 85); some combine their efforts in the construction of a common domicile. It is a huge, umbrella-shaped, roofed-over apartment house honey-combed with separate noncommunicating, warmly feather-lined cavities which serve for both nesting and shelter.

Some birds build supplementary, auxiliary, secondary, or dummy nests (terms used more or less interchangeably), for a variety of purposes. Many tropical birds construct special nests or dormitories for sleeping (p. 252). Black Terns build auxiliary nests to which the young may move, voluntarily or when disturbed, when three to five days old, and be cared for (brooded and fed) by the adults (Cuthbert, 1954). Coots and grebes may build special copulatory platforms, not necessarily used for nesting. Wrens are particularly noted for building supplementary nests. Cactus Wrens (Anderson and Anderson, 1960) work jointly in the construction of a breeding nest, then the male builds one or more secondary nests which the female uses for second broods and the male uses for sleeping. Male House Wrens commonly fill up all available crevices in their territories with sticks, then the female completes one of them for her nest. The extra or dummy nests built by Long-billed Marsh Wrens, however, are not used by the female and their function is somewhat speculative (Welter, 1935).

## NEST BUILDING

Nest-building techniques and construction materials vary widely. Materials used are commonly, but not invariably, those close at hand, but the innate requirements of the species apparently govern selection. A dove must have its twigs, the Robin its mud and grass, a duck its special down—materials all readily available to the builder. On the other hand a Chipping Sparrow may be hard pressed, in these days, to find horsehair or a suitable substitute for lining its nest, a Tree or Barn Swallow may risk its life for the inevitable chicken feathers it uses, and the Great Crested Flycatcher may possibly have to go far afield to find a cast-off snakeskin for decorating its doorway. Snow Buntings often range widely for coveted items; in one case all the buntings in the neighborhood visited a dead gull behind an Eskimo tent for feathers for their nests (Tinbergen, 1939). Thistledown is so highly prized for nest construction by American Goldfinches that it cannot be controlled for exclusive use by a pair on its territory; in fact, it is often acquired by dismantling the nests of its own and other species. The Red-breasted Nuthatch, for unknown reasons, commonly smears the entrance to its nest hole with pitch from evergreens.

Thus innate requirements enter in an interesting way into the nesting habits of birds. A list of the natural materials used by birds would be long, perhaps including items from nearly every species of higher plants, as well as the hair, feathers, skin, shells, or skeletal fragments of many animals. Of 794 nests in the Museum of Vertebrate Zoology at Berkeley, California, 622 (78 per cent) contain hair from various mammals (Riney, 1951). Barn Owls utilize both fur and bones from dissected pellets of their prey for nest materials. Kingfishers make similar use of fishbones and regurgitated scales. More than 30 species of birds are known to use cast-off snakeskins in their nests; 8 of them do it so regularly as to suggest that the incorporation of the skins in the nest is deliberate (a species habit) and not accidental (Rand, 1953b).

Many birds have learned to supplement natural items with materials made available by man. Pieces of cleansing tissues and other roadside and picnic litter, unfortunately, are readily available. On a more cheerful note perhaps, Gross (1958) describes a nest of a bananaquit (Coerebidae) on

Tobago Island (West Indies) which was built chiefly of tinsel and placed in a Christmas tree in a hotel. In spite of some inconveniences (the birds also nested on a chandelier and left droppings on the carpets), the management condoned the birds because guests were amused. Broley (1947) found an interesting assortment of curios in Bald Eagle nests in Florida. These included golf balls, electric light bulbs, a bottle, a fish plug with seventy feet of line, a child's dress, a shoe and a white rubber ball which an eagle "incubated" for six weeks after her real eggs had hatched.

Birds use their bills and feet, often in ingenious ways, for collecting, carrying, and weaving together the materials used in nest construction. Rotary motions of the body in the nest make the usually cup-shaped cavity conform to the size of the sitting bird, thus forming a more efficient watershed during incubation and brooding. Birds that drill holes in decaying trees chisel out chips with their strong beaks and carry them away or drop them at the nest site. Kingfishers tunnel into banks with their bills, but kick the dirt out behind them. The weaving of a pendulous nest is an arduous task in which both beak and feet are employed. The Tailor-bird is said to puncture sixteen holes in each edge of the single leaf which forms its nest, then sews the leaf up with plant thread, even to tying the knots.

The time required for nest construction of course varies with the elaborateness of the job to be done and the diligence of the workers. Song Sparrows (Nice, 1937) took from 3 to 13 days to build their fairly simple nest, but 4 or 5 days was usual. Field Sparrows in Iowa (Crooks and Hendrickson, 1953) usually took only 3 days, with a maximum of 5. Ovenbirds (Hann, 1937) required about 5 days to build their first nests, but the main body was constructed rather rapidly, in about 2 days, while the lining was added more leisurely. Robins have been observed to take from 6 to 20 days, but intervening spells of rainy weather account for the longer periods. One nest was built in a single day, with both sexes working, perhaps of necessity, as an egg was laid the next day. Stokes (1950) found that goldfinches averaged 13 days for July nests, but only 5 to 6 days for August nests. Lewis (1952) gave 12 days as an average, with one nest-building period of 22 days, and a mid-August record of a 3-day construction period.

In general, northern birds, often working under pressure of a short breeding season, take less time for building than southern species. Derby Flycatchers in Mexico take 24 days for nest construction (Pettingill, 1942), whereas their northern relatives require less than half that time. Arctic-nesting passerines commonly save time by reoccupying old nests; one

Wheatear had an eight-layered nest which suggested occupancy over an eight-year period (Wynne-Edwards, 1952). Birds that use their own saliva in nest construction may be delayed by its rate of flow (see p. 199 for Cayenne Swift building time). Another time-consuming operation is that of the Hammerhead (a stork) in Africa which requires about four months to build its enclosed, clay-lined domicile of sticks and grass; but once built the nest is used year after year.

Nest building is not normally a steady or uninterrupted process. Birds may work actively at the nest for a few hours in the morning, then cease building for a time. First nests, particularly those started early in the season, are built more slowly, but second nests, or nests built late in the season, are constructed more rapidly. Inclement weather may temporarily halt nest-building operations or cause desertion of partly built or even completed structures. Some nests, especially those with mud walls, are allowed to "set" a day or two before the lining is added; then one or more days may intervene before the first egg is laid. In many species (herons, hawks, doves), nest building and incubation overlap, with fresh materials being brought to the nest more or less continuously. A bird's attachment to its nest is not very strong at first, and it readily deserts if disturbed. Even if undisturbed, the female may decide on another nest site, sometimes deserting her mate and territory. Nest building is apparently largely instinctive, for though a Baltimore Oriole may improve its technique with age and experience, many birds do as thorough a job with their first nest as with subsequent attempts.

The role of the sexes in nest building is of interest. Typically the female takes the initiative, selecting the site and doing most or all the building. In many species the males help gather materials; these may be merely token presentations which the female as likely as not discards; or in other cases, the male may bring all or nearly all the material, leaving the female to work it into the nest. In still other cases the male and female work cooperatively, on a nearly equal basis (Fig. 107). The male House Wren, as already mentioned, builds the nest foundation, often before acquiring the mate which later completes its construction. In the Phainopepla, a handsome black and white passerine bird in southwestern United States, the male does most of the nest building before the female joins in on the finishing touches (Rand and Rand, 1943). In still other birds—the Ostrich and its allies, kiwis, tinamous, and some shorebirds—there is a nearly complete sex reversal in family affairs with the male usually constructing the nest if one is needed. In ducks, most gallinaceous birds, hummingbirds, and

*Fig. 107. Avocets, unlike phalaropes, but like many other shorebirds, work cooperatively at domestic chores. Both sexes join in group courtship activities, and share nest-building and incubation duties. The peculiar recurved bill is used with a sweeping motion to rake aquatic invertebrates from shallow waters. (Photo by Allan D. Cruickshank.)*

"arena" birds, however, the male usually has nothing to do with the nest. The onerous chore of chiseling out woodpecker holes or kingfisher tunnels is usually a joint enterprise, the male and female working in shifts. In the Black-capped Chickadee, the female does two-thirds of the drilling and the pair may work together or in shifts, but apparently only the female carries nesting material (Odum, 1941). Mountfort (1957) reports that a pair of bee-eaters (Meropidae) in France alternated in swooping at a hard-baked earthen bank, striking it with their bills, then one sitting exhausted after 15 to 18 strikes while the other worked. Not all nest sites, however, were as difficult as this one.

## *The Eggs*

### GENERAL CHARACTERISTICS

The eggs of birds vary in size, shape, color, and texture. Not surprisingly the smallest eggs are laid by the smallest birds, the hummingbirds, and the largest eggs by the largest bird, the Ostrich (Fig. 108). Egg size or weight, however, is not always strictly correlated with the size or weight of the bird. The eggs of precocial birds, for example, which contain more nutritive material (yolk and albumen) and hatch out more fully developed young, are comparatively much larger than the eggs of altricial birds (Fig. 115). The eggs of Old World cuckoos are peculiarly small for the size of the parent, as an adaptation for deposition in the nests of small host species. The Ruddy Duck lays larger eggs than does the Canvasback which is three time the size of the smaller bird (Fig. 109). A 14-egg clutch of the Ruddy Duck, laid at the rate of nearly an egg a day, weighs about 3 pounds, though the female parent may weigh only 1 pound. The kiwis lay even larger eggs, but often only one, probably the largest egg known in relation

*Fig. 108. Comparative egg sizes. Ostrich, Domestic Hen, and Ruby-throated Hummingbird. (Photo by Philip G. Coleman, from specimens in Mich. State Univ. Museum.)*

to the size of the parent, although the total clutch of a Ruddy Duck would have a greater volume. The largest eggs known, probably the largest animal cells, are those of the extinct elephantbirds of Madagascar whose egg (in

*Fig. 109. Left, Canvasback female and egg. Right, Ruddy Duck female and egg. The smaller bird lays a slightly larger egg. (Drawings by R. M. Naik from specimens in Mich. State Univ. Museum.)*

the larger species) measured 13 inches by 9.5 inches, weighed about 18 pounds and had a capacity of about 2 gallons. This has been computed to be equal in volume to 6 Ostrich eggs or 148 hen eggs.

The shape of a bird's egg (Fig. 110) necessarily conforms somewhat to the limitations of the oviduct in which it is molded, but may vary from nearly round, as in the nearly sedentary owls, to extremely elongate, as in fast-flying swallows and swifts. Thus the length and breadth of the egg has some correlation with the speed of flight, or more precisely with the diameter of the oviduct during passage. The pointed, pear-shaped egg of the murres and other alcids is believed to be an adaptation for nesting on precarious ledges, the shape of the egg causing it to pivot on its axis when disturbed rather than rolling off the cliff. The 4-egg clutches of many species exhibit considerable tapering toward one end; obviously they fit in a nest better that way.

The colors and pigmentation in birds' eggs (Fig. 111) run nearly the gamut of possible hues and patterns, but the brighter colors are rather unusual. White and off-white shades predominate, with or without the brownish or darker maculations so characteristic of eggs laid in exposed nests. White eggs may be so thinly peppered with spots that the markings are hardly visible, or so heavily pigmented that they appear all brown like the eggs of the Long-billed Marsh Wren. The configuration of markings is determined by the motions of the egg in the oviduct; spots result when the egg is stationary, and scrawls and scratches when the egg is in motion. Heavier deposition of pigments on the larger end, often as an encircling wreath, is fairly characteristic, perhaps because the larger end often leads

*Fig. 110. Egg shapes. Left to right, Double-crested Cormorant, Common Murre, Bobwhite, Great Horned Owl, bee-eater (Meropidae). (Photo by Philip G. Coleman from specimens in Mich. State Univ. Museum.)*

*Fig. 111. Pigmentation of eggs. Left to right, Domestic Hen, Silver Pheasant (buff), Royal Tern, tinamou. (Photo by Philip G. Coleman from specimens in Mich. State Univ. Museum.)*

in the oviduct. Blue eggs, with or without spots, are characteristic of thrushes, while those of the Catbird are more greenish. Red eggs are rather rare, but a warbler (sylviid) in Japan lays a red egg which is almost perfectly matched by an imposing cuckoo. The tinamous in South America lay eggs of exceedingly variable colors. They may be blue, green, brown, yellow, or even purple.

Egg colors may change strikingly with age, beyond the mere tarnishing that goes with continued incubation. Rhea eggs, for instance, are said to be a rich green when laid, but later fade to yellow, then to blue, and finally to white. The Emu of Australia usually lays a dark green egg, but completely black eggs of this species have been collected. In general, white eggs are characteristic of birds that lay eggs in concealed places, such as in holes in trees or in burrows, whereas more protectively colored spotted eggs are found in exposed nests, but there are exceptions to both of these generalizations.

In texture the eggs of different species vary from those with thin, fragile and transparent shells (which become more opaque with age) to those with thick-shelled chalky coverings. The eggs of the tinamous have a smooth glossy surface, like glazed porcelain (Fig. 111), while those of the Emu and of cassowaries are rough, and those of toucans and the Ostrich pitted and grooved. Ducks and some other water birds have greasy, water-resistant eggs; those of grebes and boobies are chalky.

In several papers Preston and co-workers (see Wilson, *et al.*, for bibliography), using precise mathematical calculations, describe the variations in size, shape, pigmentation and gloss between the different eggs in a clutch in relation to laying sequences.

### NUMBER OF EGGS

Birds lay from 1 to about 20 eggs per clutch. A single egg is characteristic of some penguins and albatrosses, the California Condor, and cliff-dwelling alcids. The single egg of the Great Auk and Passenger Pigeon may have been a factor in their extinction. Two-egg clutches are common to such well-known birds as loons, eagles, doves, and pigeons, Great Horned Owls, Whip-poor-wills, nighthawks, and most hummingbirds. Boobies often lay two eggs but hatch only one; if both hatch only one young is raised. Skuas usually hatch both of their eggs but eat one of the young. Several authors suggest that this is an evolutionary step geared toward maximum production; if conditions are favorable, as they appear to be for a species of booby in food-rich waters in the West Indies, more than one young might be raised.

Many birds, perhaps the majority of our passerine species (flycatchers, swallows, thrushes, warblers, sparrows) as well as many nonpasserine birds (shorebirds) lay from 3 to 5 eggs per clutch, with 4 as a common number. Many insectivorous birds wintering in northern latitudes (titmice, nuthatches, creepers, and kinglets), as well as wrens and some woodpeckers, have larger sets with 6 to 10 or more eggs per nest. Ducks and gallinaceous birds have even larger clutches of 8 to 15 or more eggs, but higher numbers in duck nests are apt to be the product of more than one female. Dreis and Hendrickson (1952) report a Wood Duck nest with 20 eggs laid in fifteen days, obviously the product of more than one female. Such "dump" nests were found in three of nine occupied boxes. Dump nests, with a larger than normal quota of eggs, are fairly common among ducks and gallinanaceous birds, but 20-egg clutches laid by one female have been reported for the Hungarian (Gray) Partridge.

Egg number is roughly correlated with mortality. Birds that lay small clutches may be longer-lived and thus have a longer time to replace themselves, or they may nest in more protected situations, as in isolated island colonies which may be free from four-footed predators. Waterfowl and game birds, on the other hand, even before being hunted by man, have always faced many dangers; a young duck or a young grouse has many hungry eyes focused upon it. Further exploration of survival in relation to egg number, however, reveals inconsistencies. The Great Horned Owl, a much persecuted species, appears to do well with only 2 eggs per year, whereas the Barn Owl commonly lays 6 or more eggs per clutch and often raises two broods but in most regions is less common than its more hardy relative.

In many species, clutch size tends to increase with latitude, that is, tropical birds lay fewer eggs than their northern relatives, but some species (most sea birds, shorebirds, and pigeons) lay a constant number regardless of their geographic range. Two- and 3-egg clutches are common to many birds in the tropics and subtropics, whereas the same or closely related species lay double or triple that number in more northern latitudes. Thus clutch size is correlated with day length, but this may not be the critical factor (see below).

Clutch size is also correlated with the available food supply; indeed, this may be the critical determining factor in northern latitudes. Rough-legged Hawks and Snowy Owls lay larger clutches in good lemming years than in years of food shortage. The Barn Owl may breed almost continuously during peak years in the *Microtus* (meadow mouse) cycle, but slow down or skip a breeding season when its staple prey is scarce. But food is apparently not a critical factor in the tropics, since birds there do not spend all their time foraging, even when feeding young and often one parent can raise the brood.

Lack (1947, 1948), Moreau (1944), Skutch (1949a), and Wagner (1957), from whom these data are taken in part, contribute interesting discussions to this problem. Lack apparently favors a genetically fixed rate in correlation with the food supply as an explanation, but Skutch shows that this does not apply to neotropical birds. Wagner suggests that the upper limit of egg production may be genetically fixed but obtainable only under certain conditions, and governed by food reserves in the bird. That is, if a Snowy Owl uses 25 per cent of its reserves to lay one egg in low lemming years, then four eggs would be its limit, but in good lemming years that number might be (and is) doubled. Tropical species store little or no fat and have low reserves.

## LAYING SEQUENCES

Nearly all passerine birds, as well as many of the smaller nonpasserines, lay an egg a day until the clutch is complete. Often the egg is laid at a particular time during the day, such as in the early morning. Cowbirds sneak on to their victims' nests in the morning and often get driven out, but the more methodical European Cuckoo waits till afternoon, when the owner of the nest is away. After an egg is laid the female does not stay at the nest, unless incubation is started immediately, which is unusual.

Many of the larger birds do not oviposit daily, though ducks at least approximate an egg per day. Pheasants and grouse require about fifteen days to lay 10 eggs. Hawks and owls usually lay every other day, or in some cases may skip more than a day between layings. The Mallee Fowl, in Australia, is said to lay every third day, while its relative in the Celebes, the Maleo, lays its 6 to 8 eggs at 10- to 12-day intervals, thus having a long laying period which lasts two to three months.

Birds possess an unexplained control over egg production. If the complete clutch is 4 eggs, they cease laying with that number, partially formed ova in the ovary presumably being resorbed. But if the first clutch is destroyed or part of the eggs taken, more eggs are produced after a waiting period. The capacity to continue uninterrupted laying is well illustrated by the oft-cited example of a flicker which laid 71 eggs in 73 days when an egg a day was experimentally removed from the nest before the clutch was complete. A wryneck (Picidae) in Europe has been known to produce 62 eggs, 52 of them on consecutive days, and of course domestic fowl lay almost continuously (there are records of 351 and 352 eggs in a year). There is also a record of a duck that laid 363 eggs in 365 days.

On the other hand, Herring Gulls cannot be induced to lay more than three eggs or less than three, when eggs are experimentally removed from or added to the nest (Davis, 1942). Experiments with Tri-colored Blackbirds in California yielded similar results (Emlen, 1941). Later, Davis (1955) could not induce Barn Swallows or Black-billed Magpies to change the number of eggs laid when he added or removed eggs from their nests. Such birds, perhaps the majority though there are few experiments to prove it, are spoken of as *determinate* layers, as opposed to *indeterminate* layers such as flickers, ducks, and poultry.

## Incubation

As soon as a clutch is complete, or in some cases before it is complete, one of the parent birds sits on the eggs (incubates them) with varying degrees of attentiveness until they hatch. During the breeding season, incubating birds develop an *incubation patch* or *brood patch,* which is a featherless area on the ventral surface of the body containing an anastomosis of blood vessels which can be brought into close contact with the eggs. When a bird settles upon its nest, it parts the abdominal feathers so that they surround or enclose the eggs (Fig. 112). Thus the heat of the

*Fig. 112. Wilson's Plover settling on eggs. The abdominal feathers are parted to permit vascularized skin (incubation patch) to come in close contact with the eggs. Note the nest —merely a depression in the sand— and the extremely large eggs. (Photo by Allan D. Cruickshank.)*

body, through the brood patch, can be transferred more or less directly to the eggs. Ventral skin temperatures of incubating females are higher than those of the males (1.7° F. higher in the House Wren).

Studies of the incubation patch (Bailey, 1952) show that it is produced by defeatherization by molting ventral down (not feather plucking) and vascularization (increase in size and number of blood vessels in the patch). In most birds it is a simple median patch in the ventral apterium, but in charadriiform, gruiform, and galliform birds lateral patches (sometimes merging) develop. It is absent in struthious and anseriform birds, occurs only in the males in which only the males incubate, and develops in both sexes if both sexes incubate regularly. In most passerines the brood patch occurs only in the female, lending some doubt as to the efficacy of incubating males in this order. However, the Great Crested Flycatcher (Parkes, 1953), Clark's Nutcracker (Mewaldt, 1952), and some neotropical flycatchers have proved to be exceptions, with the males possessing well-developed incubation patches during the nesting season. Development of the patch is controlled by hormones—chiefly estradiol and prolactin (pp. 134–135). It is interesting to note that Selander (1960b) could not induce brood-patch formation in the Brown-headed Cowbird (which has no need for it) by estrogen and prolactin treatments.

### ATTENTIVE AND INATTENTIVE PERIODS

Most birds incubate intermittently, with attentive periods at the nest and inattentive periods away. This results in oscillating egg temperatures. Some birds bring water in their bills or wet their breast feathers, thus moistening the eggs either for cooling or humidifying purposes. Mayhew (1955) reports that Mallards often shake out their wet feathers while standing over the eggs, and that hatching success is better in wet years and higher in incubators when the eggs are dipped or sprinkled. Open nests in hot exposed situations are sometimes shaded by a parent bird to prevent the hot sun from killing the embryos. This is particularly true of nighthawks on exposed roof tops, where temperatures have been recorded up to 142° F. (Weller, 1958), or in the southwestern deserts. Most birds turn their eggs frequently or occasionally, which heats the eggs more uniformly and prevents the embryonic membranes from adhering to the shell, but this practice is not universal. Some swifts glue their eggs to the nest.

Egg temperatures averaging in the nineties seem to be about optimum; tests with 37 species in 11 different orders gave an average egg temperature of 93.2° F., with not much fluctuation between the off (92.1°) and on (93.7°) periods (Huggins, 1941). Kessler (1960), using a self-recording potentiometer, found mean egg temperatures in pheasant nests varied from 94.0° to 98.3° F. in 1955 and from 92.0° to 97.8° F. in 1956. Highest egg temperatures were in the center of the nest; the lowest, on the periphery. Graber (1955) kept incubator temperatures for six nongalliform birds somewhat higher (98° to 104° F.) with success; on three occasions, temperatures went up (accidentally) to 108°, 112°, and 120° F. without harmful consequences. Embryonic development is said to stop at about 82° F., but air temperatures can drop much lower for short periods without killing the embryo.

In experiments conducted at a state game farm in Michigan, pheasant eggs were subjected to temperatures as low at 45° F. for periods up to 8 hours during the first two weeks of incubation with only slight lowering of hatching success, but exposures of 16 hours or more at that temperature (45° F.) resulted in heavy losses during the last week of incubation (MacMullen and Eberhardt, 1953). Large eggs, of course, can stand more exposure than small ones.

Attentive and inattentive periods during incubation have been checked in many nesting studies, and such data have now been quite thoroughly summarized in Kendeigh's *Parental Care and Its Evolution in Birds* (1952). Inattentive periods are often lengthened at midday and shortened in the cooler parts of the day, and the nest is seldom left unattended during storms or rains. Song Sparrows (Nice, 1937) usually have attentive periods lasting from 20 to 30 minutes, followed by 6- to 8-minute intervals off the nest, a rhythm believed to be correlated with hunger. In Cactus Wrens (Anderson and Anderson, 1960), twenty-eight attentive periods averaged 14.8 minutes (ranged from 1 to 28 minutes), and twenty-nine inattentive periods averaged 11.7 minutes (ranged from 2 to 26.5 minutes). These averages are remarkably close to those recorded for House Wrens (14.3 minutes on, 6 minutes off—Kendeigh, 1941).

Longer vigils are characteristic of some passerine birds, especially if the male feeds the female on the nest. A Red Crossbill has been known to spend 14 hours and 34 minutes on the nest and only 36 minutes off, but was fed by the male three times during her long vigil (Snyder and Castle, 1951). In the Cedar Waxwing, the female incubates 90 per cent of the observed daylight time after the last egg is laid. Attentive periods may last 2 hours or more, though commonly only 20 to 40 minutes, but the female is fed frequently at the nest by the male (Putnam, 1949).

Quite a few studies, chiefly by Alexander Skutch, now show that tropical species have longer inattentive periods (a furnariid nest watched for 18 hours was unattended 58 per cent of the time—Skutch, 1952b), yet there are exceptions. Swallowtanagers (Tersinidae) studied by Schaefer (1953) in Venezuela incubated 80 to 92 per cent of the observed time.

Larger birds commonly have longer attentive and inattentive periods. Birds of prey are sometimes gone from their nest for hours without apparent reduction in hatchability of the eggs; but they also sit for long periods. A Sandhill Crane watched by Walkinshaw (1949) sat for 16 hours and 10 minutes of continuous incubation. Long attentive periods also are characteristic of many sea birds (p. 214) in which the male and female work in shifts. Cuthbert (1954) noted that Black Terns covered their eggs 97.3 per cent of the time, the adult alternating incubatory duties and making quick changeovers.

### THE ROLE OF THE SEXES DURING INCUBATION

It is probably already evident that with certain exceptions the female is largely responsible for incubation; the absence of the brood patch in most male passerines precludes the possibility of any real incubation, although rapid cooling could be prevented by the male sitting on the eggs. The role of the male is primarily to guard the territory and to help care for the young when they hatch, but he may also assume varying degrees of responsibility at the nest at other times. Among geese and swans, the gander and the cob stand guard near the incubating female. Among songbirds, the male frequently visits the nesting site, may inspect the nest or even stand guard by it in the absence of the female. Other males actually relieve the female at the nest, either occasionally, as in the case of the Rose-breasted Grosbeak, or regularly, as in the case of many nonpasserine birds.

Kingfishers work in shifts varying from a few hours in some species to a day and night (12-hour) shift in others, and 24-hour shift in the Ringed Kingfisher of the tropics (Skutch, 1952c, 1957). In the Mourning Dove the female incubates at night, the male roosting nearby. He relieves her at the nest for an approximately 8-hour spell of daytime incubating until the female takes over again in the late afternoon. Some birds have special signals or elaborate nest-relieving ceremonies when changing places. In the Common Tern one adult may tempt its mate off the nest by offering a fish at changeover time; if unsuccessful it may push the incubating bird off the nest. In general, changing over is a more striking ceremony among birds that nest in open places (shorebirds) than at nests concealed in marshes, where one bird may slip on quickly as the other skulks away.

One of the most dramatic cases of alternation of incubatory duties is found in the Adelie Penguin which nests up to 200 miles inland from its source of food in the sea. After a prolonged period of courtship and nest preparation (p. 144) which may require nearly a month, the females leave for the sea while the males remain on the eggs for a two-week period, thus fasting for a month to six weeks before the females return to relieve them. The Royal Albatross also has extremely long periods before changing guards; Richdale (1942) reports one that sat for fourteen days without relief or food.

Cases of partial or complete sex reversal in breeding behavior, in which the male does all or most of the incubation, include the struthious birds—the Ostrich, rheas, Emu, and cassowaries—as well as the kiwis, tinamous, button-quails, jaçanas, and phalaropes. Female Ostriches may resort to brief spells of diurnal incubation, but it is the male that keeps the eggs covered during the cool desert nights. In some shorebirds, notably the phalaropes and sometimes the Spotted Sandpiper, the females desert after oviposition and leave incubatory duties to the males (Fig. 113). The

*Fig. 113. Male Wilson's Phalarope on nest. The female merely laid the eggs in a makeshift nest prepared by the male, then the male took over completely, deserted by the more colorful female. (Courtesy of L. H. Walkinshaw.)*

phalaropes have carried sex reversal so far that the females also wear the brighter nuptial plumage and do the active courting.

As already indicated some males feed their mates at the nest, thus eliminating the need for the female to do much hunting. Particularly among the corvids (magpies and jays), titmice (chickadees), and some fringillids (crossbills, towhees and goldfinches), mate feeding during incubation is a regular habit. Care of the female during nesting is carried to the extreme in the hornbills, in which the females are deliberately imprisoned by partially sealing off the nesting cavity with regurgitated castings and mud. The male then proceeds to feed her through an opening too small to permit her egress and cares for her during the whole incubation period as well as for both her and the young after the hatch (Fig. 114). In some fruit-eating species, the period of confinement may last as much as four months, but in the insectivorous species the female breaks out when the young are half grown. In both cases, the female emerges in good flesh, with a new coat of feathers, whereas the male is worn and emaciated.

## INCUBATION PERIODS

The incubation period, or time interval required for hatching an egg, varies from about 10 to 80 days in different species and is not necessarily uniform within a species. Excessive periods of inattentiveness, too much disturbance, or unfavorable weather can retard hatching. The time required is quite variable in different years in the Common Gull in Europe, being

*Fig. 114. A male hornbill (Bucerotidae) presents a food item to his mate in the partially sealed-in nest cavity. (Courtesy of the Amer. Mus. Nat. Hist.)*

shorter in some years than others (Barth, 1952). Many ornithological references give specific incubation periods for all birds included in the book, but many of them are misleading or actually wrong; some of the erroneous periods have been traced by Mrs. Nice (1954) back to Aristotle.

The incubatory period is correlated to some extent with size, the larger eggs generally requiring longer to hatch. But more fundamental is the stage of development of the young at hatching, the precocial birds usually requiring longer periods for incubation. The eggs of the precocial Killdeer take about 26 days for hatching, but the young are able to run from the nest within a few minutes of hatching. The much smaller eggs of the similar-sized altricial Robin hatch in about 13 days, but the young remain in the nest for another 10 to 14 days (Fig. 115). Daniel (1957) points out that a domestic chick hatched at 21 or 22 days is at about the same stage as a 22-day-old Red-winged Blackbird leaving the nest; the chick spent its 22 days in the egg, the Red-wing spent 12 days in the egg and 10 more as a nestling.

Passerine birds in northern climates have incubation periods varying from about 11 to 20 days, with a few records of early 10-day hatchings. House Sparrows studied by Weaver (1943) at Ithaca, New York, hatched a few of their eggs in 10 days, but the average of 22 sets was 12 days. Berger (1957), at Ann Arbor, Michigan, reported one 10-day and one 13-day

*Fig. 115. Comparative egg sizes of precocial Killdeer and altricial Robin. The larger egg has more storage material and requires twice as long to hatch. (Drawings by R. M. Naik from specimens in Mich. State Univ. Museum.)*

incubation period, but most sets hatched in 12 days. Cowbirds have a comparatively short 11- to 12-day incubation period, as an adaptation to early hatching in foster nests, but in most studies it has been found to be about the same as that of the smaller host. Chipping Sparrow eggs will hatch in 11 days in warm weather, but average 12.3 days in colder weather (Walkinshaw, 1952). The Robin averages 13 days, but some eggs hatch in 12, while others are delayed until the fourteenth or fifteenth day. Incubation periods are longer in the corvids; crows and magpies take about 18 days and most jays average 17, while the Raven is said to take about 3 weeks. Some tropical passerines require considerably longer than their northern relatives; Skutch (1945) lists several flycatchers that require more than 20 days for incubation. Lyrebirds (Menuridae) in Australia are reported to take up to 40 days to hatch their single egg, but one has been hatched under a domestic hen in 28 days (Austin, 1961).

Incubation periods for nonpasserine birds, as might be expected, are generally much longer, but there are a few curious exceptions. Skutch (1949b) recorded a 10- or 11-day incubation period for the Ruddy Quail-Dove in Costa Rica, a day or so shorter than periods for the Ruddy Ground-Dove (Skutch, 1956). Two marked eggs of a Black-billed Cuckoo in northern Michigan hatched in 10 and 11 days, respectively (Spencer, 1943); possibly retention of the egg in the oviduct an extra day accounted for the shorter period (Nice, 1953). At the opposite extreme some sea birds, including penguins, petrels, shearwaters, and albatrosses, have exceptionally long periods of six weeks or more—up to a maximum of 80 days for the Royal Albatross (Richdale, 1942). A pair of kiwis studied in captivity for several years usually required 75 days for incubation (Robson, 1948); Cottrell (1955) gave the period as 75 to 77 days, or even 80. Emus, both captive and wild, have been checked at 58 to 61 days, much longer than the 42-day period assigned to the larger Ostrich.

A curiously delayed incubation has been reported for the European Goshawk (Holstein, 1942) with the male ineffectively covering the eggs for much of the first 16 days, then the female taking over for another 26 days, giving an extremely long total (for a hawk) of 42 days. The male, however, was observed to have no brood patch, and the temperature of the eggs, checked by thermocouple, was kept too low for embryonic development. Cole and Kirkpatrick (1915) long ago called attention to the fact that incubation of the first egg in the Common Pigeon is partial—it hatches a half day earlier than the second egg although laid 44 hours earlier. Several recent life-history studies (see Anderson and Anderson, 1960) indicate that incubation is partial or irregular in some birds until the clutch is complete.

Though a number of birds are known to take advantage of solar heat and decaying vegetation to aid in incubation, the megapodes of the Australasian region are the only ones known to do so entirely. Mound-building species (Frith, 1956) scrape together a huge pile of vegetation and soil, sometimes 10 to 15 feet high, deposit eggs (18 to 24 in *Leipoa*, although large clutches may be communal affairs) in an amazingly symmetrical pattern with the pointed ends down, and then cover them. The adults, primarily the male, attend the nest for months, both before and during "incubation," and actually regulate the temperature by alternately opening and closing over the mound, testing it with bare head and neck (hence the name "thermometer birds") and keeping it at about 92° F. (90° to 100°). Decomposition heat is important at first, but solar heat is more important toward the end of the cycle. Incubation, though very variable, requires about 57 days in some species, then the young break out and *fly* away (p. 51). Relatives of these Scrub or Mallee Fowls, notably the Maleos in the Celebes, bury their eggs in volcanically heated sand instead of mounds.

Eggs lose from 10 to 20 more per cent of their weight during incubation, the rate of evaporation (which causes the weight loss) increasing with continued incubation and with rising temperatures. Weight loss can be lowered somewhat in incubators by controlling the humidity. House Wren eggs lose 13.7 per cent of their weight up to hatching time (Kendeigh,

1940). Eggs of the Common Gull in Europe (Barth, 1952) lose 11 grams (from 52.0 to 41.0) or 21.2 per cent and the emerging young weigh only 36.0 grams or 16 grams less than the original egg (a 30.8 per cent loss).

## Hatching

At the end of the period of incubation fertile eggs with live embryos hatch, or give birth to young; unhatched eggs may be infertile or contain embryos that died at some stage of development. Hatching is preceded by "pipping" of the egg (Fig. 116), which is accomplished by the activities of the struggling chick within. Young birds are equipped with an "egg tooth," a horny protuberance on the tip of the upper mandible which is used to open the shell but which disappears soon after birth. Sometimes eggs appear to hatch rather suddenly, but usually they are pipped for several hours to a day or more before the young finally emerge. Often the chick can be heard peeping faintly within the shell, even a day or two before hatching. During its struggles it utilizes air in the air chamber of the egg. Eventually the crack in the weakened shell, initiated by pipping and completed by mechanical breakage, extends completely around the

*Fig. 116. Left, White Pelican nest scene in Montana. One young has just emerged, the other egg is pipped. (Courtesy of L. H. Walkinshaw.) Right, hatching at a pheasant nest. Most eggs in a pheasant nest hatch more or less simultaneously and the young soon depart, leaving the discarded shells. (Photo by Mich. Dept. of Conservation.)*

egg, usually around the larger end, and the chick kicks itself free. The parent bird may watch the proceedings, ostensibly with great interest, and occasionally tries to help out by picking at the shell, but too much parental (or human) interference may rupture the blood vessels in the lingering yolk sac.

Soon after liberation of the chick, the parent removes the shell from the nest, often carrying it a considerable distance before dropping it. Shells and their associated membranes emit considerable odor at hatching time which might attract predators, so it is important that some disposal be made of them promptly. Some birds eat the shells, although there is probably little mineral value in them since the developing embryo has extracted much of the lime for bone formation. Precocial birds that leave the nest upon hatching, such as ducks, pheasants, and grouse, may leave the shells at the nest (Fig. 116), but precocial birds that remain for a day or more in the nest, such as gulls and terns, generally remove the shells. Eggs that fail to hatch are usually left in the nest and may even survive the tramplings of the young through nest life.

Parent birds appear to be conscious of and even "excited" by hatching events. Probably they hear or feel the pulsations of the struggling young in the egg. A female Gray-cheeked Thrush (Wallace, 1939) has been observed to hop to the rim of the nest repeatedly during the hatching process and to watch and poke at the egg. Several times she sang while perched on the edge of the nest. Once she flew away and returned with a worm which she tried to feed to an unhatched egg, as if her feeding instincts were getting ahead of schedule, but as subsequent events disclosed, the egg was probably delayed in hatching and should have hatched on that day. Putnam (1949) describes a similarly dramatic scene in the nest life of the Cedar Waxwing. At hatching time the female in some way communicated the event to the male who came and inspected the young. He then left but later returned with a mass of small caterpillars for the young, whereas previously he had brought only fruit for the female. The female Common Tern (Palmer, 1941) appears nervous at hatching time and often refuses to change over when her mate comes to relieve her; her restlessness to some extent is communicated to the male.

All the eggs in a nest may hatch more or less simultaneously, or at staggered intervals (*asynchronous* hatching). Among the ducks, gallinaceous birds, plovers, and sandpipers, which lead their young from the nest soon after hatching, it is important that they all hatch more or less at once; sometimes, indeed, an unhatched egg with a live embryo is abandoned in the nest in the haste of the mother to get away with her brood (Edminster, 1947). Among the gulls and terns, however, hatching of the two or three eggs may occur at intervals, even a day apart, but the young stay at or close to the nest site for several days after hatching. A common but far from universal sequence in passerine birds which lay four eggs is that three of the eggs hatch close together, with the fourth egg hatching several hours to a day later, indicating that incubation began with laying of the third egg and that the fourth egg was laid a day later.

In the hawks, owls, North American cuckoos and Boat-tailed Grackles (Selander, 1960a), it is common to find young of quite different ages in the nest, indicating asynchronous hatching (Fig. 117). As previously pointed out, this may result in cannabilism in some predatory birds, and may be a means of bringing family size into adjustment with the food supply (Lack, 1947). Some of the owls, notably the Great Horned, and the Gray Jay start nesting in winter even in the northern states, and must keep their eggs covered quite constantly to prevent freezing; hence the young hatch at staggered intervals.

When eggs fail to hatch, incubating birds may prolong incubation for indefinite periods. Peterle (1953) reports a Ruffed Grouse that sat on

*Fig. 117. These young Marsh Hawks hatched at staggered intervals. The one in the background is nearly ready to fly; the one at the far left is relatively helpless and is lucky to have survived trampling by his larger nest sibs. (Courtesy of Edward M. Brigham, Jr.)*

infertile eggs for 70 days, nearly three times the normal incubation period. A male Bobwhite (Jickling, 1940) sat for nearly three months. Twenty-two to 24-day vigils, roughly double the normal incubation period, have been reported for several passerines (Berger, 1953a).

(Selected References follow Chapter 10.)

# 10

# THE ANNUAL CYCLE:

## *Postnatal Life*

This final chapter on the annual cycle describes the chief events in the life of young birds in and out of the nest, including some of their activities in late summer and fall and concluding with a brief account of winter habits. Several of these topics might well be expanded to a full chapter, but are here only briefly summarized to round out the picture of the annual cycle.

### *The Young, Their Early Growth and Development*

Young birds, as repeatedly stated heretofore, are commonly divided into (1) altricial: birds born in a relatively helpless condition and wholly dependent on parental care, and (2) precocial: birds well developed and capable of locomotion at birth, covered with natal down, and able to feed themselves. Such a division, however, is not always clear and sharp. Typical altricial birds are naked or nearly so at birth, but herons, hawks and owls, though altricial with respect to helplessness and need for parental care, are well covered with natal down when hatched. Some charadriiform birds (gulls, terns, and alcids) are well covered with down at birth, but remain at or near the nest and are cared for by their parents for some time. Hence, the following more restricted terms are often used in advanced courses in ornithology (definitions—but not examples—from Van Tyne and Berger, 1959):

1. Nidicolous—birds whose young remain in the nest for some time after hatching (includes herons, gulls, terns, alcids, hawks, and owls, as well as all birds born naked or nearly naked—Fig. 118l).
2. Nidifugous—birds whose young leave the nest shortly after hatching (loons, grebes, anatids, galliform and gruiform birds, plovers—Fig. 118r).
3. Psilopaedic—naked at hatching, or having down only on the future pterylae (all passerines, woodpeckers, kingfishers, swifts and hummingbirds, cuckoos, parrots, pigeons).
4. Ptilopaedic—completely clothed with down at hatching, the down covering the apteria as well as pterylae (particularly true of anatids and gallinaceous birds, but also includes many of the nidicolous types).

At hatching time, then, most altricial birds, such as passerines, are blind, relatively helpless, and nearly naked, with varying amounts of wet natal down sparsely distributed on some of the feather tracts. Some, such as Chimney Swifts (Fig. 118l), House Sparrows, and Cedar Waxwings, are entirely naked; others, like flycatchers, may have a fairly dense coat of long down. The eyelids are completely closed; if pried open manually they do not remain open. The young bird appears to be all head (to accommodate the large eyes) and abdomen (yolk sac); its relatively undeveloped limbs will not support it in its feeble efforts to rise to beg for food. The body is of a pinkish hue due to suffusion of blood vessels beneath the thin skin through which the viscera can be seen. The interior of the mouth is usually a conspicuous red, orange, or yellow, providing a more visible target for

*Fig. 118. Left, young Chimney Swifts are naked and helpless at birth and are cared for in the nest for about three weeks. (From Hegner and Stiles,* College Zoology, *copyright 1951 by the Macmillan Company, New York.) Right, Piping Plovers, like ducklings and gallinaceous chicks, are fully clothed with natal down and scamper from the nest soon after hatching. They are well camouflaged either in or out of the nest. (Photo by Bertha Daubendiek, courtesy of* Jack-Pine Warbler.)

the parents in feeding (Fig. 119). Essentially cold-blooded at this stage, the young have to be brooded quite constantly to keep them warm. Many passerines weigh from 1 to 3 grams at birth, some even less, having lost about one-third of the weight of the egg from which they hatched.

Growth and development are rapid in all passerine species. Young Vesper Sparrows, for example, which weigh about 2 grams at birth, average about 18 grams when they leave the nest at 9 to 10 days of age (Dawson and Evans, 1960). Young Robins average 5.5 grams (4.1 to 6.7) at birth and 56.7 grams (52.2 to 63.2) at nest-leaving time at 13 days (Howell, 1942). The sparse natal down is carried out on the tips of the incoming quills of the juvenal plumage which shows as dark dots beneath the skin at first, but breaks through as pin feathers in a few days. Feathers of the juvenal plumage begin to unfold rapidly about midway through nest life (5 to 7 days in most passerines) and by nest-leaving time have expanded until they practically cover the apteria. The eyes usually open, at first a

*Fig. 119. These young Brown Thrashers raise their heads hungrily for food at the appearance of an adult. Light-reflecting papillae on the brightly colored palate aid the parents in hitting the target. (Photo by Allan D. Cruickshank.)*

mere slit, some time during the first 3 to 5 days (a little earlier in a few, considerably later in others), but the young bird apparently does not see clearly at this stage.

About midway through nest life the young birds become conscious of things about them: they rear up in the nest with loud begging cries when the parents appear with food (Fig. 119); a sense of fear perhaps correlated with improved vision begins to develop so that they "freeze" in the presence of an intruder; they stretch, preen, and jostle each other; and just before departure are so active that the nest can hardly contain them. If unduly disturbed or startled by an intruder, they explode from the nest, often prematurely, in this way perhaps escaping a predator for the moment, but perhaps later falling prey to another predator because they cannot fly at this stage. Temperature control is established rather gradually, concomitant with feather development, and is quite unstable at first, but is fairly well established before nest-leaving time (see p. 96 for development in Vesper Sparrows).

Weight is one of the best criteria of growth, but development of structural parts—bill, wings, tarsus, and tail—is also readily measurable. Growth, though rapid and fairly uniform (except for the first day or so), shows some fluctuations due to irregularities in feeding, health, and general welfare of the birds, and rapidity of feather development (a slowing down of the rate of increase in weight is characteristic during periods of rapid feather development). Some structural parts develop more rapidly than others; the bill and tarsus may have attained full length at nest-leaving age, but the wings and especially the characteristically stubby tail continue their growth for some time after departure from the nest (Fig. 120). The young bird is nearly as large as its parents at nest leaving (70 to 80 per cent of the adult weight in those that leave in pre-flight stages, 100 per cent or so for those that stay longer). It is a mistaken concept among many laymen that small individuals are young birds. In some nonpasserines, in fact, as in eagles, the immature are often larger than their parents during their first summer.

There are of course numerous exceptions to the rapid growth rates characteristic of passerines. Among the nonpasserines which are not precocial, for instance, are some species which develop comparatively slowly. The Ruby-throated Hummingbird remains in the nest for about 20 days (extremes of 14 to 31 days have been recorded—Eyer, 1949), compared to 9 to 14 days for most passerines. Chimney Swifts may stay in the nest for 20 days, then linger in the chimney another 8 to 10 days before venturing

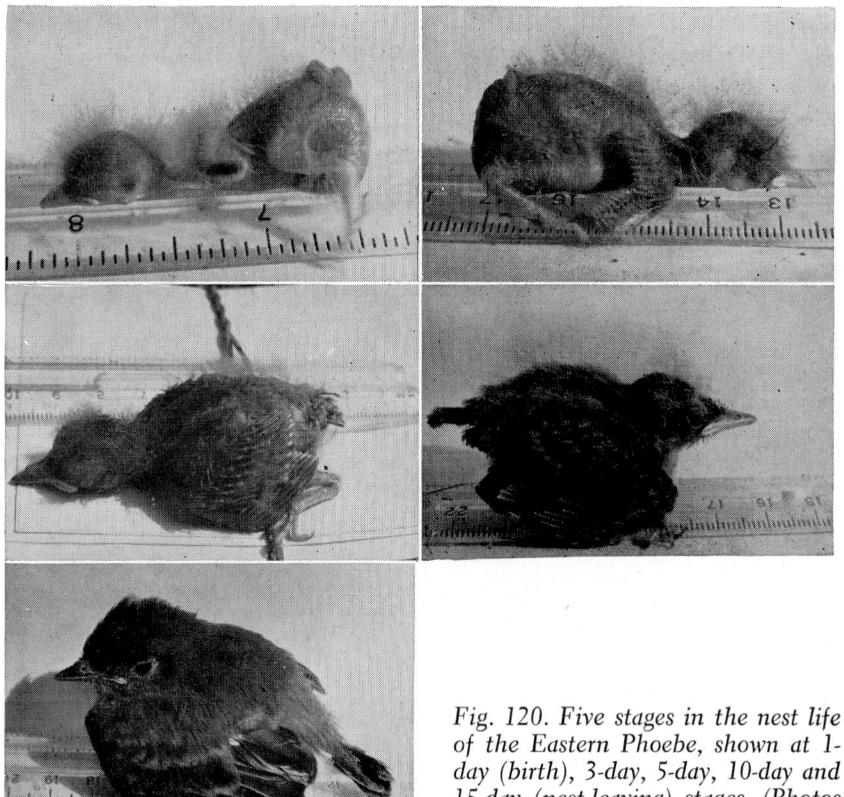

*Fig. 120. Five stages in the nest life of the Eastern Phoebe, shown at 1-day (birth), 3-day, 5-day, 10-day and 15-day (nest-leaving) stages. (Photos by Harold D. Mahan.)*

outside. Young woodpeckers are slow of growth; a flicker's eyes do not open till about the tenth day, and it may remain in the nest cavity nearly a month. The young of hawks and owls remain in the nest for six weeks or more, or for 12 weeks in the case of young eagles. Some of the oceanic birds are notoriously slow of growth. Petrels remain in their nest burrows for 8 weeks or more, penguins require several months for growth, and Royal Albatrosses remain at the nest site for 8 to 9 months (Richdale, 1942), then spend 8 to 9 years at sea before returning to their natal isle to breed (Westerskov, 1959).

This picture of young altricial birds applies only in part to precocial young, which at birth are usually alert and lively, with open eyes and a full covering of natal down. Gallinaceous chicks run about soon after birth and downy ducklings swim; both are led away by the mother and at least guided in their first quests for food. Their legs are well developed for locomotion, but their wings are retarded and the juvenal plumage develops

**Table 6. Comparative Nesting Data for Representative Species**

| Species | Family | Pair Bond | Number of Eggs/ Clutch | Incubation Period | Sex Incubating | Fledgling Period (dys) | Reference |
|---|---|---|---|---|---|---|---|
| Ostrich | Struthionidae | polygynous | 12–16 | 42 | male | 0 | Kendeigh, 1952 |
| Kiwi | Apterygidae | monogamous | 1–3 | 75 | male | 6 | Robson, 1948 |
| Tinamou (*Nothoprocta*) | Tinamidae | polyandrous (?) | 4–9 (7) | 22 | male | 22 hrs | Pearsons, 1955 |
| Emperor Penguin | Spheniscidae | monogamous | 1 | 62–64 | male | ? | Rivolier, 1959 |
| Common Loon | Gaviidae | monogamous | 2 | 28–30 | both | 0 | Kendeigh, 1952 |
| Royal Albatross | Diomedeidae | monogamous | 1 | 78–80 | both | 8–9 months | Richdale, 1942 |
| American Bittern | Ardeidae | monogamous | 4–6 | 25–26 | female | 14 | Kendeigh, 1952 |
| Whistling Swan | Anatidae | monogamous | 2–7 (4–5) | 35–40 | female | 0 | Kortright, 1942 |
| Canada Goose | Anatidae | monogamous | 4–10 (5–6) | 28–30 | female | 0 | Kortright, 1942 |
| Mallard | Anatidae | monogamous | 6–15 (8–10) | 23–29 (26) | female | 0 | Kortright, 1942 |
| Bald Eagle | Accipitridae | monogamous | 2 | 35 | both | 84 | Broley, 1947 |
| Mallee Fowl (*Leipoa*) | Megapodiidae | monogamous | 18–24 | 57 | neither | 0 | Frith, 1956 |
| Ruffed Grouse | Tetraonidae | promiscuous (?) | 11 | 23–24 | female | 0 | Edminster, 1947 |
| Sandhill Crane | Gruidae | monogamous | 2 | 28–30 | both | 0 | Walkinshaw, 1949 |
| Killdeer | Charadriidae | monogamous | 4 | 26 | both | 0 | Kendeigh, 1952 |
| Northern Phalarope | Phalaropodidae | polyandrous (?) | 4 | 20–21 | male | 0 | Kendeigh, 1952 |
| Herring Gull | Laridae | monogamous | 2–3 | 24–28 (26) | both | 0 | Bent, 1921 |
| Common Tern | Laridae | monogamous | (1–5) 3 | 21–26 (23) | both | 2 | Palmer, 1941 |
| Mourning Dove | Columbidae | monogamous | 2 | 14 | both | 13–15 | McClure, 1943 |
| Black-billed Cuckoo | Cuculidae | monogamous | 2–4 | 10–14 | both | 7 | Kendeigh, 1952 |
| Great Horned Owl | Strigidae | monogamous | 2 | 33–35 | both | 45 | Hoffmeister, *et al.* 1947 |
| Nighthawk | Caprimulgidae | monogamous | 2 | 18–19 | female (m.?) | 23 (brooded) | Kendeigh, 1952 |
| Chimney Swift | Apodidae | monogamous? | 4 | 18–19 | both | 19–26 | Kendeigh, 1952 |
| Belted Kingfisher | Alcedinidae | monogamous | 6–7 | 23–24 | female (m.?) | 28–32 | Bent, 1940 |
| Yellow-shafted Flicker | Picidae | monogamous | 6–8 | 11–12 | both | 25–28 | Bent, 1939 |

| *Species* | *Family* | *Pair Bond* | *Number of Eggs/ Clutch* | *Incubation Period* | *Sex Incubation* | *Fledgling Period (dys)* | *Reference* |
|---|---|---|---|---|---|---|---|
| Eastern Phoebe | Tyrannidae | monogamous | 5 | 16 | female | 16–18 | Kendeigh, 1952 |
| Horned Lark | Alaudidae | monogamous | 3–5 | 11–12 | female | 11–12 | Pickwell, 1931 |
| Barn Swallow | Hirundinidae | monogamous | 4–6 | 14–16 | female (m?) | 18–23 | Kendeigh, 1952 |
| Common Crow | Corvidae | monogamous | 4–6 | 18 | both | 28–35 | Bent, 1946 |
| Black-capped Chickadee | Paridae | monogamous | 5–8 (6.7) | 13 | female | 16 | Odum, 1941, 1942 |
| Dipper | Cinclidae | monogamous | 4–5 | 16 | female | 24–25 | Bakus, 1959 |
| House Wren | Troglodytidae | polygynous | 4–9 (5.5) | 13 | female | 15–16 | Kendeigh, 1952 |
| Catbird | Mimidae | monogamous | 3–5 (4) | 12–13 | female | 10 | Bent, 1948 |
| Robin | Turdidae | monogamous | 3–4 | 12–14 | female | 9–16 (13) | Howell, 1942 |
| Ruby-crowned Kinglet | Regulidae | monogamous | 5–11 | 12 (?) | female | 12 (?) | Bent, 1949 |
| Cedar Waxwing | Bombycillidae | monogamous | 4–5 | 12.2 | female | 15.9 | Putnam, 1949 |
| (California) Shrike | Laniidae | monogamous | 5–7 (6) | 16 | female | 20 | Miller, 1931 |
| Starling | Sturnidae | monogamous | 4–6 | 11–14 | both | 14–21 | Bent, 1950 |
| Red-eyed Vireo | Vireonidae | monogamous | 2–4 (3.07) * | 12–14 | both | 11–12 | Southern, 1958 |
| Kirtland's Warbler | Parulidae | monogamous | 3–6 (4.6) | 13–16 (14) | female | 9–11 (9.4) | Mayfield, 1960 |
| Ovenbird | Parulidae | monogamous | 3–6 (4.7) | 11–14 (12) | female | 8 | Hann, 1937 |
| House Sparrow | Ploceidae | monogamous | 4–6 (4.7) | 10–14 (12) | female | 12–16 (14.4) | Weaver, 1943 |
| Brewer's Blackbird | Icteridae | polygynous | 3–7 | 12–14 (13) | female | 13 | Williams, 1952 |
| Cardinal | Fringillidae | monogamous | 3 | 12 or 13 | female | 9–10 | Laskey, 1944 |
| Song Sparrow | Fringillidae | monogamous | 3–5 (4) | 12 or 13 | female | 10 | Nice, 1937, 1943 |
| Snow Bunting | Fringillidae | monogamous | 4–7 | 12.5–13 | female | 12–14 | Sutton, *et al.*, 1954b |

* Clutch size may have been reduced by heavy cowbird parasitism.

slowly compared to altricial passerines (Fig. 121). Though well proportioned, they are smaller in relation to the size of the parent (1 to 6 per cent of adult female weight) than passerines (6 to 8 per cent or more) both at birth and at the preflying stage. In anseriform birds flight feathers and flight are particularly slow to develop (see Weller, 1957, for remex development and first flights in ducks).

Temperature control in precocial birds is not fully developed at hatching time. Though in chickens and gulls the capacity to regulate temperature is known to be present to some extent before birth, regulatory ability after hatching is good only in ordinary air temperatures at first and unstable in colder weather (Bartholomew and Dawson, 1952). Farner and Serventy (1959) found that Slender-billed Shearwater chicks on Bass Straits (Australia) have adequate thermoregulation for life in burrows within the first day of hatching, surpassing both galliform birds and gulls in this respect. Occupied burrows had higher temperatures than empty burrows due to the presence of the birds.

## Parental Care

### BROODING

Brooding, or the covering of the young by the parent bird to keep them warm, is an important function in early nest life. During their first days,

*Fig. 121. Day-old Black Duck. Downy ducklings are alert and lively with well-developed legs for running or swimming, but their wings and flight feathers are slow to develop. (Courtesy of Miles D. Pirnie.)*

altricial young are brooded fairly constantly, in a rhythm somewhat similar to incubation. Thereafter, brooding gradually decreases with feather development and may cease altogether during the late stages of nest life, except that the adult generally sleeps on the nest at night. Birds nesting in colder climates and in mountainous regions, understandably, brood more constantly than those in warmer areas. Brooding is likewise correlated with local weather conditions, the adult, usually the female, remaining at the nest through rains and storms, during which time the male may have to do double duty in providing food.

The more advanced development of precocial birds at hatching does not preclude the necessity for some brooding, for they lose body heat rapidly with exposure. Nearly all species brood their young until they leave the nest and thereafter resort to frequent off-nest hovering. Duck mothers assemble their ducklings for brief spells of brooding, and gallinaceous birds brood their young at night and at intervals during the day for many days. In fact, the necessity for increased brooding during spells of bad weather seriously curtails feeding time in gallinaceous birds and may cause losses (Höglund, 1952).

## FEEDING THE YOUNG

A major task in the care of nestlings is providing sufficient food for their proper growth and development. The appetites of young birds are enormous; they often consume their own weight in food per day, or even more, although perhaps about one-fourth of the body weight is more usual. Finding and delivering this food is nearly a full-time occupation for one or both parents, especially in northern latitudes where larger broods are reared. Feeding problems are solved in many different ways by different species. Some of these interesting variations are dealt with in the following sections.

ROLE OF THE SEXES. The role of the sexes in the feeding program is a very variable feature. The somewhat exceptional cases in which the male plays little or no part in family affairs, as well as instances of sex reversal in which the male does it all, have already been mentioned; these, in most cases, apply to precocial birds which after a little parental supervision are able to forage for themselves. In most other birds, however, feeding is handled on a cooperative basis (Fig. 122), with both male and female sharing in the task. Frequently the female appears to take the initiative, the male helping out somewhat dilatorily; or again, perhaps somewhat exceptionally,

*Fig. 122. The males of most passerine species cooperate faithfully in feeding the young. Here a male Hooded Warbler brings food to the nest. (Photo by Hal Harrison, courtesy of* Jack-Pine Warbler.)

the male may bring the bulk of the food while the female remains to supervise affairs at the nest. In the Marsh Hawk, for instance, the male brings nearly all the prey for the first five days and transfers it to the female, often in mid-air, and she then portions it out to the young. Later the female also hunts prey, but the male continues to leave his contributions at the nest for the female to dole out (Hecht, 1951). A similar arrangement prevails in the Goshawk (Schnell, 1958); the male brings 85 per cent of the food to the female and she feeds it to the young. Schnell suggests that this functions in keeping the male from wasting time at the nest (the female is hostile to him) and forces him to do more hunting.

In the Black-capped Chickadee (Odum, 1942) the male does most of the feeding at first (two to four times as much) while the female broods, but thereafter they feed with about equal frequency. In the Cedar Waxwing the male does all the feeding for the first three days, the female brooding about 90 per cent of the time (Putnam, 1949).

At nests of the Gray-cheeked Thrush observed on a mountain top in Vermont (Wallace, 1939), the male and female shared feeding assignments about equally; the female was a little more regular in pleasant weather, but during the frequent mountain storms when she remained at the nest to brood, the male did double duty, bringing insects at about the same rate that both birds usually maintained. Once during a two-hour period of steady rain the female remained constantly at the nest while the male brought prey, which she took from his bill and relayed to the young or else stood aside while he fed them. Hole-nesting species, of course, do not face the problem of extra brooding during storms.

Evenden (1957) reports an unusual, though not unique, situation in which House Finches in California may have two nests operating simultaneously. At hatching time the male takes charge of one nest while the female starts another. In one case the female left the first nest *before* the eggs hatched, but the male carried on successfully. Curiously, also, the male Painted Bunting in Oklahoma (Parmelee, 1959) helps feed the young only after they are fledged and then only if the female starts a second brood.

Usually, however, among altricial birds fed for a period at the nest, feeding is a cooperative enterprise, and without the participation of both sexes the welfare of the young might be in jeopardy. An illuminating example of this is that the Yellow-eyed Penguin raises only one chick if one parent is lost, but two young if both parents survive (Richdale, 1951b).

FEEDING SCHEDULES. Frequency of feedings varies greatly with different species, but also with the age of the young, time of day, and particularly with the amount of food brought per trip. Sometimes feedings are more concentrated in the early morning and in late afternoon or evening, with a pronounced midday slackening. The young are fed less frequently, or more rarely not at all, for the first day or so, since they are still deriving some nourishment from the yolk-filled abdomen, but the feeding rate increases rapidly thereafter. Cuthbert (1954) noted that Black Terns increased their feeding rate from 1.2 times per hour on the first day to 16.8 times on the eighth day.

Some of the smaller birds have extremely rapid feeding rates. Tabler (1956) reports that a pair of Barn Swallows nesting on a light fixture on a porch fed their young about once a minute, or more often on the eighth day, a fast rate confirmed by several other observers for short periods; but Peterson (1955) gives the hourly rate as only 27.4 for Bank Swallows. A Warbling Vireo has been reported making 45 trips per hour to a nest, in contrast to the slow feeding rate of 6.5 times per hour at two nests of the Red-eyed Vireo (Southern, 1958). Nice (1943) gave the maximum feeding rate for ten passerine species as 39.7 times per hour for the Great Tit in Europe. Using daily rates, Kendeigh gives 491 feedings as the maximum of many observations on House Wrens and 845 times on the twelfth day of nest life as the climax at a nest of Eastern Phoebes. The phoebes appear to have established a record, with 8,942 total visits to the nest recorded in 17 days, or 2,275 per young bird.

Most of the birds cited above have small territories and make short trips with small insect prey. Thrushes make fewer trips, at 10-to-15-minute intervals (less than 100 per day), but usually bring enough items to feed more than one bird at a time. Still others, like the Cedar Waxwing (Putnam, 1949), which averages about three feedings per hour, may bring a whole cropful of berries, enough to go around the whole brood one or more times (Fig. 123). Goldfinches feed their young by regurgitation at half-hour intervals, but bring a gullet full of small seeds for each feeding (Stokes, 1950). A fairly typical feeding schedule for many passerines, with male and female cooperating, is described by Davis (1960) for the Rufous-sided Towhee in California (Fig. 124).

Larger birds, characteristically but not invariably, feed their young less frequently. With predatory birds, this may vary with hunting success. The

*Fig. 123. Cedar Waxwings feed their young less frequently than most passerines, but may bring a large load at one time—5 large mulberries, or 7 chokecherries, or 9–13 elderberries in one trip. (Courtesy of Edward M. Brigham, Jr.)*

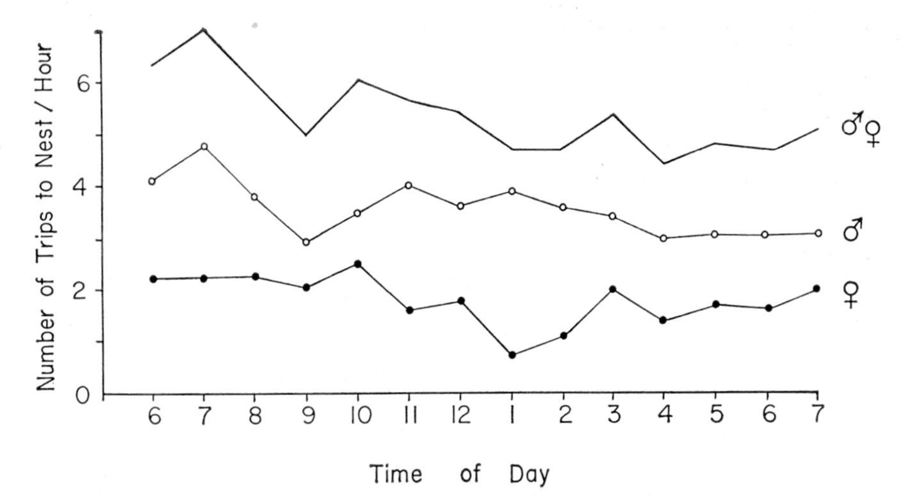


*Fig. 124. Feeding rates of male and female Rufous-sided Towhees and of the two combined. Note morning peak of male activity and mid-day slump of female. (Graphs by John Davis, courtesy of the* Condor.)

young may gorge themselves until their crops threaten to burst, if food is available, then fast for long periods if it is not. Hourly feedings are said to be characteristic of some hawks, but often a large carcass, such as a rabbit, may be left in the nest where it is available to the young whenever they feel inclined to dine. Herrick (1934) noted that Bald Eagles renewed the food supply at the nest from two to eight times per day.

One of the most extraordinary feeding programs is that of a European swift (*Apus*), which has been well documented by Koskimies (1950). Under adverse weather conditions, aeroplankton (flying insects mainly), are not available and the swifts cease hunting. During such periods the nestlings become torpid and are able to fast for long intervals, up to a recorded maximum of 21 days, though the average survival time of fourteen young subjected to starvation experiments was about ten days. In good weather, however, the adults collect large food balls of massed insects (up to several hundred per ball) which they regurgitate to their young at infrequent intervals—hence, swifts are well fed and get fat in good weather but fast and starve during bad weather.

Some fish-eating birds—gulls, terns, kingfishers, and the Osprey—bring their young whole fish, singly or in multiples, but others, like herons, cormorants, and pelicans, bring larger loads from more extended fishing excursions and feed their young by regurgitation. White Pelicans nesting on Gunnison Island in Great Salt Lake, where fish are not available, have to make long flights, apparently twice daily, to fishing waters that are 50 to 75 miles away (Low and Rasmussen, 1950). Sea birds also feed their young infrequently; Yellow-eyed Penguin chicks are usually fed once daily (sometimes twice) and young petrels are fed even less frequently (at one- to ten-day intervals in late nest life when they are no longer guarded).

Long absences of such birds as albatrosses and other petrels from their nest sites have given rise to a *starvation hypothesis*, namely, that the adults desert their young in late nest life for weeks or months (three months in the Wandering Albatross) until the starving young go out to sea and learn to forage for themselves. Richdale has shown that this is not always true, since the adults may come back at several-day intervals to feed their young; yet there appears to be no question about such a starvation period during late nest life of many of the Procellariiformes. In many land birds less frequent feedings toward the end of nest life are thought by some to function as an incentive for young birds to leave the nest.

FEEDING TECHNIQUES. Most birds bring food items in their beak (predatory birds also use their talons) and feed directly by cramming the food deep down into the throats of the young. A special muscular mechanism in the throat facilitates swallowing, as many a novice has discovered in trying to rear nestlings which appear unable to swallow food unless it is placed deep down in the throat. The oral cavity of many birds is brightly colored, in some cases even equipped with papillae or light-reflecting knobs that aid the adults in hitting the target quickly (Fig. 119). The red spot on the bills of several species of gulls apparently aids the young in spotting the food. Swaying movements of the head, special food cries or vocal signals of either adults or young, and even the draft of air created by Chimney Swifts descending a chimney (Barton, 1958) provide other stimuli for feeding.

Some birds utilize the pharynx and the crop for carrying food. Such birds feed largely by regurgitation. Hummingbirds deliver predigested food (nectar and insects) by thrusting their long rapier-like bills deep into the gullets of the young until it appears that the nestlings would be stabbed to death. Young herons grasp their parent's beak at right angles in their own and shake it vigorously. This seems to initiate the release of the prey which is then dropped in the nest for the young or else taken directly from the bill of the adult. Pelicans simply open their huge maw and let the hungry nestlings go exploring.

Hunger reflexes apparently determine to some extent the rotation in which the young are fed. The hungriest bird is apt to reach higher or clamor more loudly, then when satisfied drops back relaxed while another bird is fed. If the food placed in the mouth of the young is not swallowed promptly, it is taken out and fed to another. Young cowbirds flourish, usually at the expense of rightful occupants of the nest, by being larger and able to command the lion's share of the food. Such a process of food distribution, to the one that appears hungriest, is called *automatic apportionment*.

The nature of the food fed to the young usually reflects the food habits of the species, dealt with in more detail in Chapter 13. Young birds, however, even in primarily seed-eating species, are fed animal food at first, mainly insects in the smaller forms, and larger prey, such as fish and other vertebrates, in the larger forms. Cedar Waxwings feed their young on insects for the first three days, then shift largely to fruits. A male Cardinal has been observed to visit a feeding station with his beak full of green worms, lay down the worms, crack and eat sunflower seeds, then pick up the worms and go to the nest site, presumably feeding the young (Van Tyne, 1951). The American Goldfinch, however, which postpones nesting until fresh pulpy seeds of thistle and other composites are available, feeds its young on seeds from the beginning of nest life, but they are fed to the young in somewhat predigested form. Pigeons, which are primarily grain-feeders, produce pigeons' milk (p. 80) for the early nourishment of their young.

## NEST SANITATION

In species in which the young are cared for in the nest, some system of sanitation is almost imperative. Considering the large amount of food consumed, and the fact that a nestling's digestive apparatus does not function perfectly at first, it is natural that excreta are expelled frequently and in considerable quantity. Sanitation of the nest is usually carefully provided for by cleaning it at nearly every feeding. Excreta are voided by the young in a convenient fecal sac which can be readily picked up by the adults (Fig. 125). Usually the young defecate immediately after being fed; frequently the adult waits at the nest after feeding, then picks the fecal sac off the elevated cloaca, sometimes even nudging the young to prompt it to perform.

Oddly enough, the parents often eat the feces, presumably getting some nourishment from them because of the incomplete digestion in the

*Fig. 125. Nest sanitation. Left, an Old World Babbler (Timaliidae) in India removes a fecal sac from the nest. Right, a Common Grackle disposes of a fecal sac, which in this species is eaten or carried away with about equal frequency. (Photos by R. M. Naik and Lester E. Eyer.)*

young at this stage. Eating the excreta is not universal, however, either as to species or individuals; often they are merely carried away and dropped at a distance. Wible (1960) noted that a Yellow-bellied Sapsucker in Montana used a bracket fungus on a tree for fecal disposal; the male regularly brought the sac from the nest hole to the fungus, ate the sac, and allowed the contents to dribble over the shelf to the ground. No other method of fecal disposal was observed. The feces are eaten less frequently as the young mature. Laskey (1944) noted that the female Cardinal ate them the first five days, the male the first four days, and that thereafter both sexes carried them away. Artifacts, such as wads of paper or plasticene models of feces placed in or on the nest are also removed (Smith, 1947). Sometimes adults try to remove shiny leg bands from nestlings, even dumping the young out of the nest.

There are numerous exceptions to the scrupulous sanitation described above. Swallows are untidy about their nests, letting the droppings accumulate until they may become a distraction in and around farm buildings. For reasons not fully understood, but in some way perhaps related to a seed diet and the lack of formation of convenient fecal sacs, the otherwise beautiful nest of the American Goldfinch may become much soiled toward the end of the nest cycle. The "white-washed" nests in heron rookeries and the "white-washed" ledges in sea-bird colonies are familiar scenes. In dry climates, where such accumulations are not subject to leaching, rich deposits of guano result (Fig. 160). Kingfishers and woodpeckers apparently make no effort at nest sanitation. In sandy soil in Kingfisher burrows, the liquid is quickly absorbed, but when drainage is poor it may ooze out of the entrance almost continually. Kingfisher tunnels reek with ammonia gases, and the adults often plunge into water on emergence and bathe (Skutch, 1952c).

## Nest Leaving

The days just prior to departure from the nest witness interesting preparations for the event. Exercises, which actually began in a limited way before birth, now reach a new peak. The nestlings stretch and yawn, extending first one foot and then the other, elevate and flap their wings, and preen their feathers. They become increasingly interested in affairs outside the nest. Sometimes they snap at passing insects, but seldom catch one. A nest with several well-developed young becomes so overcrowded that a great deal of pushing, pecking, and jostling takes place. Two birds may stage a sparring match on the nest, perhaps standing on top of one or more nest mates to do it; loss of a bird or two out of a tree nest because of such activities is not uncommon. When an adult appears with food they all make a lunge for it, the boldest perhaps even venturing out of the nest momentarily to meet its parent. Such exercises probably help prepare the young bird for its first flight, yet experiments with binding the wings of young birds show that they can make a good first flight instinctively without benefit of preliminary wing exercises. Hole-nesting birds emerging from cramped confinement may take off well on their first flight, but may have remained in the nest longer than species in open nests.

These activities eventually culminate in departure from the nest (Fig. 126), but the manner of leaving varies considerably. Often, as previously mentioned, nestlings may be startled into a premature departure by an intruder. Birds leaving thus prematurely usually cannot fly but merely flutter over the ground to a hiding place; in fact most ground-nesting passerines regularly leave the nest before they can fly, but tree-nesting species that stay the full term are capable of short flights at nest-leaving time. Young Dippers remain in their cozy streamside nest an unusually long time—24 or 25 days—but deliberately flutter to a safe landing, sometimes across a stretch of water, when they finally leave.

When nest leaving is normal, the young may depart gradually, one at a time, although often the departure of the first seems to be the signal for all to leave. At a hawk nest it is not uncommon to see the least developed bird crouched in the nest, another perched precariously on the edge of the structure, and still another out in the branches of the

*Fig. 126. Two stages in the nest life of the Gray-cheeked Thrush. Left, restless and getting ready to leave. Right, safely fledged. (Courtesy of* National Geographic Magazine.)

nest tree or even an adjacent tree. Herons commonly crawl out into the branches of the nest tree before flight (Fig. 127). Some birds seem so hesitant about leaving that they may have to be coaxed away by the adults which appear to tempt them with food just outside the nest, though whether or not this is a deliberate and functional device to promote proper nest leaving has been a controversial question.

The extended nest life of hole-nesting species may be an important survival factor. Black-capped Chickadees, for instance, remain in the nest for about 16 days and Tufted Titmice for 17 or 18 days, compared to 10 to 14 days for other tree-dwelling passerines and 8 to 10 days for ground-nesting passerines.

## *Postnest Life*

Details in the life of young birds are difficult to secure after fledging, but the parents usually accompany them and continue to care for them until they are able to shift for themselves. Mrs. Nice found her Song Sparrows being cared for by the parents for 18 to 20 days after nest leaving. Ovenbirds, which leave the nest at the early age of 8 days, are described by Hann (1937) as having a 3-day hopping stage (when 8 to 11 days of

*Fig. 127. Young Black-crowned Night Herons, like young hawks, usually clamber about the branches of the nest tree or adjacent trees before taking flight. These young Black-crowns look so unlike their parents that there is little resemblance in plumage. (Courtesy of Edward M. Brigham, Jr.)*

age), then a 10-day early-flying stage (11 to 20 days of age), an 11-day semidependent stage (20 to 30 days of age) when they do some feeding for themselves, and then the independent stage beyond 30 days when they leave their parents and shift for themselves. They apparently stay in or near the nest area by traveling in circles, rather than going long linear distances at first. Other birds may disperse more rapidly. Sutton and Parmelee (1954a) found a whole family (male, female, and four young) of Wheatears on Baffin Island a mile and a half from the nest 8 days after nest leaving.

Postnatal care of precocial birds follows a similar pattern, with an adult, usually the female, supervising their activities until they become independent. Young ducklings are led to the water, can swim and dive instinctively, and are quick to learn to glean surface insects from the water. Geis (1956) found that the young of Canada Geese in Montana left their island nest sites within forty-eight hours and travelled two to ten miles to brood-rearing areas. The young of gallinaecous birds accompany their parent on their first explorations, and may remain associated with her until fall.

Edminster (1947) gives a somewhat fanciful but probably representative account of a Ruffed Grouse family after hatching. The mother led her ten newly hatched chicks away from an eleven-egg nest, deserting in her haste to get away an unhatched egg containing a live embryo. She called them together and brooded them at intervals, taught them how to look for and find the proper kinds of insect food, how to freeze at a given signal, and how to scurry for cover at another. In spite of parental teachings, one of the ten was soon lost to a plundering Sharp-shinned Hawk, another lost track of his mother one evening and perished of cold, and then, a week later, a blundering skunk one stormy night accidentally broke up and scattered the family, so that three more failed to respond to the breakfast call. By the end of a month the five survivors were becoming more and more independent, until a Cooper's Hawk picked off an insubordinate youngster that failed to heed his mother's danger signal. Only four of the ten that hatched survived to the time of the fall shuffle which scattered the family.

Thus it may be seen that most young birds go through a period of postnest training under parental supervision, but the extent of family ties varies greatly. At one extreme are the megapodes (p. 218) which hatch out in the sand or brush and go their way without any parental care at all; at the other extreme are the geese and swans, which maintain strong family ties through the fall and winter until another breeding season separates them (Fig. 128). California Condors are dependent on their parents so long that the adults nest only every other year. The young of some tropical birds remain in association with their parents for a long time, roosting and sleeping in family groups over winter and sometimes even helping the adults at the nest the following year. Aside from these somewhat exceptional cases, however, family ties are of short duration and the young separate from their parents during their first summer.

Birds inherit many traits of behavior, such as feeding, singing, and bathing, without necessarily having to learn them from their parents. A young Gray-cheeked Thrush, kept in confinement away from others of his kind after his seventh day, learned to pick up food for himself on his fifteenth day of age. Clumsy and inaccurate at first, in a short time his aim was so precise that on his seventeenth day he picked thirty to forty leaf hoppers (Cicadellidae) in quick succession off a window pane

*Fig. 128. Geese maintain strong family ties—the gander guards the goose at the nest, both participate in rearing the young, and the family migrates as a unit, remaining together over winter. (Photo by Allan D. Cruickshank.)*

when held on the finger up to the glass. He started to sing an off-tune song at twenty-four days of age (another young thrush sang at fifteen days) and when twenty-five days old plunged into his drinking receptacle and took a complete bath. Thereafter he bathed daily, but another young thrush was irregular about this feature (Fig. 129).

First song and self-feeding have been observed in other young birds. Three young Song Sparrows kept by Mrs. Nice started to sing at thirteen, fourteen, and fifteen days, respectively. Two young Cardinals kept by Mrs. Laskey started warbling at three and four weeks, added two adult songs at two months, and sang songs indistinguishable from adults by late January and February. One young Cardinal picked up its own food thirteen days after nest leaving, another at twenty days, but cracking sunflower seeds was not mastered until nine weeks. Young Song Sparrows attempted to shell seeds at seventeen days of age, but were not successful until twenty-five days old.

*Fig. 129. Young birds learn to bathe instinctively. This Gray-cheeked Thrush, separated from his parents when 14 days old, jumped into his drinking water one day for his first bath. Another young thrush kept in captivity bathed frequently, but this one was irregular and often only splashed water over himself without jumping in.* (*Courtesy of* National Geographic Magazine.)

## *Mortality and Longevity*

One of the features of bird life that comes as a surprise to most laymen is the apparent wastage in reproduction. Heavy losses occur among birds, not only during the nesting season but also throughout the first year of life. Many eggs never hatch, either being infertile or containing defective embryos; sudden storms destroy some nests, others are broken up by predators; accidents of many kinds to one or both adults interrupt or terminate the nesting cycle; prolonged cold rainy weather may cause heavy loss of nestlings, particularly among the aerial insect feeders; and ectoparasites, and diseases exact their toll. Of course, when nests are deserted or destroyed in early stages, the adults renest, often repeatedly, and thus have an opportunity of nullifying earlier failures. A detailed history of an individual Song Sparrow at Ann Arbor, Michigan, revealed that she nested five times in 1949, with only two of the nests successful, and four times in 1950, with none of the nests successful (Berger, 1951b).

Many life-history studies now show that a nesting success of about 50 per cent may be normal for passerines with open nests. Greater losses may represent a decreasing population for one season, but of course could be atoned for in the following season. Nice (1957) figured that success for 7,778 nests of altricial species with open nests ranged from 38 to 77 per cent (average, 49). Fledging success for hole nesters (thirty-three studies involving 94,400 eggs) ranged from 22 to 94 per cent (average, 66). Sometimes species with open nests gain temporary benefits by safe-nesting situations: goldfinches nesting in dense thistle-grown wasteland in Minnesota were 78.2 per cent successful, but predators and humans stayed out of the dense thistles, and cowbirds were through breeding (Lewis, 1952).

Precocial birds may show a high hatching success at times, in spite of longer periods of vulnerability during incubation. Nests of Clapper Rails, in salt marshes in Virginia, in 1950 showed a hatching success of 94 per cent in the absence of storm tides during the nesting season, but in 1951 storm tides lowered the hatching success to 45 per cent (R. E. Stewart, 1951, 1952a). Similarly, M. Geis (1956) found that 73 per cent of her Canada Goose nests in Montana were successful in 1953, but only 51 per cent in 1954. High water is often disastrous to the nests of aquatic birds (Fig. 130).

Postnest losses of either precocial or altricial birds are hard to evaluate, but they continue to be heavy. The sequel to Edminster's chronicle of a Ruffed Grouse family (p. 242) is that after the fall shuffle separated the mother and her four surviving young, the hunting season accounted for another victim, the long, hard winter witnessed the demise of the mother and another young, and the spring breeding season saw a weasel pick an inexperienced male off his drumming log. Thus the annual cycle was complete, with one young female and the original father, who had not been with the family, left to carry on—no gain, no loss in relation to the number that started out the previous year.

Some of the factors responsible for high mortality in bird life are discussed in Chapter 14. Natural factors that account for fall and winter (postnest) losses include further inroads by predators, particularly among the inexperienced immature birds; storms during migration; freeze-ups on the wintering grounds which sometimes produce severe mortality among

*Fig. 130. Nests and eggs of the Common Tern destroyed by high water in Saginaw Bay, Michigan. (Photo by Mich. Dept. of Conservation.)*

insect-eaters in the southern states (Wallace, 1943; Dennis, 1958b); and ectoparasites and diseases (p. 373). Additional, man-induced factors include hunting, road kills, such obstructions as light houses, monuments, television towers, and picture windows; pollution of waters and poisonous pesticides; and loss of habitats (pp. 376–382). Birds possess an amazing capacity to recover from or adjust to the natural factors (e.g., weather and predators) and from some of the man-induced factors (e.g., regulated hunting), but how well or how long they can withstand increasing habitat restrictions is a moot question.

Annual mortality during a bird's first year is high—according to some estimates two-thirds to three-fourths of the immature birds die during their first year of life, compared to one-fourth during their second year. A. Geis (1959), using band-recovery records, estimated the first-year mortality for immature Canvasbacks at 77 per cent; adult mortality ranged from 35 to 50 per cent. Hunting accounted for half of the losses. Burton (1959) figured adult mortality in the American Coot at 57 per cent and that of the immatures at 79 per cent. He estimated the egg-to-first breeding mortality at 85 to 88 per cent. Owen (1959) gave the mortality rate of

***Table 7. Maximum Age Records for Some Banded Wild Birds***

| *Species* | *Age in Years* | *Remarks* | *Reference* |
|---|---|---|---|
| Great Blue Heron | 21 | Oldest of 349 | Owen, 1959 |
| Glossy Ibis | 20 | USSR | Turček, 1958 |
| Canada Goose | 23 | Shot, Swan Creek, Mich. | Douville, *et al.*, 1957 |
| Mallard | 16 | USSR | Turček, 1958 |
| Common Teal | 20 | USSR | Turček, 1958 |
| Common Goldeneye | 17 | USSR | Turček, 1958 |
| Red-tailed Hawk | 13+ | ——— | Hann, 1953 |
| Osprey | 21 | ——— | Hann, 1953 |
| Oystercatcher | 27 | Europe | Bergstrom, 1956 |
| Herring Gull | 28–29 | Oldest wild bird? | Bergstrom, 1956 |
| Common Tern | 25 | England | Bergstrom, 1956 |
| Arctic Tern | 27 | Killed by cat, Germany | Bergstrom, 1952 |
| Least Tern | 21 | Cotuit, Mass. | Bergstrom, 1952 |
| Caspian Tern | 26 | Oldest N.A. bird? | Bergstrom, 1952 |
| Chimney Swift | 13+ | ——— | Dexter, 1960 |
| Hairy Woodpecker | 11 | Oldest woodpecker? | (Fig. 107) |
| Blue Jay | 14 | L.I. to Md. | Beals, 1952 |
| Barn Swallow | 16 | Europe | Thomson, *et al.*, 1952 |
| Mockingbird | 12 | Another 10+, Cal. | Michener, 1951 |
| House Sparrow | 13(2) | Killed at feeder, Ohio | Dexter, 1959 |
| Common Grackle | 14+ | ——— | Hann, 1953 |
| Cardinal | 13.5 | ——— | Laskey, 1944 |

*Fig. 131. An 11-year-old Hairy Woodpecker. Banded at Pleasant Valley Sanctuary in Massachusetts on Jan. 19, 1939, this bird was observed nearly every winter through March of 1949, but did not reappear the following winter. (Photo by Alvah Sanborn, courtesy of* Jack-Pine Warbler.*)*

Great Blue Herons, based on the recovery of banded nestlings, as 71 per cent for their first year *after* leaving the nest.

This rapid death rate among wild birds means, of course, that their *average* or *mean natural longevity* (in the wild) is very low. Their *potential natural longevity* is much higher, and can be increased by confinement (*potential* as opposed to potential natural) in birds well adjusted to captivity (parrots, pigeons, swans). There are now many records of banded wild passerines living 10 to 20 years and nonpasserines for more than 20 (Table 7), but computed averages usually are less than two years. Farner (1949) computed statistically (from voluminous banding records) the mean longevity of 10 species of passerines in Europe and America. These ranged from 1.1 years in the English Robin (the American Robin was given as 1.3 and 1.4 years) and several other European birds (Redstart, Starling, and Great Tit) to a maximum of 2.0 in Mrs. Nice's Song Sparrows. Marshall (1947) computed the average natural longevity of Herring Gulls, a notoriously long-lived species, as only 1.75 *after* September 1 of their first year, thus not including high nesting losses.

Table 7 gives some maximum age records of wild banded birds. Banding of small birds has been going on long enough (since 1920 in this country) and in sufficient volume to produce some reliable age records, but banding of some of the larger potentially long-lived birds, such as hawks and owls, are not yet adequate to produce sufficient return or recovery records.

Many birds, understandably, attain a much greater longevity in captivity. Parrots, swans, and eagles have often been credited with attaining ages of 50 to 100 years, or even more, but unfortunately many of these records are open to doubt. Hann (1953), apparently citing records from Old World zoos, lists 9 species that are known to have attained records from 27 to 68 years. Only three of them—a South American condor at 52, a cockatoo at 56, and an eagle owl at 68—exceeded 50 years of age.

## *Some Late Summer Activities*

One of the major events in the late summer schedule is the postnuptial molt of the adults and the postjuvenal molt of the young, already described in Chapter 3. Both adults and young, with a few exceptions among those that postpone molting until *after* migration, thus get a complete or nearly complete renewal of plumage before the fall journey. During these molts the birds are relatively quiet, often going into semiretirement, thus making late summer an unrewarding time for bird watching. But of course not all species are molting at the same time. Those that completed their molt earlier, or postpone it till after migration, may be gathering in flocks in late July or August, preparatory to migration. Summer assemblages of swallows, shorebirds returned from their brief nesting season in the Arctic, and early warbler movements prevent late summer from being a period of complete inactivity. Several aspects of this late summer and fall flocking behavior were described on page 153.

Another late summer feature of interest is random wandering of many species. Banding of young birds shows that they may travel long distances from their birthplace, not necessarily southward at first. Some birds, notably egrets and herons, journey northward after the nesting season. Every summer witnesses invasions of such birds into the northern states from a southern source. Bald Eagles hatched in Florida invariably travel northward, even up into Canada, during their first summer (Broley, 1947). Possibly such movements are correlated with the development of the gonads in the young until unfavorable climatic conditions in the north reverse the trend of the gonads and the direction of travel.

## The Fall Journey

The journey south is the complement of the trip north in the spring (pp. 158–161), but differs in several important features. In the first place, many of the participants in the fall are birds of the year that have never made such a journey, yet they seem to know when, how, and where to go, without adult guidance. For though some families (e.g., geese) migrate together, so that the adults could guide the young, in some species (e.g., plovers) the young go separately, at a different time, and even by a different route.

The fall journey is usually more leisurely than that of spring. Though some birds make long spectacular flights (p. 270), many progress more slowly, lingering for days or weeks in favorable localities. The span of the fall migration period is also long, lasting from late June to December. Many shorebirds, perhaps mainly males and unsuccessful females (Pitelka, 1959), leave their Arctic nesting grounds in late June and July, and reappear in the northern states. Most of the swallows, the Bobolink, and some flycatchers and warblers start moving out of the northern states in July. Fall migration probably reaches a peak in the northern states in mid-September, but in spite of swollen numbers due to numerous young birds, the spectacular waves characteristic of spring are largely lacking because static late summer weather is not conducive to waves, and by the time cyclonic weather is established many birds have gone. Many hardy species, however, mainly seed-eaters and water birds, but also including some insectivorous types, linger until virtually "frozen out" in November or December.

As with the spring journey, progression south in the fall is correlated with internal physiological changes in the bird and with environmental features. Apparently the stimulus to migrate is internal, and the response is full and hearty in birds that go long distances early in the season, but many birds respond only to the extent that environmental conditions—weather and available food—dictate.

Autumn bird watching, as a pastime, has never attained the popularity it enjoys in the spring, presumably because both adults and young are often in drab colors and do not sing regularly, but there are many rewards for those who attempt identification in the fall. Fall flights of waterfowl and hawk migrations are more spectacular than they are in spring, and the warbler migration, though largely lacking in color, is a challenge in identification.

## Wintering Habits

This brief account of the activities of birds on their wintering grounds is appended largely to round out the picture of the annual cycle. Most birds have a rather specific winter home, although it may cover half a continent or more or be within fairly circumscribed limits. The Common Crow's winter range includes most of the United States, and that of the Sanderling (a sandpiper) extends from Cape Cod to Cape Horn, but the Whistling Swans, which breed in the far northwest, winter largely in the Chesapeake Bay area or along the Atlantic Coast (Stewart and Manning, 1958), and the Blue Geese winter almost entirely on the Gulf Coast. Four-fifths of the Canvasback population, which nests largely in the Canadian prairie provinces, winter in the eastern third of the United States (Stewart, *et al.*, 1958), and the American Woodcock, drawn from a large breeding area in eastern North America, winters mainly in lower Mississippi Valley. The nonmigratory Wrentit winters on its localized breeding grounds in California and Oregon. A few birds have divided winter ranges; some ducks and geese winter in part on the Atlantic Coast, in part in the Gulf of Mexico. The Lesser Snow Goose divides its wintering population between the Gulf of Mexico and Lower California.

The wintering grounds of birds, though often far removed from the breeding grounds, nevertheless cover practically all habitable portions of the globe. Some birds (ptarmigans) remain in the snow-bound Arctic; other Arctic nesters go across the equator into nearly all parts of the southern hemisphere. Some Antarctic species seek winter homes *north* of their breeding grounds, but some are essentially nonmigratory.

Not only does a particular species have a fairly specific winter range, but banding now discloses that individuals may return each winter to the same locality. The Tree Sparrow, which nests near the tree limit in northern North America and winters over most of the northern and central states, is an excellent example. Three Tree Sparrows, banded by Dr. Allen at Ithaca, New York, in the winter of 1921, returned in 1922; two of the survivors returned in 1923 and the sole survivor returned in 1924. Another Tree Sparrow apparently returned for eight successive winters to a sanctuary in Lenox, Massachusetts (Wallace, 1942). Though not recaptured every winter, it at least spent its fifth, sixth, seventh, and eighth winters in the same place, usually returning in early November and leaving in April. Snow and Snow (1960) reports a banded Northern Waterthrush that returned for two successive winters to Trinidad, an island off the coast of Venezuela—an indication that migrants wintering in the tropics may have a similarly strong attachment to a specific place.

Still other birds, however, are influenced by the distribution of winter food supplies. Some hawks will linger in the northern states in a relatively snow-free winter, but go on to more southern feeding grounds if heavy snows persist, or congregate in regions where rodent outbreaks prevail. Ground-feeding seed-eaters are similarly affected by snow cover and may do considerable roving in quest of new weed fields (Fig. 132). "Winter finches" are erratic in their distribution, for they depend on a particular food supply whose local availability varies from year to year.

Perhaps needless to say, the winter habits of our North American birds on remote southern wintering grounds are not well known, except that they often, but not invariably, seek habitats and probably other environmental conditions that are quite comparable to those on their northern breeding grounds. Within the states, however, many winter studies have been made. The shortened winter day, which curtails feeding time, and low temperatures, which necessitate a good food supply to maintain body heat, make it imperative for birds to spend the day foraging. Then at the end of the short day they seek shelter in a cavity of a tree, a protective grove of

*Fig. 132. Ground-feeding seed-eaters, like this Slate-colored Junco in Massachusetts, are affected by snow cover, and may have to wander widely in winter in quest of suitable feeding grounds. (Photo by Alvah W. Sanborn.)*

evergreens, or tangle of vines, usually sleeping with their heads tucked under the wings or buried in the scapular feathers to conserve heat.

In the selection of a nightly roost, many birds show a preference for the type of place in which they were born: hole nesters seek cavities in trees, House Sparrows resort to crevices and vines, and Red-winged Blackbirds, though foraging over fields by day, may congregate in the marshes at night. Many birds tend to roost at low elevations on winter nights, where it is often more sheltered and warmer due to radiation, but crows, hawks, and owls do not. Ptarmigans and sometimes other grouse burrow in the snow. Many birds, perhaps especially tropical species, build special nests or dormitories for winter. Central American wrens (at least 11 species of the 22 found in Costa Rica) construct sleeping quarters; some sleep singly, some in pairs, some in family groups (Skutch, 1940). Cactus Wrens in the Southwest also construct special sleeping or roosting quarters for winter, the male and female in separate nests though sometimes in the same bush (Anderson and Anderson, 1957). Winter Wrens and Pygmy Nuthatches in the western states also roost in cavities or nest boxes, sometimes in large groups (Phillips and Black, 1956; Knorr, 1957). The woodpeckers commonly drill new roosting cavities separate from their nest holes, the male and female usually living singly (Kilham, 1958b).

The narrowly circumscribed winter ranges characteristic of some birds are well illustrated by Black-capped Chickadees. Flocks of a half dozen to a dozen individuals assemble in the fall and remain together in close association until spring. If one is transferred to an adjacent territory or taken several miles away, it promptly returns to its former territory and associates. In three winters of observations, in Massachusetts, most individuals did not cross between feeding stations that were a half mile apart (Wallace, 1941). White-breasted Nuthatches and Downy and Hairy Woodpeckers appear to cover only slightly larger areas, but Blue Jays and Tree Sparrows (Sargent, 1959) may range considerably farther.

Social relations and flock composition of birds in winter are interesting and relatively new fields of study. Apparently individual bonds or social ties exist among certain birds which stay together during the winter. In the Black-capped Chickadee the same individuals can be found together in close association day after day and, if survival permits, year after year. At Lenox, Massachusetts, in the winter of 1937–1938, ten chickadees, color-banded for individual recognition, were often observed together at a woodland feeding stand. The following winter nine of the ten birds were back at the same station. Sabine (1955) found winter flocks of Oregon Juncos quite stable, but in Tree Sparrows (Heydweiller, 1935; Sargent, 1959) flock organization is less stable with loose associations. Similar group associations exist in migratory Slate-colored Juncos and White-throated Sparrows wintering in eastern Massachusetts (Whittle and Fletcher, 1924) and in Indigo Buntings wintering in Guatemala (Van Tyne, 1932).

Such winter associations terminate with the coming of another breeding season, when individuals segregate, establish territories, and mate for another annual cycle.

## *Selected References Pertaining to Life Histories and the Annual Cycle*

(Others listed in literature cited, pp. 438–462)

Allen, A. A. The Red-winged Blackbird: A Study in the Ecology of a Cat-tail Marsh. *Abst. Proc. Linn. Soc. of N.Y.* (1914), **24–25**:43–128.

———. *The Book of Bird Life.* Princeton, N.J.: Van Nostrand, 1961. Chapt. 9 and 10.

Allen, R. W., and M. M. Nice. A Study of the Breeding Biology of the Purple Martin (*Progne subis*). *Amer. Midl. Nat.* (1952), **47**:606–665.

Anderson, Anders H., and Anne Anderson. Life History of the Cactus Wren. Part I, *Condor,* **59**:274–296; Part II, *Condor,* **61**:186–205; Part III, *Condor,* **62**:351–369; Part IV, *Condor,* **63**:87–94. (1957–1961).

Bent, A. C. Life Histories of North American Birds. *U.S. Nat. Mus. Bull. 107 to 211* (1919–1958). Twenty volumes covering loons through blackbirds; still incomplete.

Blanchard, B. D., and M. M. Erickson. The Cycle in the Gambel Sparrow. *Univ. Calif. Publ. in Zool.* (1949), **47**:255–318. Refers also to earlier comprehensive paper on White-crowned Sparrows.

Bump, Gardiner, *et al. The Ruffed Grouse: Life History, Propagation, Management.* Albany, N.Y.: N.Y. State Cons. Dept., 1947.

Davis, John. Nesting Behavior of the Rufous-sided Towhee. *Condor* (1960), **62**:434–456. See Lit. Cited at end of article for other towhee papers by Davis.

Edminster, Frank C. *The Ruffed Grouse, Its Life Story, Ecology and Management.* New York: Macmillan, 1947.

Erickson, Mary M. Territory, Annual Cycle, and Numbers in a Population of Wrentits (*Chamaea fasciata*). *Univ. Calif. Publ. in Zool.* (1938), **42**:247–334.

Fisher, James. *Watching Birds.* London: Penguin Books, 1951. Chapt. IX and X.

Friedmann, Herbert. The Cowbirds. *A Study in the Biology of Social Parasitism.* Springfield, Ill.: Charles C Thomas, 1929.

Hann, Harry W. Life History of the Oven-bird in Southern Michigan. *Wilson Bull.* (1937), **49**:145–237.

Herrick, F. H. Nests and Nest Building in Birds. *Jour. Animal Behavior* (1911), **1**:159–192, 244–277, 336–373.

———. *The American Eagle.* New York: Appleton, 1934.

———. *Wild Birds at Home.* New York: Appleton, 1935.

Hochbaum, H. Albert. *The Canvasback on a Prairie Marsh.* Washington, D.C.: Amer. Wildl. Inst., 1944.

Howard, H. Eliot. *Territory in Bird Life.* London: J. Murray, 1920.

Howell, Joseph C. Notes on the Nesting Habits of the American Robin (*Turdus migratorius* L.). *Amer. Midl. Nat.* (1942), **28**:529–603.

Kendeigh, S. Charles. Territorial and Mating Behavior of the House Wren. *Ill. Biol. Monographs* (1941), **18**(3):1–120.

———. Parental Care and Its Evolution in Birds. *Ill. Biol. Monographs* (1952), **22**(1–3):1–356.

Kortright, Francis H. *The Ducks, Geese and Swans of North America.* Washington, D.C.: Amer. Wildl. Inst., 1942. Data on waterfowl life histories.

Koskimies, Jukka. The Life of the Swift, *Micropus apus* (L), in Relation to the Weather. *Ann. Acad. Scient. Fennicae*, 4 (Helsinki) (1950), **15**:1–151.

Lack, David. *The Life of the Robin.* London: Witherby, 1943.

Lanyon, Wesley E. The Comparative Biology of the Meadowlarks (*Sturnella*) in Wisconsin. *Publ. Nuttall Ornith. Club* (1957), **1**:1–67.

Laskey, Amelia R. A Study of the Cardinal in Tennessee. *Wilson Bull.* (1944), **56**:27–44.

Lindsdale, Jean M. The Natural History of the Magpies. *Pacific Coast Avifauna*, No. 25, Cooper Ornith. Club (Berkeley, Calif., 1937).

McClure, H. Elliott. Ecology and Management of the Mourning Dove, *Zenaidura macroura* (Linn) in Cass County, Iowa. *Res. Bull.* **310** (*Iowa State Coll. Agr. Exp. Sta.*, 1943).

Mayfield, Harold F. The Kirtland's Warbler. *Cranbrook Inst. of Science Bull.* 40 (Bloomfield Hills, Mich., 1960).

Michener, Harold, and J. R. Michener. Mockingbirds, Their Territories and Individualities. *Condor* (1935), **37**:97–140.

Miller, Alden H. Systematic Revision and Natural History of the American Shrikes (*Lanius*). *Univ. Calif. Publ. Zool.* (1931), **38**:11–242.

Nero, Robert N. A Behavior Study of the Red-winged Blackbird. *Wilson Bull.* (1956), **68**:5–37; 129–150.

Nice, Margaret M. Studies in the Life History of the Song Sparrow, I and II. *Trans. Linn. Soc.* (New York, 1937, 1943), Vols. 4 and 6.

Odum, Eugene P. Annual Cycle of the Black-capped Chickadee. *Auk* (1941), **58**:314–333; 518–535. *Auk* (1942), **59**:499–531.

Palmer, Ralph S. A Behavior Study of the Common Tern (*Sterna hirundo hirundo* L.). *Proc. Boston Soc. Nat. Hist.* (1941), **42**:1–119.

Peterson, Arnold J. The Breeding Cycle of the Bank Swallow. *Wilson Bull.* (1955), **67**:235–286.
Pettingill, Olin S., Jr. The American Woodcock, *Philohela minor* (Gmelin). *Mem. Boston Soc. Nat. Hist.* (1936), **9**:167–391.
Pickwell, Gayle B. The Prairie Horned Lark. *Trans. Acad. Sci.* (St. Louis, 1931), **27**:1–153.
Putnam, Loren S. The Life History of the Cedar Waxwing. *Wilson Bull.* (1949), **61**:141–182.
Richdale, L. E. *Sexual Behavior in Penguins.* Lawrence, Kans.: U. of Kans., 1951 b.
Saunders, Aretas A. *Bird Song.* Albany, N.Y.: N.Y. State Museum Handbook 7, 1929.
———. *The Lives of Wild Birds.* Garden City, N.Y.: Doubleday, 1954.
Skutch, Alexander F. Incubation and Nestling Periods of Central American Birds. *Auk* (1945), **62**:8–37.
———. Life Histories of Central American Birds. *Pacific Coast Avifauna,* No. 14 and No. 34, Cooper Ornith. Soc. (Berkeley, Calif.) 1954, 1960.
Smith, Stuart. *How to Study Birds.* London: Collins, 1947. Chapt. 1–7.
Soper, J. Dewey. Life History of the Blue Goose, *Chen caerulescens* (Linnaeus). *Proc. Boston Soc. Nat. Hist.* (1942), **42**:121–225.
Southern, William. Nesting of the Red-eyed Vireo in the Douglas Lake Region, Michigan. *Jack-pine Warbler* (1958), **36**:105–130, 185–207.
Stoddard, H. L. *The Bob-white Quail: Its Habits, Preservation and Increase.* New York: Scribner, 1931.
Stokes, Allen W. Breeding Behavior of the Goldfinch. *Wilson Bull.* (1950), **62**:107–127.
Stoner, Dayton. Studies on the Bank Swallow, *Riparia riparia riparia* (Linnaeus) in the Oneida Lake Region. *Roosevelt Wild Life Annals,* 4 (1936), **2**:122–233.
Tinbergen, N. The Behavior of the Snow Bunting in Spring. *Trans. Linn. Soc.* (New York, 1939), **5**:1–94.
Van Tyne, Josselyn, and Andrew J. Berger. *Fundamentals of Ornithology.* New York: Wiley, 1959.
Walkinshaw, L. H. The Sandhill Cranes. *Cranbrook Inst. Sci., Bull.* **29** (Bloomfield Hills, Mich., 1949).
Wallace, George J. Bicknell's Thrush, Its Taxonomy, Distribution and Life History. *Proc. Boston Soc. Nat. Hist.* (1939), **41**:211–402.
———. The Barn Owl in Michigan. *Mich. State Coll. Agr. Exp. Sta. Tech. Bull.* (1948), **208**:1–61.
Williams, Laidlow. Breeding Behavior of the Brewer Blackbird. *Condor* (1952), **54**:3–47.

# 11

# THE MIGRATION OF BIRDS

One of the most spectacular events in the animal world is the migration of birds. It has intrigued mankind for many centuries; in ancient times it led to some critical studies designed to explain the phenomenon, but also to wild speculations, such as the persistent view that swallows hibernated in the mud and the theory that birds flew to the moon for winter. Now after more than 2,000 years of observations, climaxed by a half century of experimental studies, we are still in the dark regarding many aspects of migration. Though we now know in considerable detail the breeding range, wintering grounds, and often the migration routes of practically every North American bird, we still cannot always explain why birds go where they do at the time they do, and their manner of navigation is only partially solved.

Birds are by far the best known examples of migrants, but of course many other animals have migratory habits. Many marine invertebrates have definite but often not well-understood movements in relation to tides and seasons; aeroplankton, perhaps unwittingly as in the case of wind-blown ballooning spiders, take miraculous journeys through space; certain insects, particularly butterflies, undertake regular migrations, some going south for the winter, others merely taking suicidal journeys out to sea. Sharp periodicities in the breeding cycle of most amphibians involve short journeys to and from water, and some reptiles travel far for suitable winter quarters. Among the fishes the amazing migrations of the eel and salmon are the most publicized, and among the mammals the cyclic outbreaks of the lemmings are classic. Many other animals—reindeer and caribou on their grazing grounds, desert creatures seeking a new food supply, montane forms making altitudinal adjustments—respond to seasonal and climatic changes by undertaking regular or irregular migrations.

## Definitions and Scope of Migratory Movements

Migration in a broad sense, as defined by Cahn (1925), is "a periodic passing from one place to another." Some, notably Woodbury (1941), would add to this the concept of some correlation with environmental periodicities or with some stage in the life history of the individuals making the migration. Others would limit its use to two-way journeys of animals under their own power, thus excluding unidirectional movements and those in which animals are helplessly carried by some other agency. With regard to frequency, migration may be (1) *daily,* as of birds passing to and from a roost (Crows, Starlings) or rookery (herons); (2) *lunar,* as in the case of many marine organisms under the influence of tides (and possibly Sooty Terns which have a ten-month breeding cycle on Ascension Island corresponding to the lunar rather than calendar year—Chapin and Wing, 1959); (3) *seasonal,* which includes the regular, as well as some of the irregular, migrations of birds; and (4) *cyclic* (*emigration*), movements correlated with some cycle of longer duration than, or not associated with, the seasons. Cyclic and seasonal migrations are of particular importance in bird life and merit further analysis.

### CYCLE MIGRATIONS (EMIGRATIONS)

Irruptions of animals, typically, are characterized by a periodic overpopulation in a herbivorous form and consequent devegetation of its feeding grounds, causing an exodus of surplus individuals out of the normal range. They may be *sporadic* (irregular) or *rhythmic* (correlated with a cycle of definite length). These are often unidirectional, and thus not considered a true migration by some authorities, but among insects sometimes another generation makes the return trip. A classic example of emigration involves the lemming, a small Arctic rodent, which periodically (every three to five years) reaches population peaks apparently compelling it to undertake a death migration, sometimes taking it overland to the sea where individuals surviving the march plunge in and drown. Perhaps the concept of drowning has been overemphasized, however, since only the animals living near the coast, as in Scandinavia or Labrador, would ever reach the sea.

Such migrations are not unknown among birds. The Pallas Sandgrouse (*Syrrhaptes parodoxus*), a pigeonlike bird of central Asia, has staged several such irruptions in the past, spilling over Europe in large numbers. In the flight of 1863, some 700 individuals reached Great Britain. A few pairs remained to breed in western European countries, but failed, as on subsequent invasions, to establish themselves. Similar irruptions occur among grouse in North America. Cade and Buckley (1953) report that following a buildup of Sharp-tailed Grouse in the Tanana Valley, Alaska, a large flock, two to three miles long and one-half of a mile wide, took off en masse on a day in October and disappeared. Periodic population peaks and subsequent irruptions, within a limited range however, are well known for the Ruffed Grouse. The fall shuffle and dispersal of Bobwhites may become irruptive, though not necessarily suicidal, when populations are high (Agee, 1957). The presumed function of such outbreaks is periodic reduction, or perhaps in some cases merely more effective scattering, of rapidly breeding herbivorous forms which might otherwise completely devegetate their range.

Some other similar journeys of birds are correlated primarily with fluctuations in the food supply. These may be in tune with known cycles, as in the case of the three-to-five-year movements of the Snowy Owl, Rough-legged Hawks and Northern Shrike, or more irregular, as in the case of crossbills and other wandering seed-eaters. The Snowy Owl (Fig. 133) in particular is affected by the three-to-five-year lemming cycle. When these rodents on which the owls depend largely for food fail, the birds are forced to seek new feeding grounds or starve. Many of them move southward, spilling over into the northern states in large numbers. In the record flight of the winter of 1945–1946, 13,502 reports were received by an international committee collecting records of the flight over northern United States and southern Canada. Presumably the largest flights are correlated, not alone with lows in the lemming cycle, but also with population peaks in the owls, so that if a summer of high production is immediately followed by a winter of scarcity of lemmings, a large southward flight will be staged.

The crossbill movements are much more irregular, and not necessarily southward in direction nor confined to winter. These birds are dependent

*Fig. 133. The periodic winter invasions of Snowy Owls into the United States arouse great interest; and trophy collectors, even in states according legal protection to these birds, practically exterminate the visitors before they can return to their Arctic home. Unlike most owls this species is largely diurnal, living on lemmings and other vertebrate life of the tundra. (Photo by Allan D. Cruickshank.)*

on seed production in northern conifers and move erratically, sometimes in large flocks, irrespective of place or season, in quest of a new cone supply. Even their breeding season seems to be correlated with this peculiar situation, since the birds are very irregular as to time and place of nesting. Svärdson (1957) correlates "invasion" migrations of certain species in Sweden with high fruiting of trees every three or four years; redpolls raised two broods in good years, one in March on seeds, one in June on insects. Davis and Williams (1957) describe similar irruptions of Clark's Nutcracker in California; population buildups during years of heavy pine-cone production were usually followed by years of pine-cone failures and a consequent exodus of the nutcrackers.

Vagaries in weather cycles are responsible for some of the irregular movements of birds. In Australia, for instance, there appears to be no particular incentive for regular northward and southward migrations, for winter and summer as we know them here are not a conspicuous feature on that continent. Consequently bird movements in Australia may be associated with the highly irregular dry and rainy spells, with seed-eating as well as insectivorous and predatory birds following the rains to new feeding grounds, and raising their young during the staggered periods of maximum food production. Such peculiar breeding cycles are fairly characteristic of some birds in dry climates, with the species involved showing a remarkable adaptability to adjust to weather cycles.

## SEASONAL MIGRATIONS

Some of the seasonal movements of birds are quite irregular and include random wanderings, sometimes in quest of new food supplies, and the summer dispersal of young birds in all directions from their birthplace. These are sometimes called *vagrant* migrations, but they nearly always involve a subsequent return to the regular wintering and breeding grounds. The most noteworthy of these vagrant movements are the northward exodus of herons from southern breeding grounds (p. 248) and the random dispersal of gulls, terns, Barn Owls, and other species far and wide from their nest sites before migrating southward. Young gulls hatched in the Great Lakes island rookeries almost invariably drift northeastward along the St. Lawrence waterway in late summer and fall, apparently traveling with the prevailing winds, and thence proceed southward along the Atlantic Coast (W. Smith, 1959; Hofslund, 1959).

Tropical and subtropical countries witness a type of seasonal migration not well known in northern latitudes. These movements, termed *moisture rhythm* migrations by Woodbury (1941), are like those described above for Australia except that they are regular migrations of the seasonal type. They apply to the spacious savanna lands of South America and Africa, which are broad belts characterized by sharply divided wet and dry seasons. The breeding season of the birds in these regions coincides with the rainy season, or period of maximum food production, and their migratory movements follow the seasonal rains. In Africa in particular this means that some migrants cross the broad equatorial rain forest twice yearly between the northern and southern savanna belts.

The regular seasonal migrations of birds in northern latitudes may be divided into (1) *altitudinal*, as up and down a mountain (the term *vertical* migration is perhaps more properly restricted to aquatic organisms); (2) *longitudinal* (east-west migrations); and (3) *latitudinal* (north-south). Altitudinal migrations are well-known phenomena in western United States, where various species of jays, chickadees, nuthatches, kinglets, and certain fringillids (juncos) avoid long north-south migrations by merely changing altitude with the seasons. Some of these species are much less migratory in the western mountains than in the eastern parts of their range, where latitudinal migrations prevail. Most western species nest at the higher altitudes and seek more favorable lower levels for winter, but the Blue Grouse reverses this trend and goes to higher elevations in fall and winter (Mussehl, 1960, and others), a movement that appears to coincide with the fruiting of certain plants. The Clark's Nutcracker also seeks higher levels after nesting, but may not remain there over winter.

East-west migrations are well illustrated by the peculiar route taken by Redhead Ducks nesting in the Bear River marshes in Utah and wintering on the Atlantic coast, in about the same latitude as where they were reared. Evening Grosbeaks and California Gulls are also good examples of east-west migrants.

Aside from these somewhat exceptional altitudinal and east-west migrations, most journeys of birds take them between a northern summer (breeding) and more southern winter home. Migration is best developed in the northern hemisphere, where the largest land masses, and thus the greatest extremes of winter and summer, occur. The less extensive land areas in the southern hemisphere, with their more equitable climate, witness some interesting migrations, but these are not comparable in magnitude to those of northern hemisphere birds. Some southern hemisphere birds, in South America and Africa, merely move short distances toward the equator; others, as previously indicated, actually cross the equator. Perhaps the most spectacular example of the latter (excluding oceanic birds) is a race of the Blue and White Swallow (*Atticora cyanoleuca*), which nests in southern South America and has been taken in Costa Rica, 2,200 miles north of its northernmost breeding limits (Howell, 1955).

The annual migration of birds, from a summer to a winter home and back again, may be extremely short or extremely long. Some birds, of course, are strictly sedentary. The Wrentit (Chamaeidae) in California is nonmigratory; certain individuals at least probably never range over more than a few acres within their lifetime. Gallinaceous birds, in general, are also essentially nonmigratory. The Bobwhite, except for unusual irruptions which may take it up to 26 miles (Agee, 1957), is perhaps the least mobile of American game birds; some spend their entire lives within one-quarter of a mile of their birthplace, and most others stay within the square mile where they were hatched (Murphy and Baskett, 1952). Some of the owls (Screech, Great Horned, Barred) are nonmigratory; others (Barn, Snowy, Short-eared) are very irregular in this respect (Fig. 134). Most of the titmice, in this country at least, are quite sedentary, although they may move to more sheltered locations in winter. White-breasted Nuthatches are essentially nonmigratory, but Red-breasted Nuthatches are not.

In some cases adult birds, established on their breeding grounds, are nonmigratory, whereas their young go long distances during their first year

*Fig. 134. This nonmigratory Screech Owl may inhabit this same cavity throughout its lifetime, though the chances are that it had to move from its natal nest site, if one of its parents still occupied it. Some other owls are highly migratory, at least on occasions. (Photo by Allan D. Cruickshank.)*

or two. Herring Gulls hatched in New England coastal colonies may go to Florida for their first winter, to the middle Atlantic Coast their second winter, and then remain in northern waters after their first breeding season. A pair of Barn Owls in East Lansing, Michigan, apparently occupied the same barn almost continuously for three years, but one of their banded young was taken in Alabama during its first winter. Mueller and Berger (1959) report that two Barn Owls banded as nestlings in Wisconsin on July 1 were taken in Florida, over 1,200 miles distant. Yet there are records of migrating adult Barn Owls also, up to 850 miles in one case (P. Stewart, 1952).

Widely ranging young of sedentary parents are apparently far from universal; there are records of banded broods of titmice in England, some of which migrated and some did not. Among Mockingbird broods in California, the Micheners found some which migrated and some which did not. Starlings are quite irregular; some migrate and some do not, some migrate some years and not other years, and range expansion is accomplished by young birds (not adults) invading new regions (Kessel, 1953). And to add another quirk to the peculiarity of migration patterns, Ludwig (1960) reports that of two young Mourning Doves banded in the same nest in Michigan on May 24, one was recovered in Georgia on December 11, the other in Texas on the following day.

Why certain individuals in a highly migratory species sometimes fail to migrate is not known. Every winter produces records of thrushes, warblers, orioles, and other birds remaining in the northern states when normally they would have gone south. Conversely, sometimes shorebirds remain in Central or South America over summer when their other members have gone to the Arctic to nest (Eisenmann, 1951). In some cases, physical injury may have prevented migrating at the proper time, and then the urge to go subsided. Again improper metabolic condition, or prevailing weather conditions, may have been the underlying cause.

It has already been pointed out that species that are migratory go variable distances for suitable wintering grounds. In many species the northern part of the winter range overlaps, broadly or narrowly, with the southern part of the breeding range. In other species the summer and winter ranges are widely separated. Many of our northern summer birds winter in the southern states; still others go to the West Indies, Central America, or northern South America, and a few make even more spectacular journeys across the equator into southern South America.

## *Origin and Possible Causes of Migration*

Though it is generally assumed, and rightly so, that winter weather and the consequent scarcity of food, particularly insects, cause birds to migrate, it is well known that this is an inadequate explanation in many cases. While it is true that a flycatcher or swallow can hardly be expected to find enough flying insects in the north in winter, it is not clear why the Eastern Phoebe winters in the states when other flycatchers go to Central America or beyond, or why the Tree Swallow can make a go of it in New Jersey, when the Cliff Swallow travels across the equator. Within most families of birds there are examples of species, closely related and ostensibly with similar food habits, some of which winter in the northern states while others go long distances. Some ducks winter as far north as open waters permit, but the Blue-winged Teal goes to Mexico and beyond. The Red-tailed Hawk winters in the northern states or southern Canada, but the Broad-winged Hawk reaches South America. Similarly, among the wrens, the warblers, the blackbirds (icterids), and fringillids, there are hardy forms readily weathering northern winters while others go to South America.

Another serious objection to the view that food supplies and cold weather are the underlying causes of migration is the fact that so many birds leave their northern breeding grounds in midsummer, long before food supplies are exhausted or even before they have reached a peak. Thus shorebirds often desert their breeding grounds on the Arctic tundra in late June or July, with insects swarming in abundance. Most of the swallows, some flycatchers and warblers, and even seed-eating Bobolinks abruptly terminate their nesting activities in July and start southward. Conversely, Robins and Eastern Bluebirds often leave their wintering grounds, where food is usually adequate, and hurry northward into a region of questionable food supplies.

Often, however, a reasonable explanation can be found for some of these distributional peculiarities. The Eastern Phoebe has learned to exploit a special food supply—aquatic winter insects. All flycatchers could not be supported in this way, because there would not be enough food for all. Wintering Tree Swallows in New Jersey subsist in part on bayberries or other fruit, but Tree Swallows in Florida do not and sometimes starve during prolonged freezes while their northern relatives survive. Shorebirds that leave their Arctic nesting grounds early are the unsuccessful females, and males no longer needed in the breeding cycle (Pitelka, 1959); their early departure may function in leaving more food for families with young. The Louisiana Waterthrush is one of the earliest warbler arrivals in spring and perhaps the first nester; Eaton (1958) notes that rearing of the young coincides with the heavy hatches of stoneflies and mayflies in the streams where the birds feed. Thus there may well be explanations to the enigmas of migration, but we have yet to find the right answers to many of them.

Several theories have been advanced to explain the origin and perpetuation of the migratory habit in birds. None of them is entirely adequate; probably there is no single factor or workable hypothesis explaining migration as a whole, which is presumably a phenomenon of multiple origin. Lincoln (1950) summarizes these various theories and their modifications into four main hypotheses: (1) the *northern ancestral home theory*, (2) the *southern ancestral home theory*, (3) *continental drift*, and (4) *photoperiodism.*

The northern ancestral home (ice-sheet or glacial epoch) theory postulates that in remote geologic times, nonmigratory birds inhabited the northern hemisphere, and as a mild climate prevailed, with palm trees and elephants occurring in Alaska, there was no incentive to migrate. Pleistocene glaciation ended this phase in the earth's histoy, and birds were forced by the first great ice sheet to go south or perish. As the icecap gradually receded, those birds that had formerly inhabited northern regions worked their way back toward their ancestral nesting grounds, thus avoiding the more crowded tropics. Subsequent glacial periods and the gradual establishment of sharp winter and summer seasons in the north introduced a migratory rhythm in birds that became a hereditary habit.

Though this view of the possible origin of migration is now largely discredited (the migratory habit in birds probably preceded Pleistocene glaciation by many millions of years), it can readily be seen that birds of northern climates might well be influenced by the continent's past glacial history. Glaciation has profoundly affected present-day distribution and migration routes of northern birds, both in North America where persistent glaciation in the western mountains separated eastern and western forms, and also in Europe where ice-bound mountain ranges split populations into eastern and western segments creating subspecies. Hence, glaciation in the late Tertiary had a profound effect on the details of distribution, speciation, and the working out of specific migration routes, but probably had little to do with the origin of the migratory habit.

In some respects the second hypothesis, the southern home theory, is diametrically opposed to the above. This theory presupposes that the ancestral home of birds was in the tropics, which eventually became so congested that the more venturesome birds spread northward to seek isolation during the breeding season and then returned to their home in the tropics as soon as nesting was over. Such a view helps explain why some long-range migrants leave their breeding grounds as soon as nesting is over, long before the food supply is a critical factor. Hummingbirds, tanagers, and flycatchers, all of South American origin, may simply be returning home as soon as they have raised their young in the north. Moreover, by moving northward in the spring, birds have a longer day (sixteen to twenty or more hours of daylight compared with twelve near the equator) for the arduous task of gathering food for the larger broods characteristic of northern regions. However, many northern species, perhaps a majority, are not of southern origin; hence their migrations cannot be explained by the southern home theory.

The concept of continental drift, which postulates southern and northern land masses that later split up into our present continents, with the origin of birds in the south, has been advanced by several authors (see Wolfson, 1948) to account for the evolution of migration patterns. Most geologists, however, believe that the separation of the continents occurred long before the origin of migratory birds.

A more modern and realistic approach toward explaining migration involves photoperiodism, which accounts for recrudescence of the gonads in the spring with increasing day length and regression with decreasing light in the fall. Photoperiodism is no longer theory, as far as its influence on the state of the gonads is concerned, but its exact relationship to migration is.

The first detailed experimental work demonstrating the effect of the daily photoperiod on birds was carried out by Rowan (1931 and earlier papers) at Alberta, Canada. He kept Slate-colored Juncos and Common Crows in outdoor aviaries in subzero fall and winter temperatures but with artificial lighting simulating spring. Birds thus exposed to increasing daily photoperiods showed enlarged gonads when dissected (the controls did not) and experimental releases in winter apparently "migrated," some of them northward, but the evidence was not very conclusive. Later Bissonette (1937, 1939) conducted similar experiments with Starlings and Blue Jays with similar results, but thought that increased light stimulated activity of the anterior pituitary (p. 134) which in turn caused recrudescence of the gonads. Rowan, as well as subsequent workers, felt that increased wakefulness in the longer day, or perhaps more properly, the increased exercise associated with wakefulness was an important factor in the development of the gonads.

More recently many workers, notably Wolfson, Farner, and Miller and their associates (see bibliographies) have conducted extensive experiments with caged birds, trying to measure the effects of various external stimuli on the internal or physiological state of a bird. One of the results has been the elucidation of a postbreeding refractory period—a quiescent or preparatory period into which the gonads relapse before they can be stimulated by increased photoperiods to start another cycle. Another important physiological condition disclosed by these experiments as well as by dissection of many migratory birds is a premigratory buildup of fat reserves (15 to 40 per cent or more of the body weight), quick exhaustion during long flights, and quick replenishment during resting and feeding periods. Neither fat accumulation nor depletion during migration, however, appears to be universal, even among closely related birds. Migratory *Zonotrichia* species (White-throated, White-crowned, and Golden-crowned Sparrows) build up fat reserves prior to migration, but apparently Tree Sparrows (Helms and Drury, 1960) do not. Mourning Doves (Hanson and Kossack, 1957) do not ordinarily store up fat, perhaps because of their leisurely migration. And Irving (1960) found male Water Pipits arriving on their Arctic breeding grounds after rapid migration from a probable winter home in Texas, fat and in good condition; they then lost weight during courtship when they spent much of their time singing instead of eating.

Various shortcomings are evident when one tries to correlate migration with photoperiodism *per se*. It operates principally in birds that breed in northern latitudes, less so in tropical species where changing photoperiods are largely lacking. Here, however, other factors, such as intensity of insolation or humidity or rainfall, may be crucial. Moreover, increased light could not *initiate* migration in transequatorial migrants, as they would have to start out their journey under conditions of uniform or even decreasing light. According to Griscom (1945) such migrants may be well on their way up into the southern states before there is any perceptible increase in their gonads. Hence, it may be that the development of the gonads is coincident to, rather than a cause or effect relationship of, migration. East-west migrations, such as the annual winter excursions of Evening Grosbeaks into New England (Fig. 135), seem to have no correlation with length of day. Heerman's Gulls on the Pacific Coast actually move northward in the fall and winter.

The breeding season of many birds does not conform to annual light cycles. The Barn Owl breeds irregularly; nests with eggs and/or young have

*Fig. 135. Evening Grosbeaks, which formerly bred exclusively in the northwest, now visit New England feeding stations each winter in large numbers, often dominating the feeders and consuming large quantities of expensive sunflower seeds. Now they breed in limited numbers in the Adirondacks, northern New England, and eastern Canada. (Photo by Alvah W. Sanborn.)*

been found in every month in both northern and southern states. Though most tropical birds have a specific time for breeding, it is not necessarily in the spring. Recently Miller (1959) has disclosed an amazing six-month cycle, perhaps the only one known, in the Andean Sparrow (*Zonotrichia capensis*); marked individuals had *two* breeding seasons annually, each characterized by four months of high reproductive activity followed by two months of rest and reconstruction. The ten-month cycle in Sooty Terns on Ascension Island, possibly triggered by the phases of the moon, has already been mentioned. Well known also are some two-year breeding cycles (albatrosses, California Condor) in which the young mature so slowly that the adults breed every other year. Changes in or postponement of the breeding season in response to special environmental conditions, such as the Short-billed Marsh Wren in Arkansas delaying nesting until dense growth of rice fields is available in late summer (Meanley, 1952) and Rufous-winged Sparrows waiting until summer rains make food more plentiful for their young (Phillips, 1951), are also interesting contradictions to the correlation of breeding with maximum light.

Hence, in summary, it is evident that the factors governing migration and breeding are exceedingly complex and that no one of them alone can explain either phenomenon in all birds. The annual stimulus for migration, as outlined by several recent authors (see particularly Farner, 1950, 1955; and Marshall, 1961) is the development of a particular metabolic or physiological condition, called *Zugdisposition* by some Europeans, prior to migration. This may be reflected in the state of the gonads in some species but not in others, and in fat accumulations in some but not others. Most migratory species exhibit nocturnal restlessness (*Zugunruhe*) in captivity just before migration but not at other times, and nonmigratory species (House Sparrows) do not. Weather conditions as external factors may be very important in early spring migrants ("weather" migrants), less so, if at all, in later long-distance ("instinct") migrants. The early experiments on photoperiodism emphasized the importance of day length, and discounted temperature, but it is now believed that warm temperatures and other favorable vernal conditions supplement light in stimulating recrudescence of the gonads. It is also now generally conceded that light acts on the anterior pituitary whose secretions in turn stimulate gonadal development which is correlated, with great variations, with migration and breeding.

## Some Mechanics of Migration

There are many interesting features concerning the manner in which birds migrate. Migrants are divided into *nocturnal* and *diurnal* types, with a few birds (notably waterfowl) that migrate either by day or night. Most of the smaller insectivorous species migrate at night, resting and feeding by day, with prolonged stopovers at certain stations, either for replenishing depleted fat supplies or waiting for more favorable flight conditions. Swallows and swifts, however, which feed on the wing, migrate by day. Hawks are also conspicuous diurnal migrants and often have specific routes of travel, along coasts or mountain chains where they take advantage of thermals or updrafts created by mountain slopes. One such strategic and well-known route passes Hawk Mountain, Pennsylvania, formerly a rendezvous for hunters who gathered to shoot the birds as they passed by at close range, but now a sanctuary where thousands of observers assemble, particularly in the fall, to watch the miracle of migratory hawks (Broun, 1949). A less publicized station, known to hunters for a long time, is at Duluth, Minnesota, where hawks in the fall converge from flight lines along the shores of Lake Superior. Hofslund (1954) tabulates a total of 29,300 hawks of 18 species observed at the "pass" during the 1951–1953 period.

Most migratory flights at night are now known to take place at about 3,000 feet, not at the great altitudes formerly depicted, but there are great variations under different weather conditions and of course for different species. Birds fly higher on clear nights, but not necessarily at the same height for all stages of the flight; perhaps they fly higher during the middle of the night, thus accounting for slack periods in flight calls (Ball, 1952; Graber and Cochran, 1960). Birds fly dangerously low on cloudy nights with a low ceiling and often strike high obstacles, such as monuments, tall buildings, and television towers (p. 378). Certain species fly at much greater heights, characteristically, or under special conditions, such as crossing mountain barriers. Lapwings and cranes have been recorded at high altitudes in migration, the former up to 8,500 feet, the latter at 15,000. The highest recorded altitude seems to be of a flight of geese crossing the Himalayas at 29,000 feet.

Reverse migrations, in which nocturnal migrants in particular appear to be travelling in the wrong direction during their daytime maneuvers, have been commonly observed at such strategic migration points as Point Pelee in Ontario and along the New England coast. Baird and Nisbet (1959, 1960) describe this phenomenon and attribute it to "redetermined passage," or attempts to regain a preferred migration path after having been carried off course by unfavorable winds.

Though the daily rate of migration for most birds is relatively slow (p. 160), some birds make nonstop flights over portions of their routes. The eastern form of the American Golden Plover (Fig. 141) makes its 2,400 mile trip from Nova Scotia to South America in about forty-eight hours and many birds cross the Gulf of Mexico in a single flight. Blue Geese and Lesser Snow Geese, in both spring and fall, are believed to make long flights between their Arctic breeding grounds and wintering areas in Louisiana and Texas (Fig. 136). Apparently a part of the population assembles at James Bay in the fall, then takes off on a 1,700-mile journey for Louisiana, usually but not invariably without stopping en route (Cooch, 1955). Another segment of the population takes off from York Factory and goes more

*Fig. 136. Blue Geese nest in large colonies in a few places in the Arctic (e.g., Baffin Island and Southampton Island) and winter chiefly in a coastal strip bordering the Gulf of Mexico, making the 3000-mile journey with few stopovers en route. (Photo by the Mich. Dept. of Conservation.)*

or less directly to Texas (2,100 miles), sometimes stopping at Sand Lake, South Dakota, sometimes not.

Some birds migrate singly, or as somewhat scattered associations, yet apparently often keep in contact by frequent calls. Other birds, as is well known for ducks, geese, shorebirds, and the more gregarious passerines, migrate in close flock formation. Sea birds, such as shearwaters and petrels, sometimes travel in enormous flocks. Occasionally the whole population of a species moves together. It is believed that all the Greater Snow Geese on the continent, about 70,000 individuals in 1957, stop in a strip of marsh along the St. Lawrence on one lap of their journey to the Atlantic coast (Morrison, 1960).

The timing of migrating flights in relation to wind and weather has already been mentioned (pp. 158–161). In both spring and fall, birds travel chiefly with a tail wind and stop when they meet a reverse condition such as a cold front ahead. Bennett's (1952) studies of fall migration at Chicago disclosed birds coming in chiefly with northwest or northerly winds. Static weather, common in late summer, produced few or no waves, but a cold front from the north, then or later in the fall, brought in heavy flights. Possibly vagaries of the weather explain why some migrants, such as White-throated Sparrows, are seldom if ever retaken at banding stations along their migration routes, for their exact paths and stopover places vary so much from year to year.

There have been many recent stimulating discussions regarding the influence of weather on migration patterns (see Lack, 1960, for a six- to seven-page bibliography on the subject). Lack (1960) sums up some of these features and variations as follows: "There is more migration in fine weather than in rain, more with clear than cloudy skies, and more with light than strong winds. . . ."; and that there is "more migration in spring with warmth and in autumn with cold."

Studies on trans-Gulf migration in Louisiana by Lowery (1945, 1946) and associates have disclosed a peculiar situation. Trans-Gulf migrants of certain species are abundant along the Louisiana coast in spring *only* when precipitated down by meeting a cold front from the north or northwest; in good weather they keep on to northern Louisiana or Tennessee before coming down, creating the "coastal hiatus" (gap) described by Cooke (1915). Williams (1950, 1952), however, maintains that the coastal hiatus results from converging lines of flight from Texas and Florida coming together north of the Gulf, and that flocks out over the Gulf are due to birds blown off course. No doubt all available routes are used, some species detouring the Gulf, via Texas or Florida, others making the 500-mile or more trans-Gulf flight directly.

## Orientation

One of the great unsolved problems relating to migration is a bird's means of orientation, or direction-finding ability. By some little understood method, birds are able to find their way through thousands of miles of space, usually flying at night without apparent aid of landmarks, the young often going separately from the adults, over routes they have never traveled before. Yet, they arrive at the place where they are supposed to go—perhaps a remote island in the Pacific, a specific nest site on the northern tundra, or a particular niche in the Amazonian rain forest.

Many homing experiments now demonstrate this remarkable direction-finding sense in birds. Among the earliest are those of Watson and Lashley (1915) in which marked Noddy and Sooty Terns were shipped in various directions away from their breeding colonies on the Dry Tortugas Islands, off the southwest coast of Florida. Some of the transported birds returned promptly to their nests on the Dry Tortugas, within a few hours from short distances (55 miles), or within a few days from points hundreds of miles north of their regular range.

Similar experiments conducted by Griffin (1940) with Leach's Petrels from their nesting burrows on Kent Island, near Nova Scotia, demonstrated this homing ability even more dramatically. The majority of the 220 petrels involved in these trials returned to their burrows, some of them over 360 miles of relatively featureless ocean and 470 miles from their nests.

Various homing experiments with Manx Shearwaters in Europe (Fig. 137), which previously indicated that they would return from long distances with remarkable promptness, reached a climax when one was flown to Boston after being taken from its nest burrow on Skokholm, an island off the southwest coast of Wales. The bird was back in its nest burrow 12½ days after its release at the Boston harbor, having traveled over 3,200 land miles at an average rate of more than 250 miles per day (Mazzeo, 1953). Equally astonishing are homing experiments with Laysan Albatrosses (Kenyon and Rice, 1958). Eighteen adults were shipped by air from their nest sites on Midway Atoll to six different localities. Fourteen birds, representing all six localities, subsequently returned, the farthest from the Philippines, some 4,120 miles in 32 days; the fastest from Whidby Island, Wash-

*Fig. 137. Long-winged, skillful aerialists, the shearwaters perform some of the most amazing migrations known. The Manx Shearwater, the species shown above, has been used in several remarkable homing experiments. (Courtesy of Amer. Mus. Nat. Hist.)*

ington—3,200 miles in 10.1 days or at the average rate of 317 miles per day.

Apparently land birds have similar homing ability. Cowbirds trapped at Waukegan, Illinois, by W. I. Lyon (Hann, 1953), were shipped to Denver (925 miles), New Orleans (875 miles), and Washington, D. C. (620 miles). Some birds from each of these three localities found their way back to Waukegan, though some of them were not retaken until the following year and many were never seen again. As in the case of the sea birds, the cowbirds were shipped to places they presumably had never visited before. Similar results, over shorter distances, were secured by Wood (1952) and Wharton (1959). One of Wharton's cowbirds, released in Ithaca, New York, on June 15, headed east and was back in Groton, Massachusetts, on June 29, in spite of intervening spells of cold rainy weather. Much faster flights were recorded by Southern (1959) for Purple Martins. Sixteen birds released at various distances from their nest boxes at Douglas Lake, Michigan, all returned—the farthest from a 234-mile deportation to Ann Arbor, Michigan. It returned over night, in 8.58 hours!

None of the several theories that attempt to explain this direction-finding ability in birds gives a wholly satisfactory answer. Of course some diurnal birds can and do follow landmarks; observations by Rudbeck (1950) in Sweden indicate that some migrants will actually deviate up to 90 degrees from a direct flight line in order to follow a coast, but will strike out across the open sea when the coastline takes them too far off their course. But landmarks are presumably of little help (though not necessarily invisible) to nocturnal migrants or to oceanic birds. Some think that landmarks, or familiarity with a region, are used by short-distance migrants, and that long-distance migrants might utilize such features at the beginning and the end but not the main course of their journeys. Blake (1959) tries to distinguish "terminal" migrants which proceed from landmark to landmark by visual clues, and "transmigrants" which use a true navigational sense.

Several largely discredited theories attempting to explain this navigational sense in birds have been advanced from time to time. One theory is that a bird might be able to judge its latitude by the *Coriolis Force* produced by the rotation of the earth, but several authors (H. Odum, 1948; Griffin, 1952; and others) estimate that the effect of Coriolis Force is so small, especially toward the equator (it is stronger toward the poles) that its effect on a bird would be negligible. Yeagley (1947, 1951), in particular, after extensive experiments with homing pigeons, feels that a combination of Coriolis Force and a bird's sensitivity to a magnetic field might set up a grid pattern so that a bird could judge both its latitudinal and longitudinal field, but in spite of considerable experimental data Yeagley's views have not been widely accepted. Still another theory, that a bird might be able to judge its position by the amount of infrared radiation, which increases toward the equator, has received even less support (Griffin, 1952).

During the past decade, however, work has progressed remarkably on apparently much more fruitful lines of research. Kramer (1952, 1961) disclosed that Starlings in aviaries in Germany could orient themselves quite unerringly, southwest in the fall and northwest in the spring, by the sun's position. Later, homing pigeons, Herring Gulls, and sylviids were found (by Kramer and others) to behave in a similar manner. They lost this directional sense when the sun was obscured and they could be fooled by an artificial sun. Even more remarkable was the fact that nocturnal migrants (sylviids) could orient themselves after the sun had set. Bellrose (1958) tested these hypotheses by releasing marked Mallards in fall, winter, and spring, both day and night, and in both cloudy and clear skies. He concluded that Mallards oriented by sun in the day (even under 70 per cent cloud cover, if the sun was visible) and by stars or constellations at night, but used random dispersal under cloudy skies. Significant also are experiments by Hamilton and Hammond (1960) in which pinioned geese in the midwest, when released or escaping from pens in spring, headed true north and walked overland, covering about one-half mile per day for a period longer than the regular migration period of wild geese. Captive birds also persistently crowded the north fence in spring.

At first it was felt that sun navigation might be useful mainly to diurnal migrants, although it was evident that nocturnal migrants might set their compass directions correctly at or near sundown, when they take off, and continue on their course until they lost their bearings. Brackbill (1952) has reported ducks taking off on such flights. Some observations on nocturnal migrants, particularly those utilizing flight calls (Ball, 1952), suggest heavier flight patterns before midnight and in the early morning, thus supporting the theory of evening and morning sun orientation. Later, however, several investigators, particularly the Sauers (Kramer, 1961) showed that birds in cages could orient themselves properly at night by the moon, if present, or by the stars. Birds in planetaria reoriented themselves when the heavens were rotated and the position of the stars changed.

In most of this experimental work, birds apparently lost their sense of direction when the skies (sun, moon, or stars) were obscured, yet it is well known that in nature there are often heavy migrations on cloudy nights. In such cases, Graber and Cochran (1960) suggest that birds might be able to utilize wind direction to enable them to fly along a proper course.

In spite of these remarkable discoveries on celestial navigation, there are still unanswered questions, and not all experimental work has supported the earlier conclusions. Yet it would appear, from the evidence now available, that birds use a variety of devices to find their way: random wandering to regain their position when lost or experimentally displaced in homing experiments; use of landmarks in familiar territory; and a true navigational sense by some sort of celestial orientation on long flights over unfamiliar territory.

## *Routes of Migration*

Although studies on nocturnal migration by Lowery (1951), Lowery and Newman (1955), and others, as well as more casual observations, indicate that birds migrate over a broad front, and perhaps spread out pretty much over the whole continent of North America in migration, there are nevertheless some special routes and preferred lanes of travel. Birds that pass between North and South America have their choice narrowed down to several possible exchange corridors over land or water, producing a funneling effect which is just the opposite of the situation in Europe where birds flare out over broad Mediterranean routes.

North American waterfowl are believed by some (Lincoln, 1950) to sort themselves in migration into particular flyways, so much so that the flyways have become the basis of the administration of regulations and policies in the Fish and Wildlife Service. The accompanying maps (Fig. 138) show two of the four major flyways defined by the Fish and Wildlife Service, and some of the detailed paths that contribute to the main networks. These special routes, if they actually exist (see Phillips, 1951), are used not alone by waterfowl, but by many of the smaller birds as well. Some birds use different routes in the spring and fall; Connecticut Warblers and the western race of the Palm Warbler, for instance, commonly detour through New England in the fall but almost universally use the Mississippi flyway in the spring. Some of the shorebirds (see Fig. 141) also use different routes in the spring and fall, the adults and immatures sometimes going separately. Among waterfowl it is not uncommon for a part of the population to go by one route to one destination (Atlantic, Pacific, or Gulf Coasts) and another segment of the population to go by a different route to another destination.

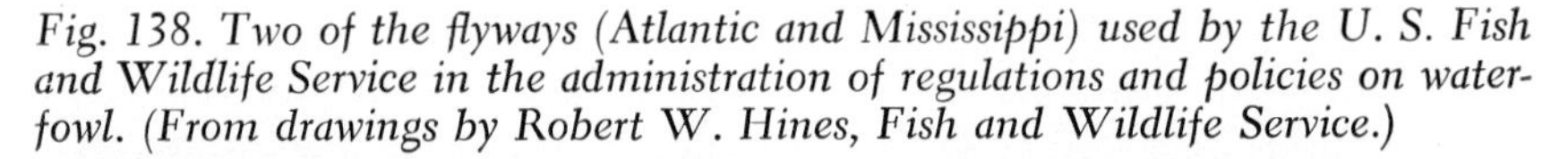
*Fig. 138. Two of the flyways (Atlantic and Mississippi) used by the U. S. Fish and Wildlife Service in the administration of regulations and policies on waterfowl. (From drawings by Robert W. Hines, Fish and Wildlife Service.)*

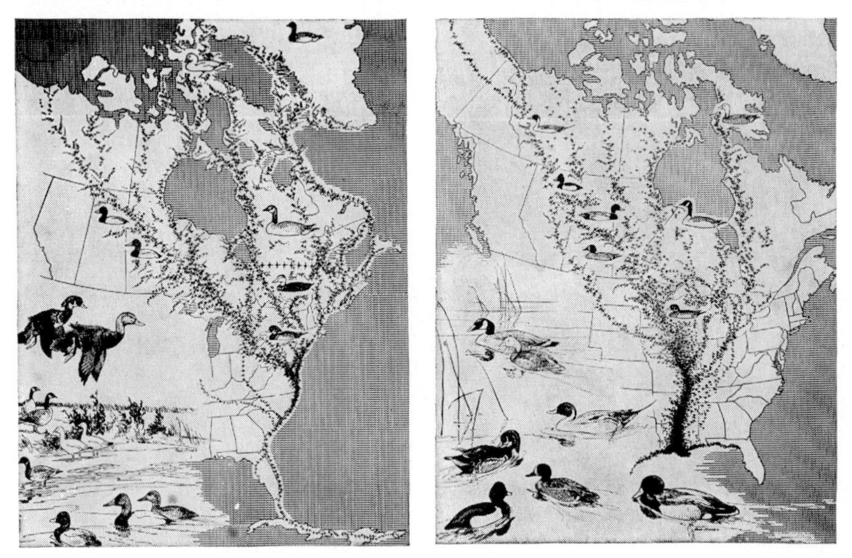

Figure 139 shows the various routes used by birds passing south of the United States. Route 1, for instance, from Nova Scotia to South America, is used mainly by adult Golden Plovers in the fall. Route 2, from Florida to the West Indies, as well as Route 3, serves many North American warblers and other birds that winter in or cross these islands. Route 4, passing directly over the Gulf and involving a hazardous nonstop 500-mile flight for many land birds, is believed to be used extensively (Cooke, 1915; Lincoln, 1950; Lowery, 1946), but some birds (or many according to Williams, 1950) take the more circuitous land routes (5 to 6) around the Gulf. Route 7, through western Mexico, is taken by Pacific Coast birds.

The accompanying illustrations (Figs. 140–142) show, and the legends explain, the migration routes of three outstanding travelers—the Arctic Tern, the Golden Plover (Atlantic and Pacific forms), and the Bobolink. The peculiar routes of the Arctic Tern and the (Atlantic) Golden Plover

*Fig. 139. Principal migration routes used by birds passing between North America and their wintering grounds to the south. (From drawing by Robert W. Hines, Fish and Wildlife Service.)*

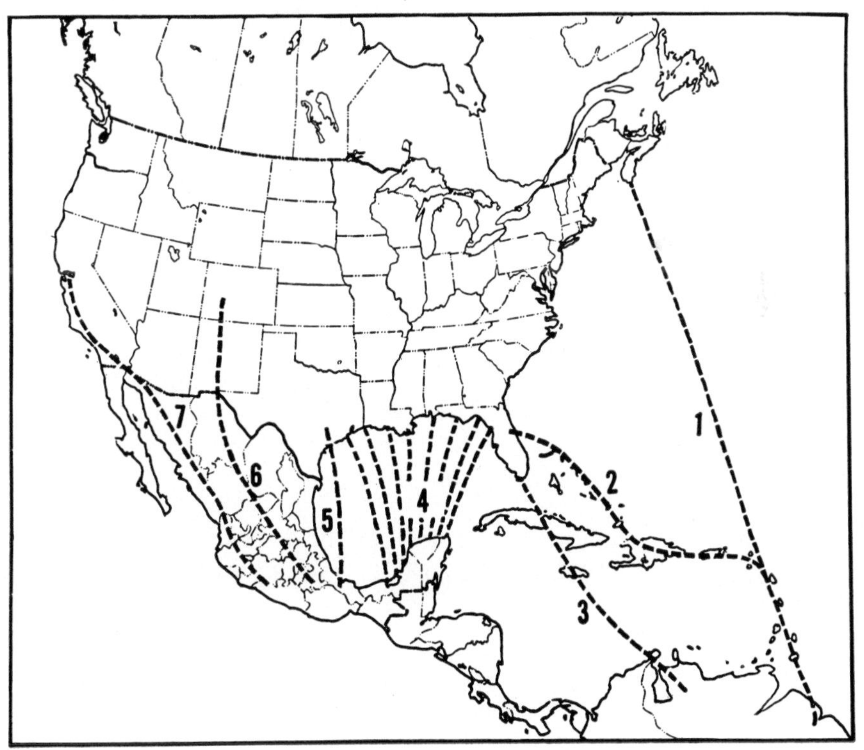

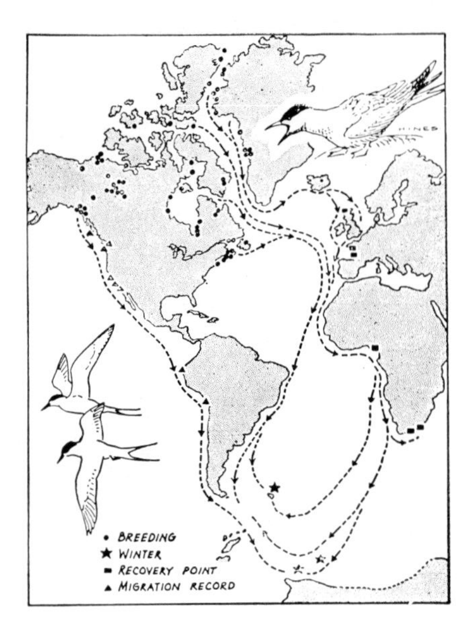


*Fig. 140. Distribution and migration of the Arctic Terns of North America. The route indicated for these birds is unique, as no other species is known to breed abundantly in North America and to cross the Atlantic Ocean to and from the Old World. The extreme summer and winter homes are 11,000 miles apart, and as the route taken is circuitous, these terns probably fly at least 25,000 miles each year. (From drawing by Robert W. Hines, Fish and Wildlife Service.)*

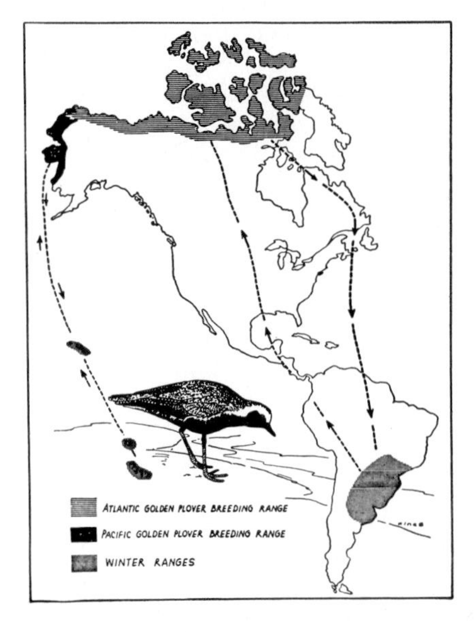


*Fig. 141. Distribution and migration of the Golden Plovers. Adults of the eastern form migrate across northeastern Canada and then by a nonstop flight reach South America. In spring they return by way of the Mississippi Valley. Their entire route is therefore in the form of a great ellipse with a major axis of 8,000 miles and a minor axis of about 2,000 miles. The Pacific Golden Plover, which breeds in Alaska, apparently makes a nonstop flight across the ocean to Hawaii, the Marquesas Islands, and the Low Archipelago, returning in spring over the same route. (From drawing by Robert W. Hines, Fish and Wildlife Service.)*

are extraordinary, duplicated by few if any other birds, but quite a few North American land birds make migrations similar to that of the Bobolink.

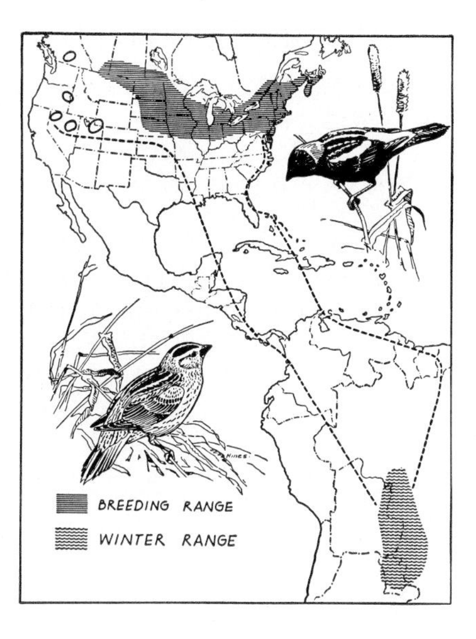


*Fig. 142. Distribution and migration of the Bobolink. In crossing to South America most Bobolinks use Route 3 (see Fig. 139), showing no hesitation in making the flight from Jamaica across an islandless stretch of ocean. It will be noted that colonies of these birds have established themselves in western areas, but in migration they adhere to the ancestral flyways and show no tendency to take the short cut across Arizona, New Mexico, and Texas. (From drawing by Robert W. Hines, Fish and Wildlife Service.)*

## Selected References


Ball, Stanley C. Fall Bird Migration on the Gaspé Peninsula. *Peabody Mus. Nat. Hist. Bull.* 7, Yale Univ. (New Haven, Conn.), 1952.

Bennett, Holly Reed. Fall Migration of Birds at Chicago. *Wilson Bull.* (1952), **64**:197–220.

Bissonnette, Thomas H. Photoperiodicity in Birds. *Wilson Bull.* (1937), **49**:241–270.

Burger, J. Wendall. A Review of Experimental Investigations on Seasonal Reproduction in Birds. *Wilson Bull.* (1949), **61**:211–230.

Cooke, Wells W. Bird Migration. *U.S.D.A. Bull.* (1915), **185**:1–47.

Farner, Donald S. The Annual Stimulus for Migration. *Condor* (1950), **52**:104–122.

———. The Annual Stimulus for Migration: Experimental and Physiologic Aspects. Chapt. 7 in *Recent Studies in Avian Biology*, ed. Albert Wolfson. Urbana, Ill.: U. of Ill., 1955.

Griffin, Donald R. Bird Navigation. *Biol. Rev.* (1952), **27**:359–400.

———. Bird Navigation. Chapt. 6 in *Recent Studies of Avian Biology*, ed. Albert Wolfson. Urbana, Ill.: U. of Ill., 1955.

Griscom, Ludlow. *Modern Bird Study*. Cambridge, Mass.: Harvard U.P., 1945. Chapt. IV and V.

Kramer, G. Long Distance Orientation. Chapt. 22 in A. J. Marshall's *Biology and Comparative Physiology of Birds*. New York: Academic, 1961.

Lincoln, F. C. *The Migration of American Birds*. New York: Doubleday, 1939.

———. Migration of Birds. *U. S. Fish and Wildl. Service Circ.* (Washington, D. C., 1950), **16**:1–102.

Lowery, George H., Jr. A Quantitative Study of the Nocturnal Migration of Birds. *Univ. Kans. Publ. Mus. Nat. Hist.* (1951), **3**:361–472.

———, and Robert J. Newman. Direct Studies of Nocturnal Bird Migration. Chapt. 8 in *Recent Studies in Avian Biology*, ed. Albert Wolfson. Urbana, Ill.: U. of Ill., 1955.

Marshall, A. J. The Refractory Period of Testis Rhythm in Birds and Its Possible Bearing on Breeding and Migration. *Wilson Bull.* (1951), **63**:238–261.

———. Breeding Seasons and Migration. Chapt. 21 in *Biology and Comparative Physiology of Birds*. New York: Academic, 1961.

Matthews, G. V. T. *Bird Navigation*. New York: Cambridge U.P., 1955.

Rowan, William. *The Riddle of Migration*. Baltimore, Md.: Williams & Wilkins, 1931.

Thomson, A. L. *Bird Migration*. Reprinted, with revisions, from the 1936 edition. London: Witherby, 1949.

Wetmore, Alexander. *The Migrations of Birds*. Cambridge, Mass.: Harvard U.P., 1930.

Wolfson, Albert. The Role of the Pituitary, Fat Deposition, and Body Weight in Bird Migration. *Condor* (1945), **47**:95–127.

———. Day Length, Migration, and Breeding Cycles in Birds. *Scient. Month.* (1952), **74**:191–200.

# 12

# THE DISTRIBUTION OF BIRDS

The distribution of birds, particularly with respect to its geographical or spatial arrangements, has long engaged the attention of ornithologists. As a result, the summer and winter ranges and migration routes of birds are now fairly well known, several classifications of regions and zones have been presented, and special habitats have been studied in great detail. But when we ask why birds are where they are today, how they got there, or why some birds are restricted to a single island or a particular habitat while others are world-wide, we do not always have the answer.

Distribution may be divided, somewhat arbitrarily, into three kinds: (1) distribution in time (geological), (2) distribution in space (geographical), and (3) distribution with respect to habitats (ecological). The geological record was examined, somewhat sketchily, in Chapter 2; it is chiefly geographical patterns, together with a consideration of some of the ecological aspects, that need to be discussed here.

Every student has some concept of both geographical and ecological distribution. Nearly everyone has learned to associate penguins with the Antarctic, ptarmigans with the Arctic, and hummingbirds, for the most part, with tropical or subtropical regions. Similarly with respect to habitat, we associate ducks with water, woodpeckers with trees, and various species of field birds with meadows.

## Origin and Dispersal

Distributional patterns involve, at the outset, a *center of origin* or *birthplace* of the species or group, then its subsequent *spread* or *dispersal* from this center, and, lastly, its degree of success in the new regions invaded. *Spreading* is a term commonly employed to denote dispersal or increase in the range of a species, as opposed to migration which is fundamentally a two-way movement not necessarily increasing the permanent range. Matthew (1939) postulates a Holarctic (northern hemisphere) origin for land vertebrates, but Serventy (1960), in part following Darlington (1957), broadens this to "the great Eurasian-African land masses as the differentiating center for main vertebrate evolution" with the tropical parts of Africa and the Orient as "the great reservoirs and apparent main dispersal centers of the vertebrates." The theory of continental drift (p. 265) also favors tropical centers of origin, which offers a solution to the problem of pantropical species (see p. 291). Glenny (1954) even postulates a tropical or subtropical Antarctica during the Jurassic as a center of origin of birds which subsequently spread northward into the Americas and the Old World continents.

Some species, or groups of species, particularly those of recent origin and those handicapped by lack of mobility, may still be at or near their place of origin, never having succeeded in occupying new regions. Other species, with greater adaptability, better means of dispersal, or a higher reproductive or genetic potential which creates population pressure and peripheral spreading, have successfully invaded new areas. Some of them, such as the hawks and owls, gulls and terns, swallows and swifts, and many water birds are now virtually world-wide. Still other forms may have moved into new homes and died out completely from their birthplace, leaving little or no trace of their origin. The rheas of South America are far removed from ostensibly similar Old World Ostrich stock, which points to the probability that they spread to the New World before Pleistocene glaciation and have survived only in South America, where they have undergone further evolution. Ecological changes, such as the development of a more favorable climate in a previously inhospitable region, encourage range expansion (Serventy, 1960), then an unfavorable climatic change may restrict farther spreading.

The Limpkin, a rail-like bird of the subtropics, is a good example of a changing range. Except for a relatively rare North American form, the Limpkins are now confined to tropical America, which might well be assumed to be their original home were it not for fossil evidence to the contrary. If the North American form dies out in the near future, only history, recent and fossil, will show that South America is probably the secondary home of a family of birds (Aramidae) that originated in North America. Apparently the New World vultures (Cathartidae) are undergoing a similar extension southward, and gradually disappearing from North America. Seven fossil species are known from the United States, and only three living forms, of which one (the California Condor) is nearly extinct. Curiously the Old World vultures (Accipitridae) once inhabited North America, and the New World vultures (Cathartidae) once inhabited Europe, but the two groups seem to have reversed their former geographic positions; or more probably each has died out from a part of its former range.

Land and water barriers influence the dispersal of birds, but not always in the same way. A barrier to one may be an avenue of travel for another. A mountain range may effectively block further spreading of a plain's species, but it is a means of further dispersion for others. The dippers, lovers of mountain streams, extend from Alaska to the Andes in the western mountains and from Scandinavia to North Africa in the Old World, but are presumably prevented from occupying apparently suitable range in the Appalachians because of the formidable barrier interposed by the great plains, and similarly blocked from mountains in South Africa by the inhospitable Sahara.

Some species extend their range by "island hopping." A recent, remarkable example believed to be attributable to this mode of travel is the Cattle Egret which appeared in northern South America in the late 1930's, presumably from Africa or Europe, and spread rapidly up the coast of North America to Newfoundland and sporadically into the interior. Though other explanations of its origin in South America are conceivable (cattle boats, escape from zoos), the recent recovery in Trinidad of a Little Egret banded in Spain (Downs, 1959) lends strong support to the island-hopping theory.

## WIDESPREAD VS. RESTRICTED SPECIES

Several interesting dispersal problems are raised by a comparison of widespread and successful species with those that are restricted to a particular niche. Among the hawks, for instance, the Osprey (Fig. 143) occurs on every continent and on most of the larger islands throughout the world, whereas another hawk, the northern race of the Everglade Kite (Fig. 179), is confined to a critically small area of southern Florida, and is nearly extinct. In this case the food habits of the two species appear to provide a ready explanation, for the Osprey, an expert fisherman, lives on a never-failing supply of fish, while the kite lives exclusively on a single species of snail (*Pomacea caliginosa*). Similarly the success of the marsh hawks (harriers), both in numbers and distribution over nearly the whole earth, might well be attributed to their adaptability in diet (p. 329) and the widespread availability of marsh habitats. Another factor, however, is the higher reproductive potential of the Marsh Hawk, which may lay a clutch of six or more eggs, whereas the Everglade Kite usually lays two or three.

*Fig. 143. The Osprey is nearly worldwide in distribution, and its chief source of food appears to be unlimited. Now, however, it is declining rapidly in the eastern states, owing to loss of nesting sites and perhaps also to reproductive failure from feeding on chemically contaminated fish. (Photo by Allan D. Cruickshank.)*

Among the sparrows, to take another well-known example, the Song Sparrow is a widespread and abundant North American bird that occurs from coast to coast and from Alaska to southern Mexico, but the Ipswich Sparrow is confined in the breeding season to Sable Island, Nova Scotia. There appears to be no ready explanation for this distributional enigma other than to generalize on the Song Sparrow's adaptability and genetic potential and Ipswich Sparrow's lack of these traits.

Similarly among the warblers, the Kirtland's Warbler (Fig. 144) breeds only in the jack-pine country of a few counties in north-central Michigan (about 400 pairs in 1961), whereas many woodland warblers range over nearly all of the deciduous forests or coniferous forests of eastern North America. Apparently the Kirtland's Warbler has been evolved to fit in only a particular stage in the jack-pine forest development, in nearly homogeneous stands of small jack pines, 5 to 20 feet high. Why it does not spread to available, and to our eyes nearly identical, jack-pine range in Wisconsin, the Upper Peninsula of Michigan, and Ontario is not readily answered.

In New England a race of the Gray-cheeked Thrush occupies the spruce-balsam zone which occurs mainly between 3,000 and 4,000 feet (Fig. 145). It does not range much above or below this level, apparently

*Fig. 144. Kirtland's Warbler in a jack pine. This unique bird—limited to about 400 pairs—breeds only in a few counties of jack-pine country in north-central Michigan. It winters in the Bahamas. (Photo by L. H. Walkinshaw, courtesy of* Jack-Pine Warbler.*)*

*Fig. 145. The zone of stunted evergreens extending from the 3,000-foot contour line to the timberline on Mt. Mansfield, Vermont, and on other New England mountains harbors a race of the Gray-cheeked Thrush that is largely restricted to this zone in the breeding season. (Courtesy of* National Geographic Magazine.*)*

because the conifers run into timberline above and deciduous forest below. But the White-throated Sparrow, a common nesting companion of the rarer thrush, extends across the timberline above and into the deciduous woods below, not only throughout New England, but over most of the forests of northern United States and Canada as well. In this case the White-throat is more adaptable than the thrush in its environmental requirements; but, in addition, a greater reproductive capacity—the White-throat lays a larger clutch of eggs and more often raises a second brood—may have prompted the sparrow to invade new and somewhat different habitats.

In western North America, where more abrupt climatic, ecological, and altitudinal differences create special niches, there are many birds, particularly subspecies, with restricted ranges. Often somewhat generalized answers (adaptability, habitat preferences, reproductive and genetic potential) can be found for these distributional enigmas, but such "solutions" leave much to be desired.

## Zoological (Faunal) Regions and Subregions

Ever since Alfred Russel Wallace (1876) advanced his concept (largely adapted from Sclater) of the geographical distribution of animals, animal geographers have strongly adhered to the classical zoogeography of the nineteenth century and attempted to fit animals in zoological regions with fixed boundaries based largely on climatic conditions and topographical barriers. Though this concept of fixed regions (static zoogeography) as opposed to fluid faunas (dynamic zoogeography) has been questioned from time to time (Mayr, 1946b), these regions and the terminology based on them are still widely used, and on a strictly geographical basis perhaps no better land divisions could be devised. Hence, Sclater's and Wallace's original regions, after many suggested modifications and criticisms, have been largely adopted by Darlington (1957) in perhaps the latest thorough review of the situation.

A detailed analysis of the zoological regions of the world is beyond the scope of this book, but the major divisions, with a few birds characteristic of each, are described below, and the Nearctic (North American) area is discussed in some detail, particularly with respect to the origins of its present-day bird life. Figure 146 shows these major regions and their approximate boundaries.

### THE HOLARCTIC (PALAEARCTIC AND NEARCTIC) REGIONS

Usually most of the northern hemisphere, which comprises a disproportionate part of the land area (but not species of birds) of the world, is included in one vast region, the *Holarctic*. This in turn is divided into two subregions, a Eurasian (*Palaearctic*) and a North America (*Nearctic*). The justification for treating most of the northern hemisphere as one major region is apparent when we consider the birds occupying it. At the polar extremes of the Holarctic are many aquatic birds—loons, alcids, and many waterfowl—that are circumpolar. In some cases the same species occur throughout the area, in other cases the Old and New World forms are only subspecifically distinct. South of the polar seas the tundras of both Eurasia and North America are occupied by the same, or closely related, species of plovers, sandpipers, ptarmigans, some hawks and owls, and even more recent passerines such as the Snow Bunting and Wheatear.

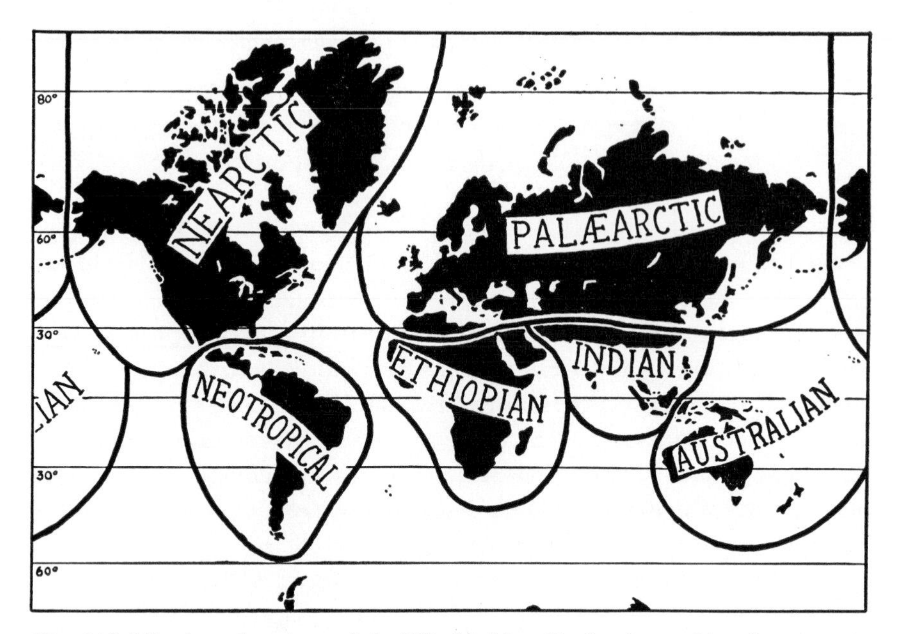


*Fig. 146. The faunal regions of the World. New Zealand, considered a separate faunal region by some, is here included in the Australian region. (Map prepared by R. H. Manville from original by Sclater.)*

The extensive coniferous forest south of the tundra likewise forms a more or less continuous belt across Canada into Siberia and northern Europe, and we find such forest birds as Brown Creepers and Golden-crowned Kinglets, at best only subspecifically separable, ranging throughout the area. Each subregion has developed a few species of its own, such as the Snow Goose and several sandpipers in the American tundra, and the Red-breasted Nuthatch and the Black-backed Three-toed Woodpecker in the Canadian coniferous forests, but many species are common to the whole region.

Southward, in the deciduous woodlands, and grasslands and deserts, the dissimilarities in the avifaunas of the Palaearctic and Nearctic naturally become greater. Udvardy (1958) describes these relationships as follows: 32 species of Arctic sea birds (86.5 per cent) are common to both regions (Palaearctic and Nearctic), 36 species (75.0 per cent) of the birds of the tundra are common to both, 28 coniferous forest species (43.8 per cent) occur in both regions, but only 7 species (3.1 per cent) of deciduous forest birds are found in both. He lists only 2 species, the Short-eared Owl and Horned Lark, as common to the open grasslands of both regions, and both of these species are members of a circumpolar Arctic fauna that have spread far south of their probable port of entry into North America, the Horned Lark even reaching northern South America.

ORIGIN OF NORTH AMERICAN AVIFAUNA. From this account of the Holarctic it is evident that not all North American bird groups are strictly endemic; some had their roots on other continents. North American bird life is derived from three known sources: (1) part of it, at least 17 families and subfamilies according to Mayr (1946b) is endemic, having undergone its main evolutionary development on this continent at an early date, probably in the Tertiary; (2) an equally large element, at least 18 families and subfamilies, is of Old World origin, with most representatives still over there but with smaller or more recent segments established in the New World; (3) still other family groups, principally the hummingbirds (Trochilidae), New World flycatchers (Tyrannidae), and tanagers (Thraupidae), apparently spread northward from South America.

In addition to these known sources of our avifauna, many of the larger and older birds—oceanic forms, waterfowl, hawks, and shorebirds, as well as the more mobile smaller birds (swifts and swallows)—have been distributed over the whole earth so long that their place of origin is obscure. The following list presents some of the better known North American groups of birds and their known, or postulated, source (condensed from Mayr's *History of the North American Bird Fauna*).

Unanalyzed Element (now so old or widespread that their origins are largely unknown):
- Oceanic birds (8 families)
- Shorebirds (5 families)
- Fresh-water birds (9 families)
- Land birds (7 families)

Old World Element (groups originating in the Old World, but now represented in North America):
- Phasianids (Phasianidae)—in part (New World quail endemic in North America)
- Pigeons (Columbidae)
- Cuckoos (Cuculidae)
- Kingfishers (Alcedinidae)
- Larks (Alaudidae)
- Titmice (Paridae)
- Nuthatches (Sittidae)
- Thrushes (Turdidae)—in part (some endemic in New World)
- Shrikes (Laniidae)

North American Element (endemic, largely confined to or originating in North America):

- New World Vultures (Cathartidae)—entirely New World
- Grouse (Tetraonidae)—have spread over Eurasia, apparently from American sources
- Turkeys (Meleagrididae)—entirely New World
- Limpkins (Aramidae)—have spread into South America
- Wrens (Troglodytidae)—have spread into Eurasia
- Mockingbirds (Mimidae)—entirely New World
- Vireos (Vireonidae)—entirely New World
- Wood Warblers (Parulidae)—entirely New World

South American Element (primarily South American but represented in North America):

- Hummingbirds (Trochilidae)—319 species, only one reaching eastern United States (18 in western United States)
- Tyrant Flycatchers (Tyrannidae)—365 species, 32 north of Mexico
- Tanagers (Thraupidae)—196 species, 4 in North America north of Mexico

## THE NEOTROPICAL OR SOUTH AMERICAN REGION

This is perhaps the most easily defined of the world regions, geographically because of its near separation from all other land areas, and avifaunally because it has so many birds (as well as other animals) restricted to it. Mayr (1946b) gives South America as the probable home (origin) of 27 families, most of them still there. These include such well-known types as the rheas, the tinamous, the Hoatzin (Fig. 58), and the toucans (Fig. 37), as well as many passerine families (14) little known to the layman.

Ornithologically South America is one of the richest regions in the world. Lush tropical forests with heavy rainfall (exceeding 275 inches per year on parts of the Pacific Coast) and coastal deserts with little or none; broad savanna lands; a temperate plateau stretching deep into the southern hemisphere; and the high Andes with four "life zones" at different altitudes provide for a great variety of bird life. Tropical regions, moreover, are noted for the development of large numbers of species; 85 per cent of the bird species of the world, according to Griscom (1945), are found in the tropics. Colombia, for instance, with a land area approximately equal to Texas and Oklahoma, has 1,532 species (2,558 forms) of birds (de Schauensee, 1948–1952), which is roughly three times the number of birds recorded in Texas or California, and nearly double the number known in North America north of Mexico.

Many tropical species are peculiarly restricted in distribution, however, and the large flocks characteristic of northern latitudes are almost unknown.

A rare grebe (*Podilymbus gigas*) is confined to a single lake in Guatemala; another (*Centropelma micropterum*) occurs only on Lake Titicaca in the high Andes. Griscom (1945) remarks further that a certain flycatcher is found only in a particular kind of palm tree, that a seed-eater dwells only in the reed beds of certain rivers in eastern Nicaragua, and that in the Amazonian basin many species are confined to the intertributary areas of wide rivers and will not cross the water. In the tall rain forest there are six strata of bird life from the forest floor to the lofty crowns of the trees. Hence, the New World tropics have an amazing diversity of bird life, but usually not large aggregations of any particular species.

Another distinctive feature of the Neotropical region is the *absence* of certain widespread groups. The titmice (Paridae), creepers (Certhiidae), and shrikes (Laniidae), for example, occur on all continents *except* South America.

In addition to its endemic bird life and the several groups that it shares with North America, the Neotropical region has eight families of birds which also occur in the tropics of the Old World. Such birds are known as *pantropical* (common to the tropics of both the Old and New World) and are oft-cited examples of discontinuous distribution. Best known of these are the parrots (Psittacidae), barbets (Capitonidae—Fig. 147), and trogons (Trogonidae) among the land birds and the snake-birds (Anhingidae) and skimmers (Rynchopidae) among the water birds. Peculiarly a warm ocean current (the Gulf Stream) has enabled the Black Skimmer

*Fig. 147. Crimson-breasted Barbet* (Megalaema haemacephala). *Barbets (72 species) are pantropical, occurring in the tropics of both the New and Old World. They are mostly gaudily colored, rather sluggish fruit eaters, with their bright colors not always in good harmony. (From Delacour and Mayr,* Birds of the Philippines, *copyright 1946 by Jean Delacour and Ernst Mayr, The Macmillan Company, New York, publisher.)*

to extend its range up the Atlantic Coast to Massachusetts, just as a cold current (Humboldt's) has permitted a penguin from the Antarctic to reach the Galapagos Islands at the equator. The explanation for pantropical occurrences has long been a controversial issue, but the prevailing belief, supported by some fossil evidence, is that the species involved once had a more or less continuous distribution over the whole northern hemisphere, until increasing aridity and cold, followed by glaciation, eliminated tropical life from the north and left segments stranded in the warmer parts of Africa, Asia, and South America.

## ETHIOPIAN REGION

The Ethiopian region includes all of Africa except the extreme northwest Mediterranean coast (portions of Morocco, Algeria, and Tunisia) which belongs with Mediterranean Europe. It also includes the portions of the Syrian and Arabian deserts, which are more or less continuous with the Sahara, and Madagascar. Some features of particular interest on this continent are the immense Sahara desert, broad savanna lands (including the veld and scrub thorn) with sharply divided wet and dry seasons, broad equatorial as well as montane rain forests, and the isolated subregion of Madagascar which has a peculiar bird life of its own. Extensive wetlands—marshes, rivers and lakes—provide for both variety and abundance of aquatic birds.

The Ostrich (*Struthio camelus*) is a characteristic bird of the Ethiopian region, the northern form (there are 6 subspecies) ranging into Arabia. The Secretarybird (Sagittariidae), which is a snake-eating falconiform bird (Fig. 148r), and two odd storks (the Whale-headed Stork and Hammerhead) are African peculiarities that occur nowhere else. The guineafowl (Numididae) and plantain-eaters (Musophagidae), the latter noted especially for unique color pigments (p. 55), are likewise confined to the Ethiopian region. Five families, little known to the layman, are restricted to Madagascar. Still other families are shared with the adjacent Oriental region, and with the Palaearctic which provides many winter visitors to Africa.

Africa, perhaps more than any other continent, is currently witnessing destructive exploitation of its animal resources. This pertains most conspicuously to big game (Grzimek, 1961), both from poaching and from government-sponsored programs to eliminate wild grazing mammals to make way for domestic livestock ill suited to the land (Grzimek and

*Fig. 148. The Wood Ibis* (Ibis ibis) *(left) and Secretarybird (right) are characteristic birds of Africa, the former belonging to a fairly widespread family (Ciconiidae), the latter a monotypic species of a family (Sagittariidae) occurring only in parts of Africa. (From Kodachromes by Roger T. Peterson and Dale A. Zimmerman.)*

Grzimek, 1960; Wright, 1960). But birds are also severely affected, not only by destruction of habitat from overgrazing but also by widespread use of insecticides to "eradicate" locusts, the tsetse fly (to protect cattle), and other insect vectors of diseases. In a recent *National Geographic Magazine*, the Rodgers (1960) dramatically describe the plight of Africa's vanishing wildlife in an article entitled, "The Last Great Animal Kingdom."

### ORIENTAL OR INDIAN REGION

The Indian region comprises tropical Asia, south of the effective Himalayan barrier, as well as such islands as the Philippines and most of the East Indies. A fairly sharp line of demarcation, known as Wallace's line, separates Borneo, Sumatra, and Java of the Indian region from the Celebes and New Guinea of the adjacent Australian region. It is fairly true that faunas of these islands, separated only by the Straits of Makassar, are surprisingly different, but a much better division between the two regions would be further eastward. Because of its continuity with the Australian region on the one hand and the Ethiopian on the other, the Indian region has few birds peculiar to it. The leafbirds or fairy bluebirds (Irenidae) are restricted to this region, and the broadbills (Eurylaimidae), a rather primitive passerine family (Fig. 149), are chiefly Oriental but also occur in Africa. The region is also rich in phasianids, including *Gallus* (the ancestors of domestic fowl) and *Pavo* (peacocks), as well as in many smaller birds (pigeons, parrots, kingfishers, babblers) which it shares with other regions. Its close affinity to adjacent regions is indicated by the fact that it shares 70 families (80.5 per cent) with the Ethiopian region and 64 families (74.4 per cent) with the Australian (Barden, 1941).

### AUSTRALIAN REGION

This region, comprising the Australian continent and its surrounding islands (Tasmania, New Guinea, Celebes, and perhaps New Zealand), probably because of its long period of isolation from mainland Asia, has

*Fig. 149. Black and Yellow Broadbill* (Eurylaimus ochromalus) *from Malaysia. Broadbills (14 species) are primitive passerines of southern Asia and the Malayan states, but a few forms occur in Africa. (From Delacour,* Birds of Malaysia, *copyright 1947 by Jean Delacour, The Macmillan Company, New York, publisher.)*

developed a remarkable bird life of its own, including many groups restricted to it. Best known of these are the cassowaries (Fig. 150) and emus (Casuariiformes), mound builders (Megapodiidae), the lyrebirds (Menuridae—Fig. 150), and birds of paradise (Paradiseidae). Still other birds,

*Fig. 150. Above, the lyrebirds (2 species) are versatile Australian songbirds noted for their extraordinary tails and spectacular courtship displays. Right, the cassowaries (about 30 closely related forms) are rather widely distributed through New Guinea and surrounding islands, including a portion of Australia. They are ferocious forest birds. (Courtesy of Australian News and Information Bureau.)*

notably pigeons, parrots, and kingfishers, reach their highest development or diversity in the Australian Region, which may well have been their center of origin. Tropical islands and a greatly varied climate, with examples of all the world's climates except the northern extremes, account for a notably rich and varied avifauna—perhaps exceeded only by the Neotropical. Like the latter, however, Australia lacks quite a few birds which have spread over most other continents. Curiously, the great fringillid group has not yet reached Australia.

New Zealand, land of animal oddities and paradox of lush meadows in juxtaposition to barren hillsides and overgrazed pastures, has been separated from all other land areas so long, and has developed so striking a fauna, that it is sometimes regarded as an independent region (but otherwise included in the Australian). New Zealand has no native land mammals except bats, which reached the islands by flying, and its bird life is quite unique. Exclusive types are the moas (Fig. 151), extinct ostrichlike birds which lived on the islands several centuries ago, and the odd kiwis (*Apteryx*). The New Zealand wrens (Acanthisittidae) also seem to have been developed only in New Zealand. As might be expected, however, the relatively small land area of the islands is not well stocked with native land birds, though of course many wide-ranging sea birds have colonized there.

New Zealand, like Hawaii and other islands, suffers from large-scale introduction of exotics—25 mammals, 24 birds, 14 fishes, and 600 plants (Cahalane, 1955). Cahalane calls New Zealand an "object lesson in biological mismanagement," but Williams (1953) notes that 13 British passerines introduced to the island appear not to be seriously competitive with native species and perhaps fill a void because of the scarcity of endemic songbirds.

## *Life Zones and Biotic Communities*

Various attempts have been made in the past to divide large continental areas, such as the Nearctic or North American, into smaller workable units composed of relatively homogeneous elements. One of the earliest and best known of these in this country was the *Life Zone Theory* developed in the 1890's by C. Hart Merriam (1894, 1898), former chief of the Biological Survey. He divided North America into broad transcontinental belts (Fig. 152), bounded on the north and south by definite isotherms or lines of equal temperature with each zone characterized by assemblages of similar

*Fig. 151. New Zealand habitat group in the American Museum, featuring a giant moa prominently in the foreground with a kiwi lurking under tall fern fronds in lower right corner. (Courtesy of Amer. Mus. Nat. Hist.)*

plants and animals. In brief, the laws stated that (1) "animals and plants are restricted in northward distribution by the total quantity of heat during the season of growth and reproduction" and that (2) "animals and plants are restricted in southward distribution by the mean temperature of a brief period covering the hottest part of the year."

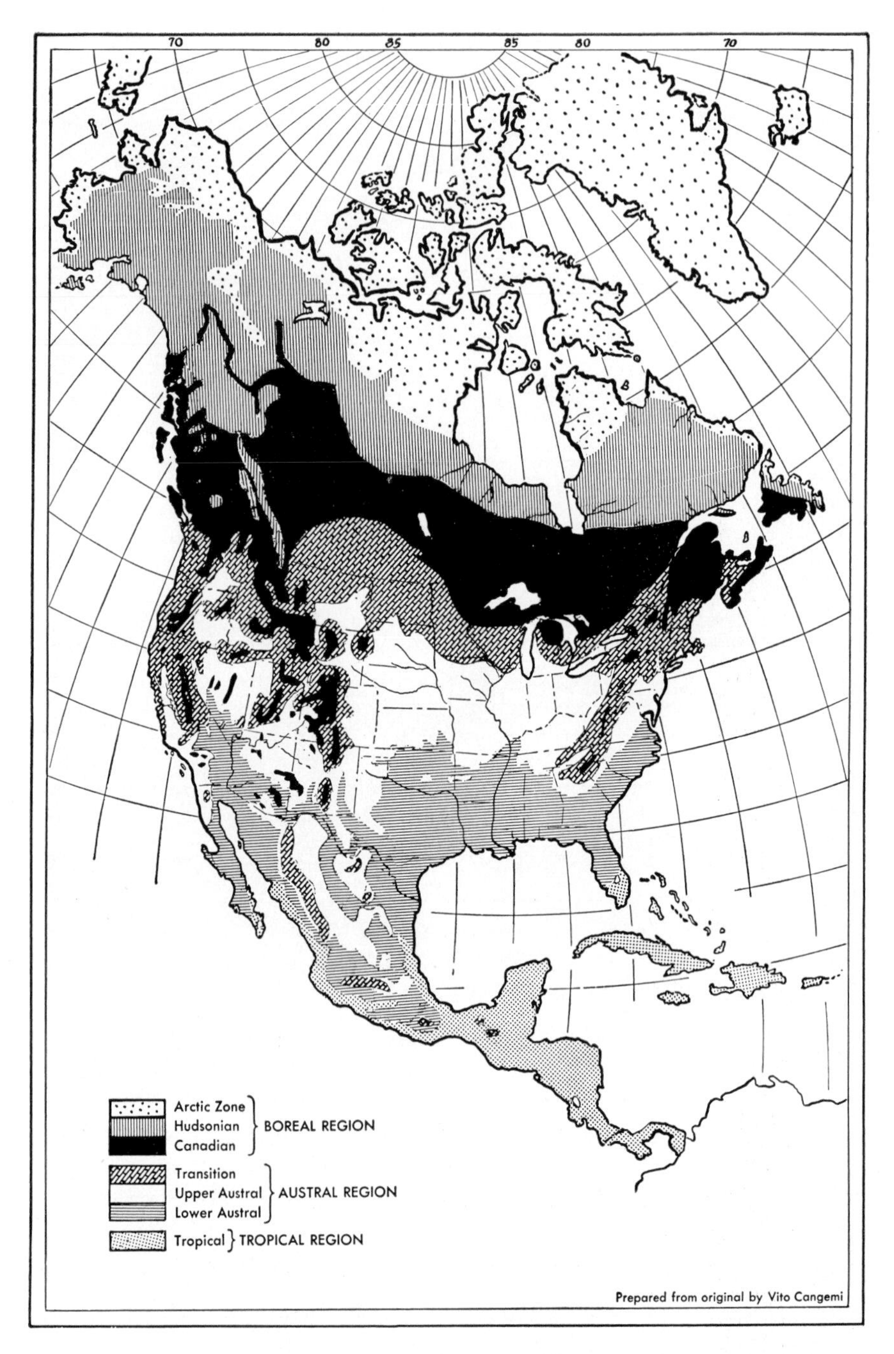


*Fig. 152. Life Zone Map of North America. (From U. S. Biological Survey Fourth Provisional Zone Map, by C. Hart Merriam, Vernon Bailey, E. W. Nelson, and E. A. Preble, 1910. Permission of Fish and Wildlife Service.)*

This life zone concept has had a wide following in the past, but has also been much discussed and severely criticized (see Kendeigh, 1932; and Shelford, 1932, for criticisms). Among its shortcomings is the fact that temperature laws (erroneously computed) were used almost exclusively in setting the limits of the zones, although other factors, such as length of day in the north, aridity and humidity, and habitat (vegetation), are often equally important. Some ecologists prefer to restrict the use of life zones or "life belts" (Dice, 1943) to the vertical divisions of fauna and flora in mountain areas. In spite of many flaws in the life zone theory, its terminology is still widely employed and such names as Boreal, Hudsonian, Austral, Carolinean, Sonoral, and Tropical are commonly applied to birds considered characteristic of these zones. Figure 152 portrays these life zones, and their geographic limits and the names applied to each.

Of the various theories developed in recent years (see also Dice's *Biotic Provinces*) to replace Merriam's perhaps outmoded life zone concept, one that is now widely employed by ornithologists is that of *biomes* or *biotic communities*, an idea advanced chiefly by Clements and Shelford (1939) and its application to bird distribution worked out largely by Pitelka (1941). Biomes are major landscape features, such as *tundra, coniferous forest, deciduous forest,* and *grassland.* These are determined and characterized by the dominant life forms, chiefly plants, that make up the unit. The early successional stages in the development of a biome are called *seral communities,* the later, more persistent stages are *subclimax communities,* and the final stage, which is self-perpetuating and cannot be replaced by natural processes, is the *climax* or *major biotic community.* Transitional areas, where two major biotic communities meet and overlap, as where elements of the deciduous forest intermingle with the coniferous forest, are called *ecotones.*

Figure 153 portrays the major biotic communities of North America and their connecting ecotones. The ones in eastern North America are fairly well defined, and quite comparable to Merriam's life zones and Dice's biotic provinces, but have the advantage of a fairly simple and probably self-explanatory terminology in common usage by botanists and zoologists, as well as geographers. They also appear to fit the facts of animal distribution more satisfactorily, for the dominant plant type of an area so often determines what animals shall live there. The western communities, because of more abrupt climatic and vegetational transitions, necessarily present a more complicated pattern; it is not certain that those shown should be considered on an equal basis with the other biomes.

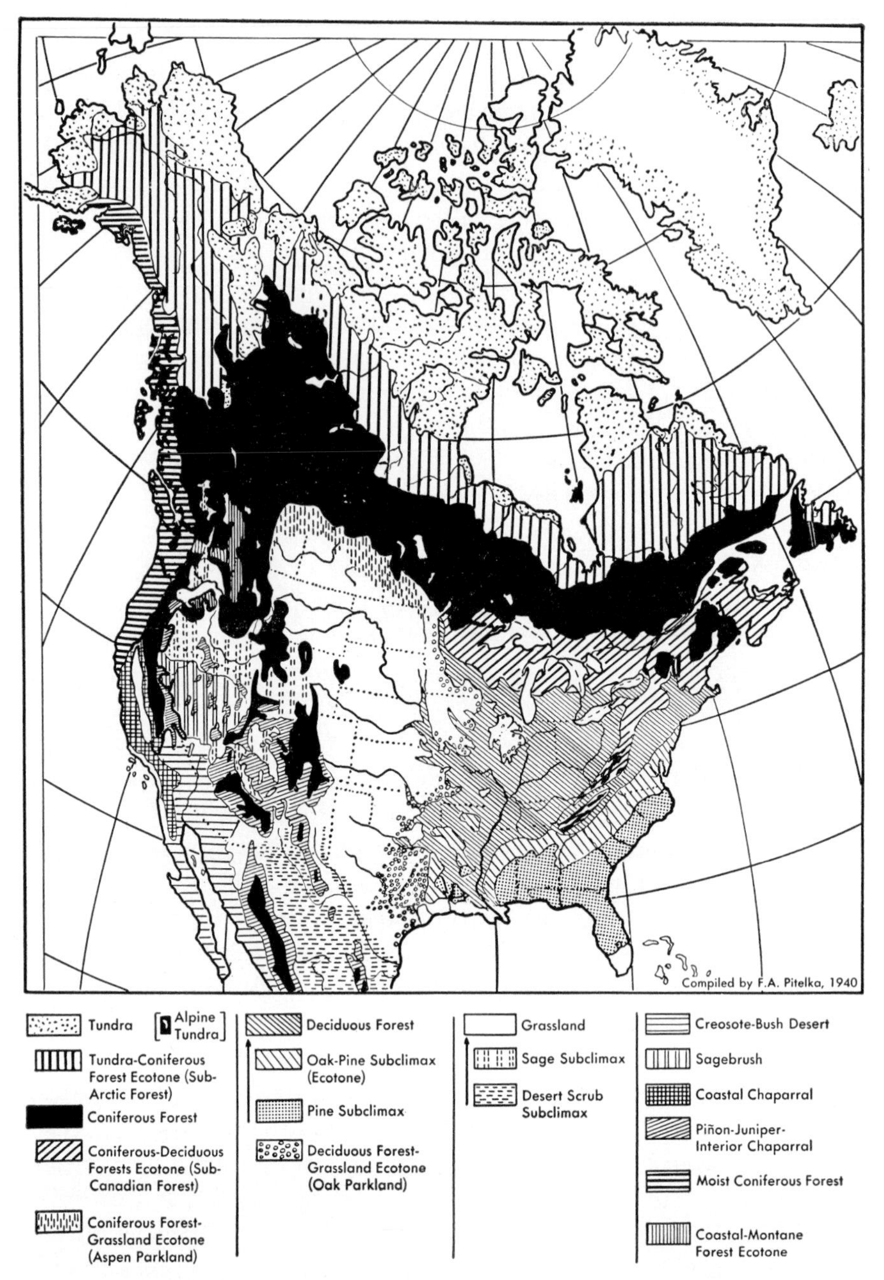


*Fig. 153. Major Biotic Communities of North America. (Redrawn by Vito Cangemi from map by F. A. Pitelka, courtesy of* American Midland Naturalist.)

It should be understood that a biome is not uniform throughout, but is composed of different developmental stages with different plants and animals. Thus a meadow in the eastern states is not a part of the grassland biome, but merely a developmental stage of the deciduous (or coniferous) forest biome. If abandoned the meadow would return, through several successional steps, to a climax forest, and the birds (and other animals) inhabiting it would change somewhat with each succession. Some birds are restricted to a particular developmental stage and others are not. A Bobolink, for example, would inhabit the area only in the meadow stage, a Catbird only in the shrub stage, whereas the more versatile Robin or Common Crow might at least utilize the area during all of its successional changes.

## NORTH AMERICAN BIOTIC COMMUNITIES

The five major biotic communities in North America—tundra, coniferous forest, deciduous forest, grassland, and desert—are briefly characterized below, and some of the birds typical of each enumerated. The ranges of some birds coincide almost exactly with major biotic communities; some are more characteristic of the ecotones or transitional areas, some spread over several or even all the North American biomes, while still others are restricted to special niches within a biome.

TUNDRA. The treeless tundra is the northernmost habitable land, merging with the permanent icecaps poleward and with the coniferous forest southward. It has a permanently frozen subsoil, but thaws out on the surface during the short summer, giving rise to much surface water and myriads of insect life. Lichens (reindeer moss), low grasses, sedges, flowers in season, and some brush at its southern extremities characterize the tundra.

Birds whose breeding range coincides quite closely with this biome, in both the Old and New World (Holarctic), are the Rock and Willow Ptarmigans, the Snowy Owl, and Snow Bunting. The latter, predominantly a seed-eater, is highly migratory in winter, the Snowy Owl migrates when its food supply fails (p. 258), and the less migratory ptarmigans wander widely in winter, often invading the tundra-coniferous forest ecotone in search of berries and herbage. It is a mistaken concept that the tundra has a heavy snow cover in winter, for precipitation is slight. Gyrfalcons hunt extensively over the tundra, but are not confined to it. Northern waterfowl (Whistling Swans, geese of several species, and ducks) and many shorebirds (Fig. 154) utilize the tundra for nesting and rearing young

*Fig. 154. The Black-bellied Plover, here shown on its nest in Alaska, is one of the many shorebirds that breeds on the tundra when myriads of summer insects are available for feeding young. It winters from southern United States into South America, and in the Old World from the Mediterranean to South Africa. (Courtesy of L. H. Walkinshaw.)*

but desert it completely in winter. Gray-cheeked Thrushes inhabit the willow-fringed streams, as do Tree Sparrows and Northern Shrikes, but these three are more characteristic of the ecotone which meets the coniferous forest southward.

CONIFEROUS FOREST (ALSO CALLED TAIGA). This occupies a broad belt around the world (the largest coniferous forest development in the world is in Siberia) and is composed predominantly of spruces and balsam fir, stunted on the north where it merges with the tundra, but forming fine stands of valuable but often inaccessible timber southward.

Strictly, or almost strictly, coniferous forest birds are the Spruce Grouse (Fig. 155), Northern and Black-backed Three-toed Woodpeckers, Gray Jay, Brown Creeper, Golden-crowned and Ruby-crowned Kinglets, several warblers, and several cone- or catkin-feeding fringillids. The Yellow-bellied Flycatcher inhabits the more boggy or swampy portions, and the Winter Wren favors the brushy undergrowth, particularly along streams. The Yellow-bellied Sapsucker and Black-throated Green Warbler are good examples of birds which extend their range southward into hardwood forests.

DECIDUOUS FOREST. This is the climax forest type that prevails over most of the eastern states, but of course it is greatly altered by cleared lands. Mature forests are chiefly oak-hickory, but a broad ecotone (sub-

*Fig. 155. The Spruce Grouse is a characteristic coniferous forest bird. Here a displaying male shows off in a Michigan jack-pine area. (Photo by Edward M. Brigham, Jr., from Wood's Birds of Michigan,* Univ. of Mich. Mus. Zool. Misc. Publ. 75.)

Canadian forest), primarily of beech-maple-hemlock, merges with the coniferous forest in the north, and a pine subclimax characterizes the southern states. The various pines (both northern and southern) and the beech-maple have their special birds, more or less distinct from those typical of the oak-hickory climax. Those characteristic of the latter include such so-called Carolinian or Austral birds as the Red-bellied Woodpecker, Tufted Titmouse, Wood Thrush, and Yellow-throated Vireo, whose ranges are fairly sharply delineated northward by the beech-maple ecotone. Many other birds, however, range over both the oak-hickory and beech-maple areas, and still others occupy particular habitats within one or several biomes. The Song Sparrow, for example, occupies a type of habitat (primarily edge) that is widely available throughout all North American biomes.

In general, deciduous woodlots have a greater diversity and density of bird life than the other North American biomes (see p. 307), but this varies greatly wtih the stage of succession, amount of dispersion (mixed stands usually have higher populations than uniform stands), presence of water, special food supplies, and other factors. Bond (1957), in a study of breeding birds in sixty-four upland hardwood stands in seventeen counties in southern Wisconsin, found the greatest density in intermediate (mixed) stands and decreased numbers toward the climax stages.

GRASSLAND. The grassland biome occupies a broad strip of the central plains, paralleling the 100th meridian on both sides, from the Rio Grande northward into the Canadian prairie provinces. Annual rainfall is inadequate for forest growth; presumably the western plains never were clothed with trees. Plantings for windbreaks and about homesteads now provide some cover for birds, but otherwise open country prevails. Particularly notable developments of similar grasslands outside this country include the pampas of Argentina, the steppes of Europe and Asia, and the parklike savannas (veld) of Africa.

Grassland birds in this country include the Burrowing Owl, prairie chickens, Horned Larks, the Western Meadowlark, Dickcissel, and several open-country sparrows. Most of these, though originally true grassland birds, have invaded cleared lands to the east, even reaching the Atlantic Coast. A possible explanation, both of the occurrence and extinction, of the Heath Hen (a form of the Prairie Chicken) on the East Coast is that it represented a relict form from a former wider extension of grasslands. Many other species, not typically prairie forms, have taken advantage of special niches provided by man or nature—swallows about buildings and bridges, doves in the windbreaks, marsh and water birds about pot holes or sloughs—but in general the grasslands have a low density of breeding birds.

DESERTS. Deserts (Fig. 156r) are characterized by deficiency of rainfall, which is low or erratically distributed. Permanent streams cannot arise in a desert, although they may flow through if they have a source in outlying humid regions. Permanent ground water is not available, so only *xerophytes* (drought-resistant plants) can survive. From the standpoint of plant and animal life deserts are inhospitable regions—day and night temperatures have sharp extremes, winds are often severe, food and cover are scarce and unevenly distributed—hence animals are highly specialized to exist under desert conditions. Many are cursorial and cover a wide range in foraging; others are nocturnal and many live in burrows to escape the heat of the day, wind-blown sand, and predators.

Bird life in the southwestern scrub, or "hot," deserts includes quite a few predatory species—hawks, owls, Loggerhead Shrikes, and the Roadrunner—which live largely on rodents, reptiles, and ground-dwelling arthropods, but erratically distributed seed-eaters take advantage of the sudden seed supply when occasional rains make any available. Dixon (1959) found 17 species (not including wide-ranging raptors) on a 33-acre plot of scrub desert in western Texas. Quite a few species nest in cactus, either in cavities (Elf Owl, Gila Woodpecker—Fig. 156l) or among the thorns (Cactus Wren). The more northern sagebrush plains, commonly called "cold" deserts, are inhabited by the Sage Grouse, Sage Thrasher, and an interesting assortment of fringillids.

*Fig. 156. Deserts vary from sandflats with little or no vegetation and practically no bird life to those that show quite a diversity, though low density, of both plants and birds. The Gila Woodpecker (left) is one of several species that utilizes cactus for nest sites. (Photos by Dale A. Zimmerman.)*

## Habitats and Population Ecology

From this account of biomes it should be apparent that each can be broken down in successively smaller ecological units, or habitats, until perhaps a single kind of tree or level in trees can serve as a microhabitat for a bird. Even the most monotonous and uniform landscapes, such as deserts and grasslands, may be quite diversified ecologically. American deserts vary from the virtually birdless Bonneville Salt Flats in Utah to southwestern scrub areas which have an interesting diversity though not a great density of birds. The veld in South Africa, a grassland which may have scattered shrubs and trees, is divisible into grass veld, bush veld, and tree (acacia) veld, each with its characteristic animal life.

The richer and more varied biomes can be subdivided even further. Batts (1958) divides nesting habitats on a southern Michigan farm (deciduous forest biome) into (1) open water, (2) marsh, (3) woods, (4) woodslope, (5) fencerow, and (6) fields (alpha and beta). Allen (1961) divides birds of the woodlands, primarily on the basis of nest sites, into (1) birds of the forest floor, (2) birds of the undergrowth, (3) birds of the lower branches, (4) birds of the tree trunks and hollow branches, and (5) birds of the higher branches and treetops. Such stratification is even more pronounced in tropical rain forests (Fig. 157). Different birds also characterize different altitudinal levels in mountains.

*Fig. 157. A tropical cloud forest in Chiapas, Mexico, showing the luxurious development and great diversity of plant life, which in turn supports a great variety of bird life, from strictly terrestrial forms to those seen only in the treetops. (Photo by Dale A. Zimmerman.)*

As already indicated, certain species (e.g., Common Crow, Starling) are very adaptable and utilize a variety of habitats; others (e.g., Kirtland's Warbler, the northern race of the Everglade Kite) are restricted to limited niches. Still others (e.g., Marsh Hawk, kingfishers) may not be abundant in any one place, but utilize a habitat that is widespread throughout the world—that is, there are many fish-eating birds in aquatic places, but only the kingfishers, in most parts of the world, fish the small streams. Such habitat selection reduces competition, and also provides for more complete utilization of all ecological units. Closely related species, occupying similar habitats, usually have slightly different requirements. Salt (1957) noted that Fox Sparrows, Lincoln's Sparrows, and Song Sparrows living in the same marsh in Wyoming occupied different niches and had slightly different food habits; the Lincoln's Sparrow fed on 40 per cent plant food and 60 per cent animal, while the Song Sparrow reversed these percentages and the Fox Sparrow was intermediate. Davis (1957) observed different foraging behavior (depth of scratching), food selection, and habitat preference in Brown and Spotted Towhees in California. Often the presence of two or more similar species in a similar habitat tends to keep them somewhat segregated (ecologically), but the absence of one or more of them allows the others to overflow the unoccupied space.

Habitats vary greatly in diversity and density of bird life. In general, deserts and grasslands are low both in number of species and numbers of individuals (birds per acre), mixed woodlots are high compared to uniform stands; marshes and swamplands, especially if harboring such semicolonial forms as blackbirds and rails, have high concentrations. Kendeigh (1948) calculated the density of breeding birds in several biotic communities in northern Michigan and found 56 pairs per 100 acres in grasslands, 112 pairs in pine-aspen, 146 in cedar-balsam, and 155 in beech-maple-pine, thus disclosing a rising trend from the more open areas to the more diversified woodlots. Dixon (1959) found desert habitats in western Texas varying from only 15 males (pairs) per 100 acres to 51 in desert scrub, but of course lower densities, presumably approaching zero, could be found in completely barren deserts. At the other extreme, much higher densities have been recorded in spruce-fir forests in Ontario (Kendeigh, 1947) and Maine (Hensley and Cope, 1951) during budworm infestations (385 pairs per 100 acres in the Maine sample). The spruce-fir forest populations were augmented by a concentration of breeding warblers with small territories.

Still greater densities, or selection for desired species, can be achieved in managed areas. Since diversity is to some extent a reflection of the amount of interspersion of different vegetation types, it is a common practice in management to create as much edge and mixture as possible by planting and cutting, or other management measures, either to improve conditions for selected species (waterfowl, gamebirds, or songbirds) or merely to create a more favorable environment for all wildlife. A "farm" in Maryland is said to have a nesting population of 59 pairs per acre, or many times the number found on ordinary farmland, but nearly half of these were box-nesting Purple Martins not confined to their nesting area. Stine (1959) listed 41 species nesting in an 18-acre woods on Bird Haven Sanctuary in Illinois over a ten-year period, most of them present every year or nearly every year. Nineteen additional species occurred on adjacent farmland in the sanctuary. The total density of bird life (pairs per acre) was not given, but the great diversity of nesting species (60) attracted to the sanctuary seems phenomenal. Sprunt (1960) has recorded an extraordinary total of 156 species at his one-acre home outside Charleston, South Carolina, but these include visitors to the grounds over a long period of time.

Some amazing aggregations of nesting birds have been recorded among colonial species on islands (Fig. 158), rocky ledges, and in marshes. A few of these, perhaps the world's greatest concentrations of breeding birds, are listed in Table 8.

*Table 8. Some Large Colonies of Breeding Birds*

| *Species* | *Density* | *Authority* |
|---|---|---|
| Adelie Penguin | 215,000 in 55-acre rookery | Eklund, 1959 |
| Slender-billed Shearwater | 150,000,000, Bass Straits, Australia | Peterson, 1948 |
| Gannet | 7,500 pairs on Bonaventure Island | Fisher, 1954 |
| Guanay Cormorant | 4–5,000,000 on one island, Peru | Hann, 1945 |
| Greater Flamingo | 3,300 nests on 1,436 sq. yds., India | Shivrajkumer, *et al.*, 1960 |
| Sooty Terns | 14,520 pairs/acre, Dry Tortugas | Peterson, 1948 |
| Common Murre | 750,000 on 17-acre island, Oregon | Peterson, 1948 |
| Dovekie | 5,000,000 in Scoreby Bay, Greenland | Snyder, 1960 |
| Auklets (3 species) | 220,000 to 1,520,000 on 2 by 1.5 mile island, Alaska | Kenyon and Brooks, 1960 |
| Tricolored Blackbirds | 5–10,000 nests/acre, California | Emlen, 1941 |

Bird populations are ascertained by inventories and censuses (see Chapter 16). One important aspect of this is to evaluate the status of various species for management purposes, either for harvesting safe numbers of a game species, or to try to preserve vanishing forms. Hence, we often know by actual count the approximate numbers of critical species—about forty surviving Whooping Cranes, 60 California Condors, 400 pairs of Kirtland's Warblers. Censuses also enable ornithologists to estimate populations over larger areas. Great Britain estimates her land bird breeding population at 60 million pairs. Peterson (1948) calculated that there are 5 to 6 billion breeding birds (3 billion pairs) in the United States.

Another important aspect of such inventories is to evaluate population changes from year to year. Bird numbers fluctuate markedly, sometimes for unknown reasons, sometimes from obvious causes. Many species have declined, or become extinct (Chapter 14), because of man's activities, but some birds have increased. McAtee (1951), in a study of bird records in the District of Columbia over an eighty-year period (1861–1942) listed 37 species that had increased, 50 that had decreased, and 44 that had suffered little or no change. Stine (1959), comparing her 1945–1955 records at the Bird Haven Sanctuary in Illinois with those of Ridgway in 1907–1910,

*Fig. 158. The several million Guanay Cormorants inhabiting this island in the Chincha group off the coast of Peru constitute one of the greatest concentrations of bird life in the world. (Courtesy of Amer. Mus. Nat. Hist.)*

found that 52 of Ridgway's species were still present but that 21 were gone, due apparently to changes in habitat.

Some of the modern hazards to birds are treated briefly in Chapter 14, but it should be noted here that population trends seem to have been drastically downward in recent years. *Audubon Field Notes,* a journal which digests and summarizes the field records of a large corps of observers all over the United States, portrayed a dismal picture of the situation in the late 1950's, but it is not certain yet that the scarcities noted were more than temporary fluctuations. Rookery birds declined sharply in the southeast, due apparently to a succession of dry breeding seasons, but recovered to some extent after a rainy season. The recent duck decline, due largely to drought and drainage in the prairie marsh lands, was reflected in the 1961 restrictions in hunting regulations. By 1958 songbird populations (except for such hardy and adaptable species as Starlings, House Sparrows, Common Grackles, and Red-winged Blackbirds) were reported to have plunged to an all-time low. This was attributed, by most observers, to the unprecedentedly severe southern winter of 1957–1958 followed in the northeast by a cold rainy breeding season, and to the unremitting use of insecticides in so many large scale "eradication" programs (gypsy moths in the northeast, fire ants in the southeast, and elm bark beetles in the midwest). By 1960, however, some of the "disaster" species seemed to be increasing again, giving hope that the reductions were only temporary, and showing that short-term fluctuations are not a dependable indication of long-term trends.

## Selected References

Allen, Arthur A. *The Book of Bird Life.* 2nd ed. New York: Van Nostrand, 1961. Chapt. III–VI.

Barden, Albert A., Jr. Distribution of the Families of Birds. *Auk* (1941), **58**:543–557.

Clements, F. E., and V. E. Shelford. *Bio-Ecology*. New York: Wiley, 1939.

Darlington, P. J. *Zoogeography: The Geographical Distribution of Animals.* New York: Wiley, 1957.

Dice, Lee R. *The Biotic Provinces of North America.* Ann Arbor, Mich.: U. of Mich., 1943.

Griscom, Ludlow. *Modern Bird Study.* Cambridge, Mass.: Harvard U.P., 1945. Chapt. VI–IX.

Kendeigh, S. C. Bird Populations and Biotic Communities in Northern Lower Michigan. *Ecology* (1948), **29**:101–114.

Matthew, W. D. Climate and Evolution. *Spec. Publ. N. Y. Acad. Sci.* (1939), **1**:xii, plus 223 pp.

Mayr, Ernst. History of the North American Bird Fauna. *Wilson Bull.* (1946b), **58**:3–41.

Merriam, C. Hart. Laws of Temperature Control of the Geographical Distribution of Terrestrial Animals and Plants. *Natl. Geog. Mag.* (1894), **6**:229–238.

———. Life Zones and Crop Zones of the United States. *Bull. U. S. Biol. Sur.* (1898), **10**:1–79.

Peterson, Roger T. *Birds over America.* New York: Dodd, 1948. Billions of Birds, pp. 56–70.

Pitelka, F. A. Distribution of Birds in Relation to Major Biotic Communities. *Amer. Mid. Nat.* (1941), **25**:113–137.

Serventy, D. L. Geographical Distribution of Birds. Chapt. IV in A. J. Marshall's *Biology and Comparative Physiology of Birds.* New York: Academic, 1960.

Wallace, Alfred Russel. *The Geographical Distribution of Animals.* 2 vols. New York: Harpers, 1876.

# 13

# FOOD HABITS AND ECONOMIC RELATIONS

This chapter deals with various economic aspects of bird life, but is concerned mainly with food habits and the relation these have to man and other animals. A few of these relationships have been brought out in a general way in Chapter 1; these need to be expanded at this point and the subject of food habits explored in more detail.

## *Birds as Food*

Undoubtedly man's first interest in birds, in prehistoric times, was as a food supply. Birds were well established long before man appeared on earth, and the number of flightless forms, far more than exist today, permitted their easy capture without modern weapons. Earliest history records the use of birds as food; the ancient laws of Moses even discriminated between "clean" and "unclean" fowl.

In many instances birds aided immeasurably in man's conquest and settlement of new regions: penguins in the Antarctic are credited with saving a Dutch expedition from starvation en route to the East Indies in 1599, the Cahow or Bermuda Petrel averted a famine in Bermuda in 1614 (Murphy and Mowbray, 1951), and the dodos and perhaps elephant-birds were exterminated primarily by navigators stopping off at Madagascar and nearby islands to replenish supplies. Similarly the early settlement of Patagonia probably would not have been possible without rheas and their eggs, and Eskimos could not inhabit Cape York, Greenland, without the Dovekie (Chapman, 1943). Archeological investigations of burial sites of prehistoric Indians in the Ohio valley testify to the abundant use of birds, particularly of the wild Turkey and Passenger Pigeon, for food (Black, 1953).

The role of game in the early settlement of this country, briefly touched on in Chapter 1, has been well documented. Figures cited for the numbers of wild game on city markets in market hunting days are literally appalling. Chapman (1943), for instance, writes of an 1864 shipment of 20 tons of Prairie Chickens, of 14,850,000 Passenger Pigeons shipped from a Michigan nest site in 1861, and of 5,719,214 game birds on the New Orleans market in 1909. Figures cited in the works of Forbush (1907), Hartley (1922), Henderson (1927), and others are equally staggering. Up to about 1913, millions of songbirds, particularly Robins, Eastern Meadowlarks, and Bobolinks in the southern states, were also included in the legal kill.

Today birds and their eggs are still used—are indeed often virtually indispensable—for food by primitive people in many lands, but in most civilized countries birds can no longer support indiscriminate hunting. Hence the harvest is now restricted to game species during special seasons, and the birds are taken primarily for sport rather than food. Nevertheless, wild game as meat on the table is no small item. The legal take of waterfowl in the United States in a relatively short open season runs close to 20 million birds annually; the pheasant harvest in South Dakota, though highly variable, usually reaches several millions each fall; and a few northern states, such as New York, Michigan, and Minnesota, take close to a million grouse per year, periodically low years notwithstanding. The harvest of Mourning Doves, in states that permit dove shooting, was estimated at 19 million in 1959. Woodcock and rails, in lesser numbers, and Bobwhite and several species of southwestern quail also enter prominently in the hunters' bag. Introduced game birds, such as Gray or Hungarian Partridges and the Chukar, are established in some states, but as in the case of the native Turkey, the legal harvest is comparatively small. Thus wild birds serve as a supplement for many people to the more extensive domestic supply of poultry and other fowl.

The history of the use of birds for food in most European countries does not closely parallel the trend in the United States. For two thousand years the game birds, carefully protected by seasonal regulations, have been more or less reserved for the people of higher rank, whereas songbirds and waterfowl were the property of the common people. After the French Revolution, in a wave of freedom for the individual, France even abolished all game laws for a time. Italy has long been noted for its systematic methods of trapping and netting songbirds, both for food and for pets, a practice that still prevails to some extent, in spite of protective laws. The Japanese are experts in the art of netting birds, for scientific purposes, to protect crops, and for food.

Eggs of wild birds are no longer harvested for food in this country, but some European countries, notably Holland and Germany, permit collecting of the first eggs of the Lapwing (*Vanellus vanellus*), but allow the birds to retain their later clutches (Fig. 159). Icelanders also take wild duck eggs early in the season, but carefully protect subsequent nestings. Indians in the high Andes have been harvesting flamingo eggs, somewhat ruthlessly, for the market for centuries, but inaccessibility of the nesting sites (14,800 feet) helps protect the birds.

## Plumages

In the past, birds have served man with a variety of economic products. Among minor items might be mentioned the beaks of Ivory-billed Woodpeckers which were in considerable demand by American Indians for decorative wear. Bird bones were sometimes used for tools and at one time the leg bones of kiwis were in demand for pipe stems among New Zealanders. But it is principally the plumages of birds that have served widespread use. Feathers have been used from time immemorial for arrow

*Fig. 159. This lapwing, an attractive Eurasian plover with spectacular aerial displays in the breeding season, is used for food in some countries and its eggs are sold on the market. (Courtesy of Georg Hoffman, Bremen, Germany.)*

making, for headgear, and for ornamental wear. Such practices still prevail among primitive people, but the commercial use of wild bird plumages is now illegal in this country.

Down from various species of waterfowl—ducks, geese, and swans—has been used since early times for clothing and bedding, but the highest quality of down comes from several species of eider ducks. In Arctic regions a number of legal eider-down industries harvest feathers on a large scale. The down is collected from nests, usually twice each season, while the ducks continue incubating minus most of their original nest material. The extreme lightness and superior quality of eider down may be inferred from the fact that it requires the feathers from thirty-five to forty nests, each profusely supplied with down, to make a pound. Though eider down has often been wastefully exploited in the past, in Iceland the natives carefully guard the supply and have practically domesticated their eider ducks.

In South America the skins of rheas are still used for rug making and their feathers extensively used for dusters. Chapman (1943) reports 60 tons of rhea feathers once found in a warehouse in Buenos Aires, baled and ready for shipment to New York. Another Argentine warehouse had hundreds of thousands of skins of the Black-necked Swan to be used solely for powder puffs. The wings and tails of Andean Condors were also in great demand. One Argentine hunter admitted shipping 16,000 to Paris, at $20 per bird, but when the price dropped to $10 he refused to participate further "in the destruction of such a noble bird for such a low price."

The history of the use of special plumes and plumages for millinery purposes and the near-extermination of many of our most beautiful birds (mentioned briefly in Chapter 14) is too long a story to relate here. In special demand were the nuptial plumes (aigrettes) of egrets (Fig. 26) and herons, which at one time commanded a price of $32 an ounce, but dried skins of many smaller species, such as hummingbirds and even terns, were also used. In 1885 Chapman (1943) counted 173 birds of 40 species on women's hats on Fourteenth Street, then the fashionable shopping district in New York City. Figures on the annual kill here and in South America (the source of hummingbirds for the world market) are appalling; Hartley (1922) reported 55 million in one season in the United States and England imported 35 million annually.

In the Old World, birds of paradise from New Guinea were in great demand in the hat shops of Paris, Amsterdam, and London. This traffic in feathers began in Magellan's time (1522) and lasted until 1924, when legal restrictions made ghost towns of New Guinea ports that lived on the plume trade (Mayr, 1945). Japanese poachers nearly exterminated the Short-tailed Albatross, which once nested in the Bonin Islands by the millions; the birds were plucked of their coveted feathers and their bodies used for fertilizer. The most elaborate feather work in the world was perfected in Hawaii. Feather cloaks worn by the nobility, sometimes composed of only the breast feathers of small birds, were valued at $10,000 (Chapman, 1943). Peterson (1960b) reports that a museum in Honolulu has a cloak composed of the yellow shoulder feathers of 80,000 oos (a Hawaiian honey-eater now believed to be extinct).

Perhaps the most valuable plume producer at the present time is the Ostrich, which fortunately, unlike egrets and many other ornamental types, lends itself fairly readily to domestication. Ostrich farms have been a flourishing industry in Africa for nearly a century, bringing in an annual revenue of $13,500,000 in 1913 (Reese, 1942). A single pair of tame birds was worth nearly a thousand dollars. Now Ostrich farms have sprung up in many other parts of the world, in Europe, Argentina, and southern United States. Feathers, particularly the numerous ornamental wing and tail plumes, are plucked or clipped once or twice (usually twice) annually. In the millinery trade the feathers are usually dyed a bright shade of red or blue, though black is also a popular color.

## Other Economic Products

Birds are sometimes used for oil, though this is hardly practical for commercial purposes. In northern South America the young of the Oilbird (*Steatornis caripensis*), which are fed on rich fruit of palm trees until they become helpless globs of fat, are collected by natives who melt out the oil into earthen pots and use it in cooking. On St. Kilda, an island off the Scottish coast, the oil regurgitated by fulmars during nesting is collected and used by natives for medicinal purposes, externally and internally, particularly for rheumatism. Another strange use is the lighting of the oily bodies of small petrels to serve as torches. Oil rendered from penguins is sometimes used for candles in the Antarctic.

The greatest single economic product (other than food) from birds is guano. In certain dry climates the unleached excrement of large colonies of fish-eating birds builds up deposits which furnish an extremely valuable fertilizer, rich in phosphates and nitrogen. The most productive region is on islands off the coast of Peru (Fig. 160), among colonies of the Guanay

*Fig. 160. Photo of guano cutting at the Chincha Islands taken about 1860, showing thickness of old beds. The present-day guano harvest, though not comparable to early days, is an extremely valuable resource. (Courtesy of Amer. Mus. Nat. Hist.)*

Cormorant (*Phalacrocorax bougainvillii*). Like most other natural resources, the guano deposits were recklessly exploited in the past; at one time revenue from them defrayed the entire cost of the Peruvian government. Fortunately the country finally became aware of the permanent value of this resource and, with the help of American advisers, set up a commendable long-range plan of sustained harvest (Vogt, 1948). The Guanay Cormorant has been called the most valuable bird in the world. (See Murphy, 1936, and Hutchinson, 1950, for more complete information on guano deposition.)

## *Aesthetic and Educational Values*

We need dwell only briefly on the well-known aesthetic and educational value of birds. Birds have figured prominently in works of art and literature from prehistoric times. They are among the most colorful forms of animal life, have a wide and usually pleasing assortment of vocal performances, and their fascinating habits have intrigued and challenged man for centuries. Birds play an important role in education—in the preschool instruction of children, among Audubon Junior clubs whose enrollees have numbered more than ten million, and in adult education as well. One need only view the many organizations devoted to the study and enjoyment of birds (Chapter 17) or cruise the spacious halls of the natural history museums of New York, Washington, Chicago, or Denver to realize the really profound part that birds play in the education and cultural enrichment of man (Fig. 161).

## *Food Habits*

The great economic value of birds in the suppression of destructive insects and other pests has long been realized. Yet strangely the Migratory Bird Treaty Act to protect migratory birds did not go into full effect until 1918 (p. 358), and even now some of our most valuable allies, the hawks and owls, are not fully protected. Longfellow's *Birds of Killingworth* portrays an imaginary but not unrealistic situation in which an unappreciative and ignorant citizenry deliberately rid their community of all birds and then reaped the presumed result of desolation and ruin. A few decades ago it was a common practice to try to place a monetary value on the services of birds or to predict how long mankind could survive without them; but we now know that the work of the birds was overrated in many of these estimates and that the chief controls of insects are among the insects themselves (parasitic and predaceous forms) and weather. Now, also, modern insecticides have taken over many of the pest-control functions formerly performed by birds.

*Fig. 161. Bird group in the Gobi Desert of Central Asia, one of the many aesthetically appealing, educational exhibits in the American Museum of Natural History in New York. Note the Great Bustard (left), Demoiselle Cranes (center), and the Pallas Sandgrouse (lower right). (Courtesy of Amer. Mus. Nat. Hist.)*

The role of birds in the complex web of life is impossible to evaluate accurately. W. L. McAtee, after a long lifetime of study on the food habits of birds, merely concludes that they play an important part in the constant suppression, rather than outright control, of insect pests, that they sometimes curb potential outbreaks, and on occasion may even avert disaster.

Perhaps the most widely publicized example of the role of birds in averting crop disaster was the "cricket plague" in Utah which threatened to destroy the Mormons' second planting of crops. A visitation of "hundreds and thousands" of California Gulls cleared the fields of crickets and saved the settlers from probable starvation. In grateful appreciation of the services of the birds and of divine providence, the Mormons erected the famous monument to the gulls in Salt Lake City at a cost of $40,000. A somewhat similar case is that of the Rocky Mountain locust plague which swept over the Great Plains states in the summers of 1873–1876. Many, but not all, fields of grain were saved by birds; in Nebraska more than 200 species were found to be feeding in part on locusts. However, great damage was done before the locust was brought under control, and it is a moot question whether it died out from natural causes (it is now believed by some to be extinct) or from man's persistent war against it.

Many such examples, mostly less spectacular, might be cited. McAtee

(1920) listed seventy instances of local extermination of plagues of insects and other pests by birds. A modern version of this was the help of woodpeckers in 1951 in combating bark beetles in Colorado spruce forests. A large buildup of woodpeckers that season, perhaps due to the local availability of food, effectively supplemented roadblocks and insecticides in preventing the spread of beetles. In some areas 75 per cent of the beetle population was taken by woodpeckers (100 per cent in some trees), and some collected specimens had 90 per cent bark beetles in their stomachs (Olson, 1953).

Exactly what birds eat and in what quantities is no longer conjecture. Ornithologists in this country have been making scientific studies of food habits for nearly a century. Staff members of the former Biological Survey and its successor, the Fish and Wildlife Service, have now analyzed more than 100,000 stomachs of birds from nearly all parts of North America. Thus, in a general way at least, the food trends of most of our birds are already known. This does not mean that such studies are no longer needed. Analysis in Washington of sample stomachs from various parts of the country is not a good criterion of what Marsh Hawks eat in Georgia's quail country or North Dakota's waterfowl marshes, nor is the diet of a Great Horned Owl in an overpopulated pheasant area a true reflection of its prey at the peak of a rabbit cycle. More detailed data are needed on regional studies, with seasonal or year to year variations, before the role of a species in a community can be evaluated.

It is convenient, though not always logical, to describe the food habits of birds by dividing them into groups, such as seed-eating and insectivorous, but of course few birds belong exclusively in one group. The Common Crow, for instance, feeds to a considerable extent on seeds and grain, but it is also insectivorous, a scavenger, a predator, and even a fisherman at times. The following summary lists the prevailing food for the most prominent families of North American birds, and succeeding paragraphs discuss the food-habit groups in more detail. It should be borne in mind, however, that there are great variations among species in some families and that the trends cited pertain primarily to North America rather than to the world as a whole.

## *Food Habits of Some North American Families of Birds*

Gaviidae—mostly fish, but consume some insects and other invertebrates.
Podicipedidae—fish, amphibians, aquatic invertebrates; ingest their own feathers regularly.
Pelecanidae—almost entirely fish.
Phalacrocoracidae—mostly fish, some amphibians and crustacea.
Ardeidae—fish, frogs, mice, miscellaneous vertebrates and invertebrates.
Anatidae:
  Swans—grazers, almost entirely vegetarian.
  Geese—grazers, mostly vegetarian.
  "Puddle" ducks—chiefly vegetarian; tubers, seeds, foliage; some animal food.
  Fresh-water divers—mixed animal and vegetable; great species variations.
  "Sea" ducks—predominantly animal, crustaceans and molluscs.
  Mergansers—chiefly fish, sometimes depredations in trout streams.
Cathartidae—scavengers, chiefly dead animals, but sometimes take nestling birds and newborn mammals.
Accipitridae—predators on animals, very variable (see Fig. 165).
Pandionidae—almost exclusively fish.
Falconidae—large birds (Peregrine); insects, mice, and birds (Sparrow and Pigeon Hawks).
Tetraonidae—browsers; buds, foliage, berries, some insects.
Phasianidae—chiefly vegetarian, grain and weed seeds; some insects.
Gruidae—omnivorous; insects and small vertebrates, grain, fruit.
Rallidae—omnivorous; rails on a mixture of plant and animal matter, coots predominantly on vegetable.
Charadriidae—mainly animal matter.
Scolopacidae—mainly animal, beachcombers and scavengers.
Laridae—gulls omnivorous, chiefly scavengers on fish and refuse, insects in fields; terns feed on living fish and invertebrates.
Columbidae—grain, seeds, vegetable matter; feed young on "pigeon's milk."
Cuculidae—chiefly insectivorous (hairy caterpillars); Roadrunner on small vertebrates.
Strigidae—mostly mammalian prey (but see discussion).
Caprimulgidae—"Hawk" insects (mosquitos, moths) on the wing.
Apodidae—nearly 100 per cent insects (aeroplankton) caught on the wing.
Trochilidae—insects, arachnids, and nectar from flowers.
Alcedinidae—mainly fish (in the United States); some amphibians and aquatic invertebrates.
Picidae—most species mainly insectivorous; some feed on cambium, sap, mast.

Tyrannidae—almost exclusively insectivorous; phoebes sometimes catch fish.
Alaudidae—mainly seeds; some insects.
Hirundinidae—almost exclusively insectivorous, but Tree Swallow eats some fruit in winter.
Corvidae—omnivorous; predators (nest robbers), scavengers, and grain feeders.
Paridae—mainly insectivorous, but consume seeds, nuts, fruit, especially in winter.
Sittidae—mainly insectivorous, but consume nuts and seeds, especially in winter.
Certhiidae—almost exclusively insectivorous; a few seeds.
Troglodytidae—almost exclusively insectivorous.
Mimidae—mainly insectivorous, but considerable fruit.
Turdidae—mainly insectivorous (or other invertebrates—earthworms, spiders); much fruit in season.
Sylviidae—almost entirely insectivorous (or other small invertebrates).
Bombycillidae—mainly fruit, some insects, buds, and flower parts.
Laniidae—predatory on small mammals, birds, and large insects.
Sturnidae—omnivorous.
Vireonidae—almost exclusively insectivorous; some fruit.
Parulidae—mainly insectivorous; some fruit (puncture grapes) in fall.
Icteridae—omnivorous; orioles and meadowlarks predominantly insectivorous; others feed heavily on grain.
Fringillidae—very variable; some predominantly seed-eaters, especially in winter, some mainly insectivorous.

## INSECTIVOROUS BIRDS

The insect-eating propensity of birds is one of their best known traits. Most passerine species, which comprise more than half of the birds of the world, are predominantly insectivorous; other passerines, even the seed-eaters, feed in part on insects, especially during the nesting season. Many nonpasserines (woodpeckers, swifts, goatsuckers, cuckoos, and most shore-birds) are also insectivorous; others, even ducks, herons, hawks, and owls, take some insects. Probably there is no family of North American birds that does not feed to some extent on insects, although pigeons and some finches (e.g., goldfinches) are almost exclusively granivorous.

It is not feasible here to attempt even a summary of how birds get their insect prey, but a few generalizations can be made. Woodpeckers drill with their powerful beaks for borers that infest trees; chickadees, nuthatches, and creepers, with their less powerful bills, merely probe into bark crevices for hidden eggs and hibernating prey. Warblers and vireos glean the surfaces of leaves and smaller branches (Fig. 162). Flycatchers catch flying

*Fig. 162. The insect-eating capacity of small birds in the nesting season, when insects are approaching their maximum abundance, is enormous. Many birds feed their young more than a hundred times a day. Here a Nashville Warbler in northern Michigan brings another load. (Courtesy of L. H. Walkinshaw.)*

insects by darting out from perches, whereas swifts and swallows pursue those found in more open spaces. When night falls, the Whip-poor-wills and nighthawks take up the quest for nocturnal forms. Thrushes and Ovenbirds take care of the forest floor, while many icterids and ground-feeding fringillids forage among planted grains and grasses. An interesting assortment of marsh and water birds cover the aquatic habitats, although often their insect fare is not of great economic concern to man. Even the cuckoos have their field of specialization in consuming hairy caterpillars which most birds avoid. In such ways are all habitats cared for by the varied activities of insect-eating birds.

Instances of insect-eating birds affecting man's interests adversely are rather rare. Kingbirds in this country and honeyguides in Africa sometimes annoy beekeepers, but stomach analyses of the former show that the bees taken are mainly the almost useless drones, and that the incidental consumption of robber flies, which prey on honeybees, is presumably of material benefit to beekeepers. Many insects are beneficial, however, and of course some of these get taken by birds. Thrushes include a small percentage of beneficial ground beetles in their otherwise highly commendable fare, and so do crows and blackbirds. House Sparrows, with so many black marks against them, make bad matters worse by consuming some beneficial insects.

GRANIVOROUS BIRDS

Though few birds feed exclusively on seeds or grain, since nearly all of them provide their young with insects at first, many fringillids, icterids, Horned Larks, and some nonpasserines are predominantly seed-eaters much of the year. Most items taken are weed seeds or waste grains, and seed-eating birds have thus often been cited as farmers' friends, but of course the actual economic gain to farmers by the reduction of weed seeds is impossible to measure. Actual quantities consumed can be estimated; a classic example is that Beal's study of Tree Sparrows in Iowa, which were estimated to consume 875 tons of weed seeds in one winter. It still is not clear, however, just what effect this truly great reduction in weed seeds had on the farms in question. Still other seed-eating species, such as crossbills and Pine Grosbeaks extracting seeds from cones of northern conifers, may feed largely on items or in areas that have less bearing on man's interests.

Instances of strictly seed-eating species doing damage under natural conditions are rather unusual. Sometimes transient sparrows, especially White-throated and White-crowned Sparrows, congregate on newly planted lawns during their spring migration and consume grass seed. Resident House Sparrows are a perennial threat to such enterprises. Nurseries and seed industries sometimes suffer heavy losses from seed-eating birds; bounties were once offered on Horned Larks in California to avert such damage. Abbott (1958) outlines some of these problems and the use of repellents to control them.

Budding on fruit trees by Purple Finches and some other fringillids in spring is sometimes extensive enough to be an economic loss, though a reasonable amount of such natural pruning may even be desirable in improving the quality of the developing fruit. The debudding of apricot and almond trees by linnets in California (Biehn, 1951) or the actual consumption of the almonds by woodpeckers and corvids (Emlen, 1937) may constitute serious crop damage. Pine Grosbeaks in the Adirondacks feed on the terminal and lateral buds of pines, particularly plantings of Scotch pine, to such an extent that their growth for timber or Christmas trees is seriously affected (Cook and Littlefield, 1945). In years of low cone production, extraction of the seeds of pines may limit reproduction; in a California study the year's supply of sugar pine seeds was found to be entirely harvested by birds and small mammals (Tevis, 1953).

Many seed-eaters include grains in their diet, often only waste grains left in fields after harvest, but in other cases extensive damage may be done to growing crops. House Sparrows add to their ill reputation by feeding on the green sprouts in spring, maturing grain in the summer, shocked grain in the fall, and stored grain in winter. Blackbirds congregate in flocks in late summer and raid grainfields, often doing extensive damage to mature or nearly mature grains, including corn in the milk. Injury to corn by Red-winged Blackbirds in Michigan in this way may be quite heavy (Fig. 163l), causing a loss of 20 per cent or more of the total crop in severe cases (Cardinell and Hayne, 1945). In marshes, large flocks of icterids sometimes completely harvest wild rice beds before migrating ducks arrive. Monocultural practices in agriculture tend to aggravate problems of grain-feeding birds by concentrating them in favorable feeding areas in the fall and winter (Buchheister, 1960; Dykstra, 1960).

*Fig. 163. Left, corn damage by Red-wings in Michigan—a somewhat exaggerated example, as only a few spots in a large cornpiece would normally suffer damage like this. Right, an acetylene exploder, set to explode with a loud report at timed intervals, has proved an economical and efficient means of dispersing blackbird flocks. It is patented and sold by the Salt Lake Stamp Company, Salt Lake City, Utah. (Photos by D. W. Hayne, courtesy of Mich. Agric. Exp. Station.)*

Formerly the Bobolink created havoc in the rice fields of South Carolina and Georgia in the fall, but later the rice-growing industry shifted to the lower Mississippi valley states, considerably west of the Bobolink's main migration route. Now, however, perhaps because of the colonization of suitable areas in the west and northwest (Fig. 142), the Bobolink is becoming a problem again (Meanly and Neff, 1953). Crows have always been a problem in grainfields, but much of the damage formerly inflicted on newly planted corn has been averted by treatment of the seed before planting. The Ring-necked Pheasant, a great economic asset from the standpoint of sport, is also often a menace to newly planted corn in the spring, to corn in the milk in the fall, and sometimes to other garden crops such as melons and tomatoes.

Control methods for preventing damage in grainfields run the gamut of shooting, trapping, scaring devices (Fig. 163r), repellents, poisons, and, more recently, attempts to develop sterility chemicals (gametocides). The United States Fish and Wildlife Service, state experiment stations, and Japanese farmers have worked on these problems for a long time, and are continually working out new techniques. However, many of the issues are still unresolved. Dykstra (1960) outlines some of the recent approaches to problems in this country, and McClure (1956) summarizes some of the Japanese techniques, chiefly scaring devices, which often utilize manpower.

## FRUIT-EATING BIRDS

In other parts of the world, particularly in the tropics, there are many fruit-eating species of birds, including parrots, fruit pigeons, toucans, hornbills, and barbets. In this country, however, fruits and berries are usually merely supplementary items in the diet of seed-eating and insectivorous birds. Normally, such items are taken wholly or largely from Nature's vast storehouse of wild fruits, and thus have little or no economic significance except for the dissemination of fruit pits. Many wild plants, trees, shrubs, and vines, mostly highly desirable from the wildlife standpoint, are planted by birds, but of course some undesirable species, such as poison ivy, are also distributed.

In many cases the depredations of birds in orchards and commercial berry fields become quite severe. One of the worst offenders is the Robin, particularly in cherry orchards, but Starlings, Cedar Waxwings, and several icterids often supplement the destructive work of the Robins. The loss to cherry growers in Michigan is very heavy (Cardinell, 1937). Sometimes small stands are almost completely harvested by birds; in large orchards the proportion of damage is smaller, but the total monetary loss greater. Usually the whole fruit is consumed, but additional damage is done by pecking into the cherries and ruining them for the market. Curiously enough, though California Gulls are still generally revered for their life-saving role in the cricket plague in Utah (p. 318), their activity in western cherry orchards is now a matter of grave concern to some fruit growers (Greenhalgh, 1952).

Similarly private and commercial berry patches, grape vineyards, olive groves in California, and even plum, pear, peach, and apple orchards suffer varying degrees of damage. Such fruits as grapes are often merely punctured and the juices extracted. Orioles and Tennessee Warblers are notorious offenders in this respect. Cultivated blueberry patches, often in settings naturally attractive to birds, may suffer considerable damage (Fig. 164), but usually the loss is not great enough to warrant much expenditure for control methods. Much of the fruit eaten is from the ground, which may reduce insect infestation, such as the blueberry maggot (Hayne and Cardinell, 1949).

No very satisfactory method of protecting fruit from birds has been devised, but most of the methods employed in grainfields can be used in orchards.

## PREDATORY BIRDS

Though in a broad sense any animal that preys on another is predatory, among birds the term has been applied chiefly to the hawks and owls, which feed largely on other vertebrates. The principal function of predators is the suppression of rapidly reproducing herbivores, which, theoretically at least, would otherwise become so abundant that they would soon devegetate their range. The hawks and owls in particular, in performing their usually useful mission, have fallen into disrepute because their prey sometimes includes game and poultry. As a result they have been needlessly persecuted, and some of the most useful species have been greatly reduced in numbers. For in spite of detailed food-habit studies which have unmistakably disclosed the generally beneficial trends in the diets of these birds, many people, farmers and sportsmen in particular, are reluctant to accept the facts; "vermin" control campaigns and costly bounties (pp. 370–372) are still in operation, and laws to protect predatory birds (p. 359) are inadequate.

*Fig. 164. Blueberries injured by birds. The center berry shows typical damage by birds; the lowest was probably fed on by insects also. (Photo by D. W. Hayne, courtesy of Mich. Agric. Exp. Station.)*

It is not feasible here to analyze food habits of hawks in detail. There are more than 200 species, world-wide in distribution and exhibiting great geographical variations in diet. Several neotropical hawks (kites) feed on snails, the Secretarybird in Africa is primarily a reptile hunter, an *Accipiter* in Korea lives largely on frogs (Wolfe, 1950), an eagle in the Philippines specializes on green monkeys, and many other species have special diets, with or without economic significance. A few comments on the North American hawks follow.

Figure 165 portrays fairly typical dietary habits in 8 species of hawks. This indicates that the *Buteos* (the Red-tailed, Red-shouldered, Broad-winged, and Rough-legged Hawks) are mainly rodent hunters; their wing structure (p. 116) and habit of soaring over open spaces favor such prey selection. The Swainson's Hawk, a western *Buteo* not shown in the chart, preys primarily on gophers, ground squirrels, and grasshoppers.

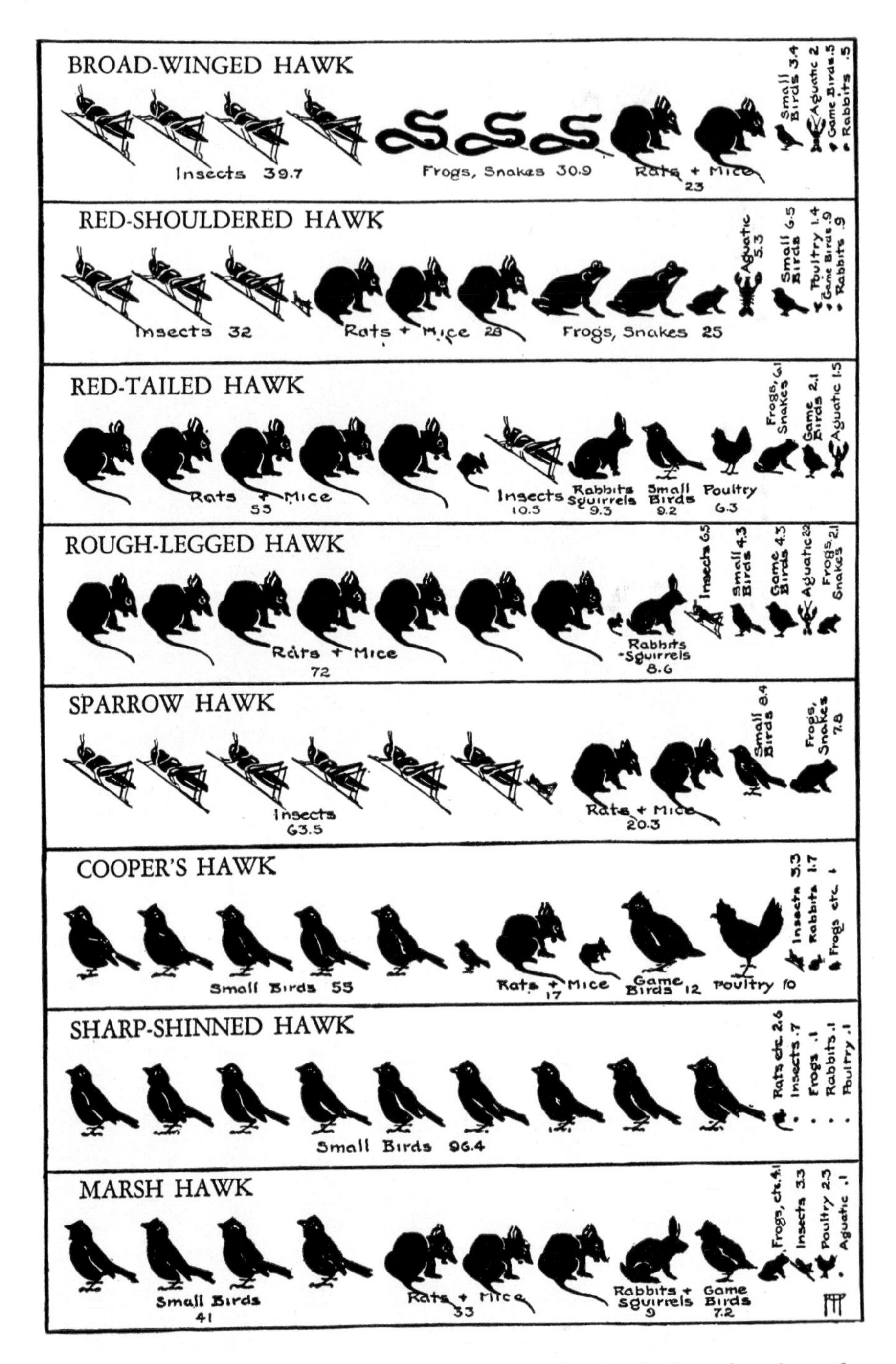


*Fig. 165. What hawks eat: a chart of representative hawk diets, based on the examination of 5,185 stomachs.* (Courtesy of Nat. Audubon Soc.)

By contrast the *Accipiters* or bird hawks—the fast-flying types which dart from concealment in a sudden sally to catch their prey—live largely on birds. The largest of these is the Goshawk, which (except for a western subspecies in the Rockies) is an uncommon winter visitor in the United States, but the medium-sized Cooper's Hawk and the smaller Sharp-shinned Hawk are widespread; all three live mainly on birds. Thus the bird hawks, from man's standpoint, are the most undesirable of the falconiform birds. Most states which have discriminatory laws relating to hawks omit the *Accipiters* from the protected list. Though the justification for this seems obvious enough, the *Accipiters* actually have an important biological mission to perform. By preying on the vulnerable surplus in populations, they tend to eliminate maladjusted individuals, such as the diseased, injured, or less alert, leaving survivors that are of a superior genetic strain. Thus populations of animals are kept at a higher level of fitness by Nature's seemingly ruthless system of predation.

The widely distributed Marsh Hawk is a particularly important species because its adaptability in prey selection makes it a potential factor for either good or harm. Quail hunters in Georgia formerly condemned the hawk, but Stoddard's monumental work (p. 255) on the Bobwhite disclosed that wintering Marsh Hawks destroy many cotton rats which in turn are serious enemies of nesting quail. A similar prejudice in New Zealand caused 200,000 harriers (*Circus approximans*) to be collected for bounties to protect introduced California Quail which, according to one investigator, the slow-flying harriers could not catch (Williams, 1952). Marsh Hawks in Manitoba, nesting in a marsh that included twenty-one duck nests, were found to be feeding on voles and blackbirds, with an occasional run of Coots and young muskrats, but not on ducks or ducklings (Hecht, 1951).

The falcons (Falconidae) are likewise quite variable in their diet. These include the far northern Gyrfalcon, largely beyond our range; the bold and picturesque Peregrine and Prairie Falcons, which though sometimes destructive are usually condoned and even protected in some states because of their aesthetic appeal; the small, largely insectivorous Sparrow Hawk; and the bird-eating Pigeon Hawk, a Canadian nester. Of these, the Sparrow Hawk is the only one sufficiently widespread and common in the United States to be of much economic significance. Beebe (1960) calls attention to interesting variations in the feeding habits of Peregrine Falcons in the Pacific Northwest; on certain islands they lived entirely on sea birds (alcids), in one case entirely on Cassin's Auklets. In some cities (e.g., New York and Montreal), Peregrines nest on buildings and live chiefly on pigeons.

The economic picture with respect to the owls is much simpler and even more commendable. With the few exceptions mentioned below, the owls in eastern North America are predominantly mousers. In a three-year study of Barn Owls at Michigan State University, identification of 6,815 prey animals in 2,200 pellets yielded more than 90 per cent mice, mostly meadow mice (Fig. 166), and nearly 99 per cent small mammals (Wallace, 1948). No trace of poultry or game birds was found, and of the relatively small number of birds taken (1.07 per cent) the majority (89 per cent) were House Sparrows and Starlings. Studies of Barn Owls in other northern states have given similar figures, but the prey varies more in the southern and western states. In Europe, where Barn Owls also occur, prey runs more heavily to insectivores, such as shrews.

Most other owls present a somewhat similar picture. The chief exception is the Great Horned Owl, a versatile opportunist which includes game

*Fig. 166. Meadow mouse* (Microtus) *skulls taken from pellets collected under a Barn Owl roost on the Michigan State University campus in the mid-1940's. The owls no longer occur on campus. (Photo by Philip G. Coleman, courtesy of Mich. Agric. Exp. Station.)*

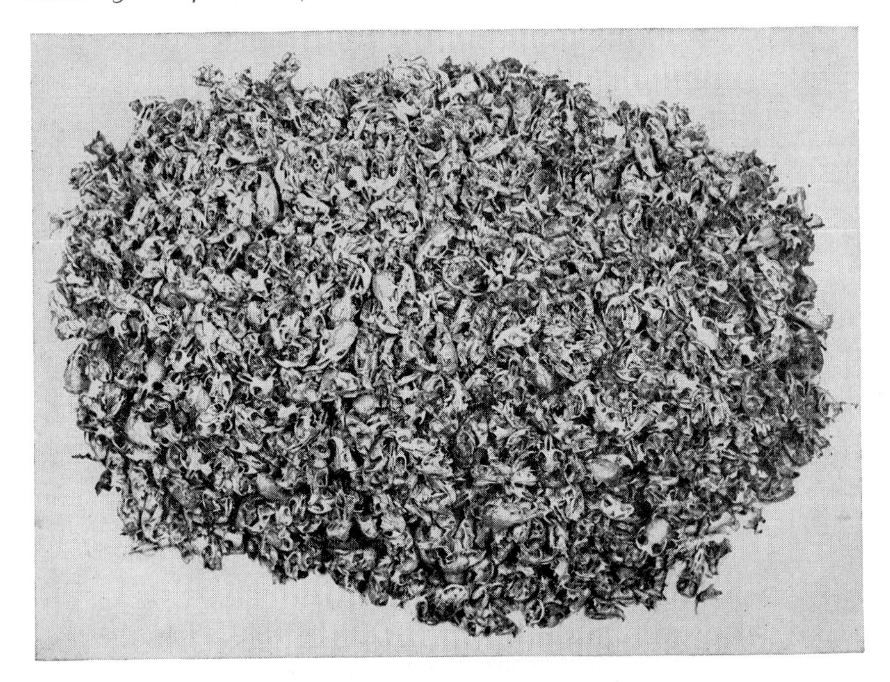

birds, ducks, and poultry in its varied diet. Comprehensive studies by Errington and the Hamerstroms (1940), however, indicate that it is predominantly a rabbit hunter (at least in the midwest), a fact probably lauded by farmers but not by rabbit hunters. Sometimes the game birds taken may appear to make serious inroads on local pheasant, grouse, or quail populations, but ordinarily only the vulnerable surplus is taken and the surviving nucleus is more or less impregnable. The Snowy Owl, another exception, which in its Arctic home feeds primarily on lemmings and some ptarmigans, takes any animal prey it can get on its periodic winter visits to the states. The Screech Owl, widely distributed throughout most of the country, feeds chiefly on insects, rodents, and sometimes small birds in the east, but in the southwest feeds largely on ground-dwelling arthropods. The Burrowing Owl of the prairies is mainly insectivorous. Ten other North American owls, not mentioned above, are primarily mousers, or, in a few cases, insectivorous.

Thus there is substantial evidence that predatory birds are a distinct asset. Predator control has often been followed by serious outbreaks of rodents or other prey animals.

### FISH-EATING BIRDS

Birds that subsist on fish, though essentially predatory, are in a special category as far as man's interests are concerned. Piscivorous species are numerous the world over, though many oceanic birds, perhaps contrary to popular conception, live largely on marine invertebrates rather than on fish. Inland regions also have a considerable number of fish-eating birds inhabiting lakes and streams, including such well-known forms as loons, grebes, pelicans, cormorants (mainly marine), herons, mergansers, Bald Eagle and Osprey, gulls and terns (partly scavengers), and kingfishers. As in the case of predatory species, there have been many misconceptions about fish-eating birds, and needless persecution.

Perhaps the most disconcerting example of persistent persecution without adequate evidence has been of the Bald Eagle in Alaska. In the years between 1917 and 1950 (not including all years), 114,000 eagles were collected for bounty at a cost to the territory of more than $100,000 (Barnes, 1951). Yet several reasonably thorough investigations have shown that aside from a few partly spent salmon taken directly on the spawning grounds, nearly the whole catch is of dead and dying fish that have finished spawning. The fish-eating preferences of the Bald Eagle, as opposed to ducks or game, have been well demonstrated in a study in New Brunswick (Wright, 1953) in which captive birds chose fish when both fish and ducks were provided. (The diet of the wild birds was 90 per cent fish, 9 per cent birds, and one per cent mammals.)

In certain situations, however, fish-eating birds become a great nuisance, especially around hatcheries and rearing pools. Herons, mergansers, and the Belted Kingfisher often have to be controlled in such situations. Even the Spotted Sandpiper can make serious inroads on trout fingerlings, if it has access to rearing pools. The Fish and Wildlife Service (see Cottam and Uhler, 1937) recommends screening of hatcheries as more practical than patrolling and shooting, but of course in some cases screening is hardly feasible.

Studies of American (Common) Mergansers wintering in the Great Lakes region (Salyer and Lagler, 1940) have shown that they normally inhabit large bodies of water and subsist largely on noncommercial fish, but some years witness the freezing over of their usual wintering areas, forcing the birds into open stretches of trout streams. Even there the catch of commercial or game fishes (32.79 per cent) was lower than that of other, mostly undesirable species. Fritsch and Buss (1958), checking on the food habits of mergansers in salmon streams in Alaska, found forty-eight salmonid eggs (less than one per cent of the total diet) and three salmonid fry in the sixty stomachs examined, although some of the birds were feeding in salmon spawning grounds.

Recent changes in the legal size limit of pan fish in some states reflect a changing attitude toward fish-eating birds, which wildlife biologists now think may actually improve fishing by the removal of undersized specimens, thus hastening the growth of the survivors (Fig. 167). Reelfoot Lake in Tennessee, for instance, affords good fishing with fish-eating birds removing 400,000 pounds of fish per year, whereas the killing of thousands of mergansers in reservoirs in New Mexico apparently resulted in waters teeming with stunted, undersized fish which yielded poor fishing (Elder and Kirkpatrick, 1952).

## SCAVENGERS

Best known of the carrion-feeders are the vultures or buzzards, terms which in the New World apply solely to the falconiform family Cathartidae, but in the Old World refer to carrion-feeding hawks (Accipitridae).

*Fig. 167. The Brown Pelican is a fisherman par excellence and consumes large quantities of noncommercial fish. It inhabits the warmer coastal waters of both New World continents and is a familiar sight along the Gulf Coast and Florida. It is Louisiana's state bird. (Photo by Allan D. Cruickshank.)*

Scavengers have a necessary but unaesthetic function to fulfill, especially in southern regions where decaying dead animals might constitute a health hazard. The automobile has undoubtedly benefited vultures by providing an abundance of highway kills. Similarly, overstocked deer areas in such states as Michigan and Wisconsin have permitted the spread of the Turkey Vulture north of its regular breeding range because of the availability of carcasses left from winter starvation.

Coincident with the spread of vultures in the north, however, sanitation on southern farms has probably decreased the food supply there. Perhaps because of this, Black Vultures in particular may have been forced to seek living prey; in Kentucky (Lovell, 1952) and Georgia (Hopkins, 1953) they are known to attack newly born pigs, picking at the vent and pulling out the intestines. In other exceptional cases, Black Vultures have been known to harass skunks and opossums until they die, thus creating their own carrion, and to raid heron rookeries containing helpless young

(McIlhenny, 1939). In Texas, farmers trap vultures extensively to prevent depredations on domestic animals (Parmalee, 1954); most of the damage is done by Black Vultures.

Petrides (1959) calls attention to an interesting hierarchy among vultures in Africa (Fig. 168). Small Hooded Vultures locate carcasses but are soon displaced by larger numbers of White-backed Vultures. Then come three larger species which successively force their way to the carcass. Petrides suggests that the larger species may not be independent hunters and may depend on the smaller species to locate prey for them.

Many other birds are partial scavengers, sometimes more or less incidentally. Nearly all predatory birds will capitalize on dead animals they find. The Bald Eagle is largely a scavenger, especially of fish, but the Golden Eagle in the west is truly predatory, living mainly on ground squirrels, rabbits, and some water birds in California and jack rabbits (58.8 per cent) and some antelope (15.7 per cent) in Montana (Woodgerd, 1952; Carnie, 1954). Crows are quick to take advantage of any obtainable carrion, and often line heavily traveled highways in the early morning hours to feed on the kills of the night. Gulls are important scavengers about harbors, fishing ports, and inland lakes, and though normally useful in this respect, large concentrations may start plundering

*Fig. 168. White-backed Vultures* (Pseudogyps africanus) *survey a stripped carcass of a Grant's gazelle killed by a cheetah, while a jackal, attracted by the descending vultures, looks on wistfully. African grasslands have an abundance of grazing mammals and a corresponding abundance of carrion feeders. (Photo, and information, by George A. Petrides.)*

the eggs and young of other birds or even cooperate in overpowering larger birds like ducks. In some New England coastal colonies, gulls have become so abundant that control measures to limit reproduction have been undertaken by the Fish and Wildlife Service.

A special and often overlooked group of scavengers are the sandpipers and plovers. Though they often wade into water and catch living prey, they also glean beaches of small animals, mainly invertebrates that are washed ashore, sometimes in windrows. Thus they have an important clean-up mission to fulfill, perhaps making our northern lakesides a pleasanter place for summer homes.

## SPECIAL DIETS

There are many special or miscellaneous diets not covered in preceding accounts, but for the most part these are not of great economic significance. The food habits of ducks have been studied in great detail, primarily for management purposes, but living as they do largely on aquatic vegetation (puddle ducks) or aquatic invertebrates (some diving ducks), they are not usually an economic problem (Fig. 169). Chief exception are ducks wintering on agricultural lands in the southwest where they do damage to winter grains and early garden produce. In California one report estimated this damage at $1,500,000, but gave the meat value of the birds harvested in the season as $4,000,000 with another $500,000 spent by the hunters. However, land usage problems (ducks versus crops) may increase greatly in the future, as demands for food production increase. In other, often unappreciated ways, grazing waterfowl may be quite useful. They keep down excessive vegetative growth in shallow water and fertilize waters for plankton (fish food) production (Sokolowski, 1960).

Many dietary oddities might be enumerated. Those of the snail feeders (Snail Kites and Limpkin), and of nectar-feeding hummingbirds, have already been mentioned. In the New World, honeycreepers (Coerebidae and Drepaniidae) and, in the Old World, the sunbirds (Nectariniidae) and honey-eaters (Meliphagidae) also feed to some extent on nectar. "Tick birds," or oxpeckers (Sturnidae) in Africa walk about on the backs of cattle and other ruminants, picking off ticks and other invertebrates. "Crocodile birds" on the same continent are alleged by historians to enter the mouths of crocodiles and clean the teeth of the huge reptiles, but both the habit and the species involved appear somewhat questionable. The peculiar habit of the Kea in New Zealand of feeding on the kidney fat

*Fig. 169. A striking formation of Lesser Scaup on the Indian River in Florida. The Lesser Scaup feeds predominantly on animal matter, and thus becomes a problem in agricultural lands much less commonly than the vegetarian ducks. (Photo by Allan D. Cruickshank.)*

of living sheep has been described (p. 148). Pigmy Parrots in the Solomon Islands live largely on fungi, an odd diet indeed, which they glean from the bark of trees by creeping about in nuthatch fashion (Sibley, 1951). Even more unusual are the cerophagous (wax-eating) habits of the honey-guides (Indicatoridae) in Africa and Asia. Friedmann (1955) has shown that these birds, which consume considerable beeswax along with bee larvae and honey, can subsist for a time on the wax alone, though it is not an adequate diet and eventually they starve without other food. Apparently microbes or bacteria in the digestive tract enable the honeyguides to digest the wax; no other birds, or other vertebrates, are known to do this.

## *Miscellaneous Damage by Birds*

Examples of birds doing damage because of undesirable food habits have already been described, but there are numerous other ways in which they come into conflict with man's interests. A few of these special cases are enumerated below.

The nest-robbing tendency of certain birds has always been a matter of deep concern to bird lovers, perhaps needlessly for it is merely one of Nature's methods of balancing populations. Notorious in this respect are the corvids (crows, jays, and magpies), grackles, gulls and, out at sea, the Skua and jaegers. As far as most nest robbers are concerned, their plundering habits are usually more or less incidental, or a supplement to their regular diet, but the Skua and jaegers are confirmed marauders, not only robbing nests but also purloining the catches of other sea birds. The House Wren, though not a nest robber, has the malicious habit of visiting the nests of other birds and puncturing the eggs so that they do not hatch.

The various interspecific relationships among birds may be mutually beneficial in some cases, or operate to the disadvantage of some in other cases. The parasitic relationships between cowbirds and cuckoos and their respective hosts take a heavy toll of the host species. Competition of aggressive, introduced species with native species for nesting sites also often seriously affects the reproductive efforts of the losers. Starlings frequently dislodge flickers from nesting holes, and House Sparrows take over the nest sites of bluebirds and other hole-nesting species, sometimes actually killing nestling occupants and building their own nest on top of the deceased.

Roosts of birds, especially of Starlings, blackbirds, and pigeons, often become a public nuisance. Starlings in particular congregate in immense flocks in late summer and fall; the chatter of the noisy birds may become almost deafening about city parks and suburbs, and accumulations of their droppings may kill valuable shrubbery or arouse public indignation in other ways. Soil fertility may be increased by moderate accumulations of droppings, but at dense roosts over a period of time undesirable ammonia compounds tend to build up.

Some of the dispersal methods mentioned for grain-eating birds have been used with varying degrees of success against Starlings, but aluminum owls have not lived up to the reputation accorded them by newspapers. At the State Educational Building in Albany, New York, where the birds have long been a public nuisance, the alcoves were electrically charged in a way that prevented Starlings from entering them, at least temporarily, but the cost of the project was prohibitive for general application. Some communities, following a procedure worked out at Pennsylvania State University (Frings and Jumber, 1954), have been successful in dispersing Starlings by playing recordings of their distress calls over a loud speaker in the streets, but in most cases success has been only temporary.

Woodpeckers sometimes do damage to trees or even buildings in their quests for wood borers or for drumming sites. The loud drumming of flickers on wood or metal surfaces about dwellings can be an annoyance, especially in the early morning hours. Pileated Woodpeckers have been known to drill holes completely through the logs of Canadian cabins, and often tunnel into trees (Fig. 170), usually already in a state of decay, in their persistent quest for deeply imbedded grubs or carpenter ants. Yellow-bellied Sapsuckers sometimes attack buildings, for no apparent reason, gouging out holes in shingles or siding. Their worst offense, however, is in their regular habit of drilling little wellholes into the bark of trees for sap. Such practices disfigure and devitalize fruit and ornamental trees and greatly reduce the value of forest trees for lumber. The loss to lumber industries in this way is extensive in northern forests. McAtee (1926) reported sapsucker injury in 174 species of trees, in 90 of which it was serious enough to spoil the appearance or workability of the wood.

An extraordinary case of birds making a nuisance of themselves is the entanglement of divers, especially Oldsquaws, in fishermen's nets. Oldsquaws dive to great depths (p. 111) for deep water crustaceans and molluscs which constitute their principal food. In several Great Lakes fishing

*Fig. 170. Pileated Woodpeckers often drill deep, rectangular holes into decaying trees in their energetic quests for carpenter ants and wood-boring larvae. Here they have been working on a red pine in northern Michigan. (Photo by Lawrence A. Ryel, courtesy of* Jack-Pine Warbler.*)*

centers and in the Finger Lakes region of New York, they get caught in the nets, tearing the mesh and restricting the catch of fish; in some cases more than a thousand birds have been brought up in a single haul of the nets. Unfortunately the dead birds, virtually tons of them, are of little use except as fertilizer.

An increasingly pressing modern problem is the frequent collision of birds with aircraft. Formerly serious collisions were largely with flocks of migrating birds, such as geese, ducks, and cranes, at high altitudes, but more recently there have been problems of smaller birds—gulls, shorebirds, Starlings and swallows—congregating on runways at airports and interfering with the take-off and landing of planes. A recent disaster in which jet engines were thought to have sucked in Starlings and caused a crash landing is an indication of the dangers involved and has caused air force officials to issue a directive for clearing airports of any wildlife menace that might interfere with flights.

Similar problems have developed at air bases on Pacific Islands. On Midway Atoll large numbers of "gooney birds" (albatrosses) congregate in and over the runways, causing frequent collisions and damage to the planes. The Navy's plan to destroy the albatrosses, which constituted 35 per cent of the world population of Laysan Albatrosses and 16 per cent of the Black-footed species, met with great public protest. Fortunately, a study by biologists of the Fish and Wildlife Service indicated that levelling the dunes paralleling the runways, and thus eliminating favorable soaring conditions, might be a more practical solution than killing the birds. Collisions decreased 80 per cent after the dunes were levelled, whereas killing 30,000 birds and breaking up their nests had only aggravated the problem by increasing the number of "unemployed" (nonnesting) birds over the airstrips (Rice, 1959).

## Diseases

Birds as carriers of diseases of man or other animals are a problem at times, but ordinarily there is not much cross-infection between birds and man, since infective organisms are rarely common to both (Worth, 1949). Pigeons are considered a menace to public health in some communities, chiefly because of *ornithosis*, a transmissible form of virus pneumonia. For this reason control campaigns have been carried out in some cities. *Psittacosis*, or parrot fever, which is similar to, or perhaps identical with ornithosis (Worth, *et al.*, 1957), is a serious and sometimes fatal disease to humans, particularly among parakeet handlers. Epidemics in 1929 and 1930 caused restrictions in importations and a decline in the disease, then following World War II came a resurgence of the disease owing to popularity of parakeets (Boyd, 1958). Tests on thirty-three bird banders, who handle wild birds in large numbers, disclosed only one case of ornithosis, but railway express agents who handle parakeets were found to be 71 per cent infected (Worth, *et al.*, 1957).

Apparently birds, not in themselves much affected, can carry several forms of *encephalitis*, or sleeping sickness, which is transmitted by mosquitos, sometimes via birds as secondary hosts. Domestic birds (poultry) and pheasants are the chief carriers, but gregarious wild birds (for example, at blackbird roosts or heron rookeries) are also suspects. Ground-nesting birds can also serve as secondary hosts of *Rocky Mountain spotted fever*, although ground squirrels (*Citellus*) and other small mammals are the chief carriers.

On the other hand, birds sometimes benefit man by consuming disease-carrying organisms, such as malaria and yellow fever mosquitoes. Avian malaria also helped solve problems in human malaria, and chicks are used in making vaccines (Boyd, 1958). The ancient Egyptians were aware that the Sacred Ibis helped keep down the incidence of *schistosomiasis* but did not know it was by feeding on the secondary hosts (snails) of the schistosome parasite.

Thus birds enter in many ways into relation with man. The relationships are primarily beneficial and enjoyable, but, as indicated above, there are some exceptions.

## *Selected References*

Allen, Glover M. *Birds and Their Attributes.* Francestown, N. H.: Marshall Jones, 1925. Chapt. I.

Chapman, Frank M. Birds and Man. *Guide Leaflet Series,* Amer. Mus. Nat. Hist. (New York, 1943), **115**:1–52.

Cottam, Clarence. Food Habits of North American Diving Ducks. *Tech. Bull.,* U.S.D.A. (Washington, D. C., 1939), **643**:1–140.

———, and F. M. Uhler. Birds in Relation to Fishes. *Wildl. Research and Mngt. Leaflet,* U.S.D.A. (Washington, D. C., 1937), **B5–83**:1–16.

Errington, Paul L., Hamerstrom, Frances, and F. N. Hamerstrom, Jr. The Great Horned Owl and Its Prey in North-Central United States. *Research Bull.,* Agr. Exp. Sta. (Ames, Iowa, 1940), **277**:757–850.

Farmers' Bulletins and Yearbooks. U.S.D.A. (Washington, D. C.). Numerous bulletins and reports on the detailed food habits of nearly all North American birds by F. E. L. Beal, A. K. Fisher, H. W. Henshaw, Sylvester D. Judd, E. R. Kalmbach, W. L. McAtee, Alexander Wetmore, and others.

Forbush, E. H. *Useful Birds and Their Protection.* Boston: Mass. State Board of Agr., 1907.

Hartley, G. Inness. *The Importance of Bird Life.* New York: Appleton, 1922.

Henderson, Junius. *The Practical Value of Birds.* New York: Macmillan, 1927.

Reese, Albert M. *Outlines of Economic Zoology.* Philadelphia: Blakiston, 1942. Chapt. 13.

Wallace, George J. The Barn Owl in Michigan, Its Distribution, Natural History and Food Habits. *Mich. State Coll. Agr. Exp. Sta. Tech. Bull.* (1948), **208**:1–61.

Weed, Clarence M., and Ned Dearborn. *Birds in Their Relation to Man.* Philadelphia: Lippincott, 1903.

# 14

# CONSERVATION AND MANAGEMENT

The following pages review some of the ornithological aspects of conservation and management and do not profess to survey the whole field, which has been well covered in books by Gabrielson, Leopold, Trippensee, Wing, and others (pp. 382–384). Here some data on extinct and vanishing birds are presented, bird-protection laws are briefly outlined, and some management techniques, old and new, which have been developed to increase, conserve, or regulate wildlife species are reviewed. Included also are remarks on some problems that birds now face in their struggle for survival in a modern world.

Though the relatively new field of wildlife management has seen many encouraging developments in recent years, the conservation idea is very old. An ancient law of Moses (Deuteronomy 22:6) decreed that a nesting bird should not be taken, but allowed to go free, though the young might be taken for food. This in a sense recognized the need for preservation of breeding stock, whereas the young might be utilized. Unfortunately this ancient principle has been slow of adoption; although some of the American Colonies had certain conservation laws before 1800 (p. 357), spring shooting of game species was not abolished in this country until 1918, by which time several game birds had become extinct.

European countries encountered similar problems earlier. The Renaissance in particular saw a clash of interests between far-sighted nature lovers who recognized the need for conserving resources and those who sought to destroy wildlife for immediate gain. In spite of concerted attempts to protect vanishing forms, England saw the Great Bustard, Crane, Spoonbill, Black Grouse, and Osprey exterminated from the British Isles; a few others (two harriers, the Ruff, Bittern, Black-tailed Godwit) conservation appears to have rescued in the nick of time (Fisher, 1942). Hunting, collecting, and loss of habitat were responsible for the disappearance of these and other birds from England.

## Extinct Birds

All conservationists regret the passing of a species. Usually it means the end of a phylogenetic line that has been millions of years in the making. The California Condor and Whooping Crane, for instance, are highly specialized end products of long lines of development that go far back into the Tertiary; within a few decades we may witness the extinction of two magnificent types that have taken 50 million years to evolve.

Commonly man assumes some responsibility, or one faction blames another, for exterminating a species, but in many cases it is a natural process with mankind perhaps putting the finishing touches to an inevitable event. Thousands of ill-adapted or outmoded species of birds died out before man's appearance on earth. Among the New World vultures, for example, there are seven North American fossil forms, compared to three living species; among the Accipitridae the number of fossil and living species in North America is about equal. Even today we see relic species, like the kiwis and rail-like *Notornis* (Fig. 171) in New Zealand (Richdale, 1951a), making a final and probably futile bid for survival on some remote island. This is strikingly borne out by the fact that more than 90 per cent of the birds that have become extinct in the last two hundred years have been island species, many of them flightless and unable to spread elsewhere when their island sanctuary was invaded by man.

Greenway (1958), in his comprehensive *Extinct and Vanishing Birds of the World*, lists 87 species and subspecies of birds that are definitely known to be extinct, 19 others that are probably extinct, 18 that are known only from osseus remains (not including prehistoric forms), 2 for which the collecting locality is indefinite, and 27 hypothetical birds (known only from pictures, descriptions or unconfirmed reports)—a pathetic total of 153 forms of bird life that have probably disappeared from the earth, largely due to man's activities, within the last 300 years. More disturbing than the total already gone, however, is the fact that the rate of extinction has

*Fig. 171.* Notornis, *a quaint, rail-like, flightless bird of New Zealand, rediscovered after 50 years of supposed extinction. Originally discovered in 1849 by a Maori native who captured a specimen with a dog, the last of four specimens brought 250 pounds cash at the Otago Museum in 1898. In 1948* Notornis *was rediscovered; at first only footprints were seen, then nesting birds were found in a remote corner of South Island. (Courtesy of Amer. Mus. Nat. Hist.)*

been increasing over the years and that the immediate future may be even more critical.

Unfortunately also, North America, perhaps because of its rapid growth and expansion in the past two centuries, has the worst record of any comparable land mass for exterminating its animal life. By contrast, Europe, over a much longer period of occupation, is not known to have lost a single species of bird from the continent within historical times, whereas North America has several glaring examples of needless extinction. Other less known birds, chiefly on peripheral islands (Guadalupe alone has lost four or five endemic forms—Howell and Cade, 1954), as well as a few questionable birds described by early naturalists but not since rediscovered, are also gone. Hence, it is well for every student to be familiar with some of the facts associated with the passing of the following forms.

### GREAT AUK (*Pinguinis impennis*)

This strange but interesting bird (Fig. 172), the largest of the alcids and the only flightless one in recent times, was apparently the first to go of the American species that could not withstand continued persecution. Though Funk Island, Newfoundland, was their main North American breeding site, they visited the North Atlantic coast in large numbers, and were killed by sailors, fishermen, and sealers who used the birds and their eggs for food or fish bait, their feathers for bedding, and their carcasses for oil. The birds showed little fear of man and could not outrun him, so

*Fig. 172. The Great Auk was probably the first of the North American birds to be exterminated by man. The little-known Spectacled Cormorant* (Phalacrocorax perspicillatus) *in the north Pacific disappeared at about the same time. (Sketch by Vito Cangemi from Fuertes' drawing on cover of the* Auk.)

they were easily clubbed to death; in fact, they were often herded into corrals or even driven on board ships where they were easily dispatched. The main stock was gone soon after 1800, but some persisted up to 1844 when two were captured on Eldey Island off the coast of Iceland on June 3. All that remain today are about eighty preserved specimens, twenty or more skeletons, and about seventy-five eggs. Aside from unrestricted killing, known factors that hastened the extinction of this species were the single egg, which hindered recovery from heavy losses, and its comparative helplessness because of lack of flight.

### LABRADOR DUCK (*Camptorhynchus labradorium*)

Little is known of this eiderlike duck (Fig. 173), which formerly visited the New England and North Atlantic states in winter from a probable summer home in Labrador or further north. Perhaps it was never abundant. Perhaps it was persistently hunted by natives for its flesh, down, or eggs, but there seem to be no records of heavy kills by white men. Some maintain that it was a stupid bird, lacking the wariness of other wild ducks. The last known member of the race was killed on Long Island in 1875 (Greenway), or in New York on December 12, 1878 (A.O.U.). About fifty specimens have been saved in various museums.

### PASSENGER PIGEON (*Ectopistes migratorius*)

The most regrettable, as well as the most dramatic, extermination of any North American bird was that of the Passenger Pigeon, whose history has now been fully documented (Schorger, 1955). So abundant was it in the nineteenth century that counts of single flocks were set at more than a billion birds, which exceeds any single species known today and out-

*Fig. 173. Labrador Duck habitat group in American Museum. (Courtesy of Amer. Mus. Nat. Hist.)*

numbers tenfold the whole continental waterfowl supply of 63 species. But the pigeons dwindled rapidly with relentless persecution and within a few decades had completely disappeared. The last two specimens were taken in Michigan and Wisconsin in 1898 and 1899. The species survived in captivity somewhat longer; a bird in the Cincinnati Zoological Gardens died on September 1, 1914, after having lived in captivity for twenty-nine years.

The full explanation of the extinction of the Passenger Pigeon may never be known, but it is mainly a pathetic example of incredible slaughter. The birds nested in dense colonies, millions at a single site, with trees so heavily laden with birds and their nests that the trees often crumbled under the weight. Such habits made them exceedingly vulnerable; they were shot, clubbed to death, captured in huge nets, burned out of trees, and wagonloads of birds were hauled away and shipped in barrels to the New York and Chicago markets. In 1861, 14,850,000 birds were shipped from the famous Petosky (Michigan) nest site. Droves of hogs were often herded into the forests at the close of day to fatten on the remains. The great nesting colonies rapidly shrank in size and number, and the persecuted birds were pursued by professional market hunters from one nesting site to another, even up into the wilds of Canada, so that in their later years the pigeons were largely unsuccessful at nesting. Ineffective legislation was enacted in some states in an attempt to save the last birds, but it was too little and too late. Michigan passed a law in 1897 to prohibit further killing, and in 1905 transferred the bird from the game to the non-game list, but apparently there were few if any birds left to protect.

Various reasons, other than obvious overkilling, are given to account for the bird's rapid decline: the lack of suitable nesting sites due to deforestation, inadequate mast supply (Wilson's flock of 2 billion birds would have required 17 million bushels of food daily), the breakup of organized flocks which eliminated the social stimulus perhaps necessary for successful breeding, the usually single egg per clutch, storms during

*Fig. 174. Passenger Pigeon Memorial Monument at Wyalusing State Park, Wisconsin (above), and close-up of plaque. (Courtesy of F. R. Poe.)*

migration, and disease. But whatever the reasons we can only reminisce with regret. The bird is commemorated only in books and museums, and in an appropriate monument (Fig. 174) at Wyalusing State Park in Wisconsin, which was unveiled in touching ceremonies on May 11, 1947 (Scott, *et al.*, 1947).

## HEATH HEN (*Tympanuchus cupido cupido*)

This race of the Greater Prairie Chicken, in contrast to the preceding species, died out with man aware that it was going and making determined but futile attempts to save it. Probably the Heath Hen (Fig. 175) was never widely distributed and perhaps not abundant, but it was known to occur from New Hampshire to Chesapeake Bay and was an important game bird in the nineteenth century. But after 1835 it was restricted to its last stronghold on Martha's Vineyard, where a nucleus of some 200 birds increased to about 2,000 by 1916 but dwindled rapidly thereafter. Persistent

*Fig. 175. Heath Hen at nest. Note close resemblance to The Greater Prairie Chicken (Fig. 91r). (Courtesy of Amer. Mus. Nat. Hist.)*

and expensive efforts were made to preserve the birds. However, a disastrous fire in 1916, disease in 1920, a heavy influx of Goshawks one winter, and an unbalanced sex ratio (two females and eleven males left in 1927) gradually reduced the population to a single much-pampered individual, which was last seen on March 11, 1932. Attempts to cross the lone survivor with its closest relative, the Greater Prairie Chicken, were unsuccessful (Gross, 1928; A.O.U. Checklist, 1957).

### CAROLINA (LOUISIANA) PAROQUET (*Conuropsis carolinensis*)

This paroquet, consisting of a southeastern (*carolinensis*) and midwestern (*ludovicianus*) form, was widespread during the nineteenth century, ranging north to North Dakota, Ohio, and central New York. But several factors combined to eliminate it quickly from the northern and finally from the southern states. The birds were very destructive in fruit orchards and grainfields; hence they were destroyed in large numbers by farmers. They were also shot as game, collected for their plumage, and trapped for cage birds. The fact that they were tame and unsuspicious made them easy prey. McKinley (1960) reports them as common visitors in Missouri into the 1840's, but the large flocks were gone by the 1850's, with the last Missouri specimen taken in 1894. In the southeast the last specimen was taken in Florida in 1901, but a flock was sighted there in 1920 and there were reports of its existence in the southeast as late as 1938 (Greenway, 1958).

### ESKIMO CURLEW (*Numenius borealis*)

The status of this bird is uncertain. Since it bred in the tundras of the far north and wintered in southern South America, it was known in this country only as a bird of passage and could be easily overlooked or confused with the somewhat similar Hudsonian Curlew. Apparently the last North American specimens were taken in Maine in 1929 and in Labrador in 1932 (A.O.U.). Occasional sight records, from the wintering grounds in Argentina as well as along migration routes, have persisted over the years; the latest are several reports summarized by Emanuel (1961) of birds seen in Texas in 1959 and 1960.

In some respects the passing of the curlew parallels that of the Passenger Pigeon. They traveled in large flocks and were not very wary; hence they were easily collected by market hunters congregating along the Atlantic flyway in the fall and in the Mississippi valley during the spring flight. On the western plains, hunters followed the flocks with wagons to haul away the kill of the day. The birds were abundant up to about 1875, after which a rapid decline took place.

## Rare and Vanishing Species

It is not practical to review here the current status of the many species of birds now facing probable or possible extinction. Greenway (1958) lists 77 species "thought to be in danger of extinction" and 50 others with "small populations." Fisher (1942, 1954) discusses some bird preservation problems in Great Britain, and Peterson (1960a) discusses the situation in conservation-conscious Japan, where the Japanese Crane, Japanese Stork (twenty-one left), and Crested Ibis (sixteen left) are in danger. Some years ago the National Audubon Society, in collaboration with the Fish and Wildlife Service, placed some 50 species of North American birds on a critical list. The current status of several of the most critical of these is discussed below.

### IVORY-BILLED WOODPECKER (*Campephilus principalis*)

Probably the Ivory-billed Woodpecker (Fig. 176) is currently in the greatest danger of extinction, if indeed it exists at all. When the small but well-studied population in the Singer Wilderness tract in Louisiana disap-

*Fig. 176. Ivory-billed Woodpecker. Photo of a painting by J. J. Audubon. There is now some doubt about the existence of this species in the United States, but a closely related form still survives in Cuba. Two other similar species inhabit Mexico and South America respectively. (Photo by Vito Cangemi.)*

peared with the cutting of the timber in the mid-1940's, the species was thought to be gone, but in 1951 two birds, perhaps not mates, were reported in northern Florida. However, persistent search failed to reveal further records of these birds, and it is now thought that the 1951 records may have been in error.

Studies of the Louisiana birds by Tanner (1942) disclosed two limiting factors, largely beyond control: (1) the birds lived on a restricted diet of wood-boring larvae that infest dead and dying trees of a certain age and thus required large tracts of mature forest for living space; and (2) though the birds mated and had nests, they were unsuccessful in rearing young. Apparently these huge woodpeckers are, or were, evolved to fit a particular ecological niche which is now practically nonexistent; if gone, they provide an example, perhaps the only one in North America, of an avian species lost through deforestation.

### WHOOPING CRANE (*Grus americana*)

The most publicized of North America's rare birds is the Whooping Crane (Fig. 177), one of our largest and most magnificent birds. Though a monographic study by R. P. Allen (1952) indicates that the species was never as abundant as popularly supposed, it used to be a fairly common migrant over the western plains. Now careful counts of the survivors on their wintering grounds and much newspaper publicity (partly to protect them during the hunting season since they are sometimes shot for Snow Geese) keep the public well informed on the year-to-year status of this spectacular bird. In 1961 there were thirty-eight known wild birds and six in captivity, an encouraging increase over the twenty-one wild birds and two captives in 1953.

Fortunately for management measures, the cranes winter on the Aransas Wildlife Refuge in Texas, where they are carefully protected. Their northern nesting grounds, in Wood Buffalo Park in northwestern Canada, formerly accorded them security for nesting. Now lumbering for pulpwood and mining for strategic minerals near the park create the need for a railroad into the area, which will bring people, fire, drainage, and damming (for railway construction) close to the crane's sanctuary. On the wintering grounds also there is urgent need for more space, as the aggressive territorial adults force the young off the refuge. More space is not available, however, because an air force bombing range and other land uses prevent expansion of the refuge. In view of these other demands for

*Fig. 177. Two Whooping Cranes (one injured), photographed on their wintering grounds on the Aransas Refuge in Texas in 1949. (Courtesy of L. H. Walkinshaw.)*

the land they occupy, R. P. Allen (1960), our leading authority on the cranes, asks the pertinent question: "Do we want to save the Whooping Crane?"

The Sandhill Cranes (Fig. 32) may well be destined to fill the niche being vacated by the larger Whooping Crane. Although they also are threatened by illegal hunting and by drainage of wetlands which robs them of nesting sites, the species as a whole, according to Walkinshaw's (1949) monograph, appears not to be in immediate danger. Though the Cuban form is nearly extinct, and the Florida race much restricted, the Greater and Lesser Sandhill Cranes, nesting in the United States and the far north respectively, are quite widely distributed and reasonably abundant (several thousand Greaters, perhaps 100,000 or more Lessers).

### CALIFORNIA CONDOR (*Gymnogyps californianus*)

Great interest attends the current status of this carrion-feeding vulture, one of the largest and most majestic of flying birds (Fig. 178), now largely

*Fig. 178. California Condor in its native haunts. (Photo by William L. Finley, courtesy of Nat. Audubon Soc.)*

confined to a refuge in southern California. Probably never abundant, though once much more widespread, its chief enemies in the past have been gunners who prized specimens because of their large size, egg collectors who coveted the rare and valuable condor egg, and ranchers who perhaps have unwittingly poisoned many of the birds with bait intended for coyotes. The actual effect of such poison bait on the birds is not well known, however, and poisoned ground squirrels may be an important source of food for the condors. Also many ranches in California have been converted into fruit farms, which do not provide carrion for the condors.

Discouraging features in the management of the condors are that they are easily disturbed by sight-seeing tourists, photographers, and bird lovers, and that their reproductive rate is very low. Among the sixty surviving birds, there are only twenty pairs (twenty nonbreeders) which, because of their slowly maturing young, nest only every other year. Thus the twenty females *average* only ten eggs per year, and raise perhaps half this number of young (Baker, 1950).

On the more encouraging side, however, is the fact that the numerical status of the condors has not changed much in recent years, and that a large tract of land has been set aside as sanctuary for the birds. Opinion differs sharply as to whether or not attempts should be made to perpetuate a few of the survivors in the San Diego Zoo. A detailed monograph on the species by Koford (1953) presents a fairly complete picture of the condor situation.

*Fig. 179. Everglade Kite at its nest in the Florida Everglades. (Photo by Allan D. Cruickshank, courtesy of Nat. Audubon Soc.)*

### EVERGLADE KITE (*Rostrhamus sociabilis plumbeus*)

This interesting hawk (Fig. 179) is now confined to the Everglade region of Florida (other races occur in the West Indies, Central and South America), and in 1951 was believed to number about sixty individuals. Since then, however, numbers have dwindled, due in part to several dry nesting seasons, until only a few pairs survive. Though formerly shot by alleged sportsmen, particularly visiting tourists, probably the chief reason for its precarious status is its peculiarly limited diet of snails (*Pomacea caliginosa*). Drainage projects for real estate and other developments, which eliminate the snail populations, threaten the survival of the kite. Evidence that diet may not be the sole factor, however, is the fact that the range of the snail is more extensive than that of the kite.

### BALD EAGLE

Currently, our national symbol, the Bald Eagle, is much in the limelight as a vanishing species, although of course its numbers are not so low as those of the species discussed above. Studies by Broley (1958) over a twenty-year period on the Gulf Coast of Florida disclosed a declining trend in reproductive success from about 150 eaglets raised annually in one hundred nests up to about 1947, to only eight young produced in 1957. He suggested sterility (often long-incubated eggs failed to hatch) from feeding on poisoned fish as the most likely cause of the decline. But another observer, in studies of nesting eagles on the east coast of Florida, pointed to loss of nest trees due to hurricanes and cutting as a more obvious cause. Further surveys, in some eastern states and in the midwest, also disclosed low reproduction and declining populations. This stimulated a nation-wide survey, sponsored by the National Audubon Society, to appraise the whole situation more carefully. If our national emblem goes, we face the sad reality that modern civilization and the type of bird life symbolized by the Bald Eagle cannot coexist.

## OTHER THREATENED SPECIES

The five species discussed above appear to be the ones in the most immediate danger of extinction in this country, but there are other birds whose populations are so low as to justify apprehension concerning their future. These include the Great White Heron (possibly only a local color phase of the Great Blue Heron) on a refuge in Florida Bay; the Wood Ibis, whose Florida populations (the main supply) dropped from a former 100,000 to 8,000 by 1957 (Sprunt and Kahl, 1960); the Roseate Spoonbill, whose Gulf Coast colonies have suffered from continued industrialization (Allen, 1952); and the Limpkin, a snail feeder which is largely restricted to southeastern Georgia (Okefenokee Wildlife Refuge) and peninsular Florida. Among the small land birds with low populations or restricted distribution, or both, are several warblers (Bachman's, Colima, Kirtland's) and several sparrows (e.g., Ipswich Sparrow on Sable Island, Nova Scotia, and the Cable Sable Sparrow in southwestern Florida). Possibly also, the Eastern Bluebird may now have to be added to our growing list of vanishing birds.

Lest the impression be left that declining species are doomed regardless of what is done for them, attention should be called to species which have responded to protection. The Trumpeter Swan (Fig. 180) became alarmingly scarce in this country in the 1930's, but with nearly complete protection of nonmigrating birds on western refuges the population increased from a low of thirty-five birds in 1931 to 642 in 1954 (Banko, 1960). Transplantation experiments in which swans were stocked on other

*Fig. 180. This Trumpeter Swan family, on a lake in Yellowstone National Park, is evidence of the usefulness of complete protection for endangered birds. These swans have increased on western refuges from 35 birds in 1931 to more than 600 in 1954. (Courtesy of Edward M. Brigham, Jr.)*

refuges have been quite successful. There is also a considerable reserve of Trumpeter Swans in Alaska and Canada. Even more encouraging was the dramatic comeback of egrets and southern herons after their near extermination at the turn of the century; with protection from shooting and preservation of their southern breeding haunts they have increased and spread over much of the United States.

Some game birds have responded well to modern management, while others have not. The native Turkey, extirpated from much of the range it occupied in colonial days, has done well in the more southern and western areas and now permits limited open seasons. The American Woodcock has stood reasonably heavy hunting, yet the more widely distributed Common Snipe has not. The Sharp-tailed Grouse has expanded its range, with transplanted birds taking well in new habitats, but the range of the prairie chickens continues to dwindle. Various species of waterfowl are periodically put on and then taken off the protected list, as fluctuations in numbers seem to dictate.

# *Bird Protection Laws*

Perhaps because of their great aesthetic and economic value, birds have enjoyed more efforts on the part of man to try to help them than any other group of animals. Although federal action on a national or international scale came late, various colonial game laws were set up much earlier. Apparently New Jersey had the first "conservation law" in 1675 (a wolf bounty). This was followed by other acts, including a deer season in 1732. Seasonal protection of game birds was initiated in Massachusetts in 1818, and in New Jersey in 1820. Other states soon established similar regulations for game and more or less complete protection for songbirds. The following paragraphs describe some of the major legislative actions that have been undertaken in behalf of birds.

## THE TARIFF ACT OF 1913

In about 1875 a sudden boom in the popularity of bird plumages in the millinery industry threatened the security of some of America's most beautiful birds (p. 314). In special demand were the breeding plumes of egrets and herons, which could be secured only in the nesting season and thus encouraged exceedingly destructive methods of obtaining them. As early as 1877 Florida passed an antiplumage law to prevent the appalling waste of bird life, but legislation was ineffective as long as feathers were in such demand—one Audubon Society warden was killed trying to enforce the law.

Eventually, however, feathers for hats went out of fashion, partly because of an aroused public sentiment, partly because of the decline of the birds most in demand. The whole matter culminated in a provision or clause of the Tariff Act of 1913 which prohibited the importation into this country of wild bird plumages from any part of the world. Feathers used for millinery purposes must come from "domesticated" birds raised in captivity. Unfortunately this law was amended in 1922 to permit importation of feathers for the manufacture of artificial flies which resulted in substantial illegal diversions to the millinery industries in New York. This loophole in the law was finally plugged in the early 1950's and the term "domestication," hitherto rather freely interpreted, was specifically defined (Baker, 1952).

## MIGRATORY BIRD TREATIES, 1913–1936

The various punitive and often ineffective efforts of the states to protect migratory birds finally culminated in federal action. A Migratory Bird Treaty, passed in 1913–1914 for the United States (Weeks-McLean Migratory Bird Law) was ratified in a convention between the United States and Great Britain in 1916, and went into full effect as the Migratory Bird Treaty Act in 1918. In 1936 a convention with Mexico extended this treaty to include that country in a remarkable demonstration of international cooperation in the protection of the bird life of a whole continent. Perhaps needless to say, Europe, with its many countries and nationalities, has not been able to achieve such international cooperation. Although there have been treaties between certain countries, it is still not unlikely that a bird protected in England may end up in a pot pie in Italy.

Birds coming under the provisions of the treaty are as follows:

1. Migratory game birds (Anatidae, Gruidae, Rallidae, Shorebirds—5 families—and Columbidae), with flexible regulations (Article II) to permit open and closed seasons and other restrictions.
2. Migratory insectivorous birds (24 families) to be protected at all seasons.
3. Other migratory nongame birds (9 water-bird families not covered above). There have been various redefinitions of families from time to time.

Birds not accorded protection under the provisions of the treaty are the nonmigratory game birds (Galliformes) which come under the jurisdiction of the states; the hawks and owls; certain fish-eating birds such as cormorants, ibises, and kingfishers; crows and jays (Corvidae); Starlings (Sturnidae); and House Sparrows (Ploceidae). Article VII in the treaty provides for the issuance of permits to deal with special cases of crop damage or other annoyances from protected birds. Bobolinks in southern rice fields, blackbirds in grainfields, sapsuckers defacing buildings, and shrikes interfering with banding traps are examples.

## SUPPLEMENTARY STATE REGULATIONS

The various states have regulations of their own, primarily for the nonmigratory game birds (grouse, pheasants, quail), but often for other species as well. Kingfishers and Blue Jays, for instance, not protected by federal law, are accorded protection in some states. "Blackbirds" are not covered by some states, but federal law, theoretically at least, makes it illegal to kill them. Mourning Doves come under Item 1 in the Migratory Bird Treaty, but eighteen northern states do not have an open season on doves, in contrast to the thirty southern and central states that do (Kiel, 1960). Hawks and owls are also subject to state laws. Some states have no regulations at all for predatory birds; others protect certain species, particularly the Bald Eagle and sometimes vultures and the Osprey. Quite a few states have laws based on the apparent economic status of the birds, affording protection to all owls except the Great Horned Owl and to all hawks except the bird-eating *Accipiters*. Recently, several states have followed Connecticut's and Michigan's "model law," which protects all hawks and owls but includes a provision that landowners can dispose of individuals actually caught doing damage to poultry or other domestic animals.

In contrast to this country, Australia, perhaps because of repeated plagues from introduced rodent pests, has long recognized the value of most of its predatory birds. All owls and most hawks are protected, and convicted offenders pay heavy fines and have their guns confiscated. Convictions for violations, as in this country, are hard to get, however. Offenders have pleaded self-defense successfully from a hawk the size of our Sparrow Hawk. Unprotected hawks include two *Accipiters* which harass chicken runs and two eagles which are believed to attack lambs.

### OTHER FEDERAL LAWS

Most states accord protection to the Bald Eagle, but the federal government formally supplemented the various state actions by a special act in 1940 which prohibited killing this species in the United States but not in Alaska. The regulation extending much needed protection for the Bald Eagle in Alaska was finally established in 1952. Currently (1961) a bill is in Congress to extend similar protection to the Golden Eagle, which heretofore has been protected in only six of the western states. Part of the motive for the Golden Eagle regulation is to give further protection to immature Bald Eagles which cannot be readily identified from the Golden in the field.

The Migratory Bird Conservation Act (Norbeck-Andresen Sanctuary Bill), enacted in 1929 and amended in 1935, was another milestone in conservation, as it provided for badly needed refuges at a critical time of nation-wide droughts. The Migratory Bird Hunting Stamp Act (1934) provided funds for the land acquisition program visualized in the Conservation Act.

## Attracting Birds

Though the art of managing wildlife, other than by the reduction of shooting and protective legislation or the various phases of predator control, is relatively new, some of the principles involved have been known and practiced by bird lovers for a long time. Among the early colonists in America, most of whom were concerned with birds merely as a source of food, were a few who erected houses for Purple Martins, following the example set by Indians who often hung out hollow gourds for birds. Storks in Europe have long been considered birds of good omen, and platforms or wagon wheels on buildings and posts were formerly provided for them (now storks are quite rare in modern cities).

Several books and bulletins, listed at the end of this chapter, deal in considerable detail with methods of attracting birds. This account briefly sketches some of the more familiar practices.

### NEST BOXES

One of the best known devices for attracting birds is the nest box for hole-nesting species. In the more settled areas, where severely pruned orchards and woodlots have deprived birds of natural nesting sites, many birds are quick to adopt man-made structures provided for them. More than 50 species in this country are known to nest in boxes or other artificial devices. Figures 181 and 182 illustrate a few of the more common types of bird houses and Table 9 gives data on the construction of houses for selected species.

Species most readily attracted to artificial housing include Purple Martins, now almost entirely dependent on boxes provided for them; Tree Swallows, which in contrast to martins prefer solitary housing but have built up large concentrations under sanctuary conditions; and House Wrens, perhaps the least choosy about housing as they will sometimes nest in tin cans, boots, scarecrows or other devices. McCabe (1961), however, has shown in numerous trials that House Wrens have color preferences and choose red or green boxes in preference to yellow or white.

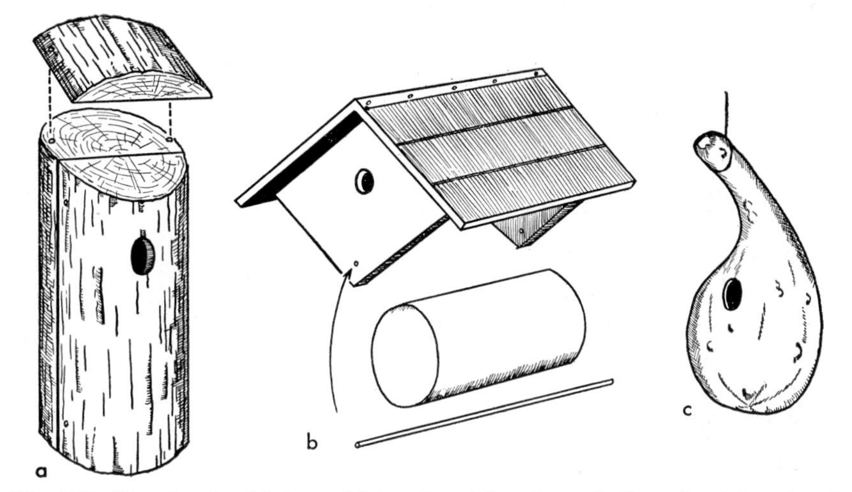


*Fig. 181. Housing for birds. a. Natural nest box from hollowed-out tree trunk. b. Wren house, unassembled to show simple construction (roof over metal cylinder prevents overheating). c. Hollow gourd house. (Drawings by Homer D. Roberts.)*

*Fig. 182. Housing for birds. a. Twelve-compartment house for Purple Martins. Martins are often unexplainably choosy about a nest site, and are repeatedly plagued by House Sparrows and Starlings appropriating their houses, but once established they may reoccupy the box each spring. (Drawing by Homer D. Roberts.) b. Wood Duck box. Elliptical entrance in metal-covered front keeps out racoons. (Drawing by Homer D. Roberts after Bellrose, "Housing for Wood Ducks,"* Ill. Nat. Hist. Survey, *Circ. 45, 1953.)*

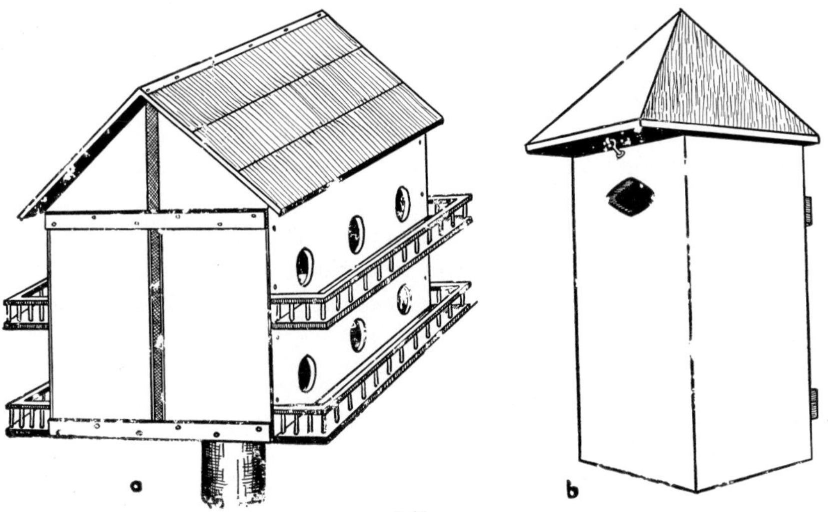

*Table 9. Nest Box Dimensions for Selected Species*

| *Species* | *Floor of Cavity (inches)* | *Depth of Cavity (inches)* | *Entrance above Floor (inches)* | *Diameter of Hole (inches)* | *Height above Ground (feet)* |
|---|---|---|---|---|---|
| Wood Duck | 10 x 10 | 24 | 18 | 3* | 10–25 |
| Screech Owl | 9 x 9 | 12–15 | 9–12 | 3¼ | 10–30 |
| Flicker | 7 x 7 | 16–18 | 14–16 | 2½ | 6–20 |
| Downy Woodpecker | 4 x 4 | 8–10 | 6–8 | 1¼ | 6–20 |
| Crested Flycatcher | 6 x 6 | 8–10 | 6–8 | 2 | 8–20 |
| Tree Swallow | 5 x 5 | 6 | 3–5 | 1½ | 6–15 |
| Purple Martin | 6 x 6 | 6 | 1 | 2½ | 15–20 |
| Chickadee | 4 x 4 | 8–10 | 6–8 | 1¼ | 5–15 |
| House Wren | 4 x 4 | 4–6 | 3–5 | ⅞ x 1¼ † | 6–10 |
| Bluebird | 5 x 5 | 8 | 6 | 1½ | 5–10 |

* An elliptical entrance keeps out raccoons.
† An elliptical entrance facilitates entering with sticks and keeps out House Sparrows.

Bluebirds are more difficult to attract to suburban homes, but several roadside and pasture box-erecting projects (Musselman, 1935; Laskey, 1939; Tillinghast, 1952) have been eminently successful in the past. Now, however, the Eastern Bluebird has become quite rare over most parts of its range, and many formerly occupied boxes are deserted; competition with House Sparrows and Starlings for nesting sites and loss of old orchards (modern orchards are not favorable habitats for bluebirds) are presumed to be among the reasons for the decline.

Woodland species are not so readily attracted to boxes as are birds of more open situations, for even in fairly clean woodlots they can usually find a place to build their own home. Nevertheless, chickadees, titmice, and nuthatches sometimes accept boxes. Providing boxes for Wood Ducks (Fig. 182b) is an important and often highly successful management procedure in the restoration of this endangered bird. In a Massachusetts project the Wood Duck population was approximately doubled (45 per cent of 2,000 boxes erected by state personnel were occupied by the ducks—McLaughlin and Grice, 1952).

### FEEDING STATIONS AND RATIONS

Supplementing a bird's natural fare by artificial feeding is a time-honored practice among bird lovers. For seed-eating birds special mixtures of selected and tested items are usually available. The principal ingredients are sunflower seeds (high quality protein, though nearly one-third useless fiber), various millets (for carbohydrates), corn (carbohydrates and vitamin A), peanut products and pecan meats (proteins and fats), grit (to aid digestion of hard seeds and to provide calcium and phosphorus), and often other items in addition to or in place of some of the above (Dennis, 1951–1952). Formerly hemp seed was a valuable proteinaceous, high-calorie ingredient of bird-food mixtures, but its illegal use in the manufacture of marijuana has placed a ban on the sale of raw seed and sterilization increases the cost. Sunflower seed is the first choice of Cardinals, grosbeaks, and titmice. It is quite expensive, however, and a large flock of Evening Grosbeaks or other finches may consume several hundred pounds in a season.

Suet and meat scraps are standard rations for insectivorous winter birds, such as woodpeckers, jays, titmice, and nuthatches. Too much salt is poisonous to birds, but a little is needed. Usually sufficient amounts are obtained from such items as bread crumbs and peanut butter. Some winter finches seem to crave salt especially, perhaps because of mineral deficiencies in their customary diet. A few birds, notably hummingbirds, have a liking for sweets; this can be provided in vials or nectar cups filled with a concentrated sugar or honey solution (Fig. 73).

Water is difficult to provide in the northern states in winter, but birds can usually meet their limited drinking needs by picking at melting ice and snow. Now electrically warmed drinking receptacles are available from some supply houses. Figure 183 illustrates some devices recommended for attracting birds.

Sportsmen are more familiar with devices for helping game birds in winter—corn-shock shelters for pheasants and quail and lean-tos in woodlands for the usually indifferent grouse. Waterfowl feeding programs are often carried out on refuges, especially in northern areas where the birds often become crowded into restricted areas of open water in winter. Coarser grains, such as corn, wheat, oats, and barley, are commonly fed to waterfowl, but such a diet, as opposed to a more normal diet of pondweeds, increases mortality from lead poisoning (p. 374). In fact, the whole program of artificial winter feeding has certain drawbacks, for building up concentrations increases the chances of disease and sometimes results in local crop damage. The view that birds may become unduly pauperized by feeding them is seldom justified, however, for most birds merely supplement their regular diet by occasional pickups at stations. All in all, winter feeding gives

*Fig. 183. Devices for attracting birds. a. A simple window shelf, with raised border to keep seeds from blowing off. b. Suet log for insectivorous birds. c. Feeder de luxe, with suet tray, feed hopper, and perches. d. Bird bath. (Drawings by Homer D. Roberts.)*

many people a great deal of enjoyment and usually aids the birds during the leanest time of year.

### PLANTINGS

A more practical method of supplying permanent rations for birds is the planting of fruit-bearing shrubs or other food plants, arranged in a way to provide natural foods over the whole year. Such plantings often furnish shelter and nesting sites as well, and are popular with home owners because many of the plants most useful for birds are also highly ornamental. Now, however, care of the home grounds often involves the use of so many pesticides (p. 380) that trying to attract birds may not be desirable. Several of the references dealing with attracting birds (p. 383) treat planting programs in considerable detail, and should be consulted by those planning such an enterprise.

More costly and more difficult to maintain are food patches of selected grains and seeds (Fig. 184). In the northern states food patches often get

*Fig. 184. A food patch of sunflower or other grains is very useful for attracting birds, but is usually quickly harvested and is expensive to maintain. (Photo by Mich. Dept. of Conservation.)*

snowed under at the time of year when they are most needed, or the seeds may be largely harvested by migratory sparrows and blackbirds before critical winter weather arrives. A less expensive method of providing for the larger birds is merely leaving corn, standing or in shocks, or leaving islands of unharvested grain in corners or along fence rows.

Farm and forest wildlife often can be helped by management of the more desirable plants already on hand. Many woodlots need regulated thinning. Brush piles of the thinnings form shelters for many species; fence rows and waste corners can be left wild rather than debrushed and burned, and eroding gullies can be reclothed with soil binding and sheltering plants such as multiflora rose.

## *Sanctuaries and Refuges*

Sanctuaries and refuges for birds, initiated in a small way long ago, have increased over the years, until now many millions of acres are in federal, state, municipal, or private holdings where wildlife is held more or less inviolate. It is not possible to deal at any length with these vast sanctuary areas, but a few remarks about them are pertinent here.

## NATIONAL PARKS AND MONUMENTS

More than 20 million acres of sanctuary are available for birds in the 181 national parks, monuments, and historic sites held in government ownership. These not only furnish badly needed nesting grounds for critical species, such as the Everglade Kite in the Everglades National Park and the Trumpeter Swan in Yellowstone, but feature valuable instructional programs for visitors as well. Some of the more popular or conveniently located parks attract more than a million visitors each year (Fig. 185); the total for all units in 1960 exceeded 72 million. Bird watchers, particularly easterners in the west, have found the national parks meccas of bird life, and usually posted lists and museum exhibits, as well as trained park naturalists conducting nature hikes, help visitors in their identification of new forms.

*Fig. 185. Acadia National Park, Maine. Accessibility for summer visitors and diversified terrain—seacoast, mountains, woods, and fields—account for an abundance of both human and avian visitors. More than 250 species of birds have been recorded in the park. (Courtesy of R. H. Manville.)*

FEDERAL REFUGES AND STATE GAME AREAS

The development of wildlife refuges was inaugurated in 1929 with the passage of the Migratory Bird Conservation Act (p. 359). There had been earlier efforts toward refuge development, the first in 1903 when Pelican Island was set aside for the then much persecuted Brown Pelicans, which promptly showed their lack of appreciation by deserting the place completely. But in the 1930's, largely by means of funds obtained through the Migratory Bird Hunting Stamp Act, a vast program of land acquisition got under way. Now some 275 wildlife refuges, comprising nearly 18 million acres, primarily for waterfowl but often also for other species, are well distributed over the continent.

Some of the more northern refuges, particularly in the northwest (Fig. 186), are strategically located for breeding grounds, though of course they are not comparable to nesting areas in the Canadian prairie provinces. Other refuges are along migration routes, and others are scattered over Atlantic, Gulf Coast, or southwestern wintering grounds. A few are strategically located for jeopardized species: the Aransas Refuge in Texas as the wintering grounds of the Whooping Crane (Fig. 177), Okefenokee for the Limp-

*Fig. 186. Lower Souris National Wildlife Refuge in North Dakota. The marshes created by impounding waters here produce more than 100,000 waterfowl annually. (Fish and Wildlife photo by C. J. Henry from Gabrielson,* Wildlife Refuges, *copyright 1943 by The Macmillan Company, New York.)*

kin, and the Florida Keys for the Great White Heron. Such refuges have also become important research centers for the study of the many current problems relating to waterfowl management.

Whereas waterfowl are primarily a federal responsibility, nonmigratory game birds come under the jurisdiction of the states. State game areas, usually operated as public shooting grounds, and experiment stations primarily for research, serve as refuges where the birds find partial protection and good habitat. Such areas are also important as research centers for the study of game problems and for the training of wildlife personnel. State game areas are not necessarily exclusively for upland game, for often the states own and operate areas for migratory waterfowl as well as for nongame species. Often state parks are also wild areas where essential habitats are preserved for many species that might otherwise be eliminated by commercial developments. However, the current trend in many state parks is for increased recreational facilities at the expense of wildlife (Fig. 187).

*Fig. 187. Egrets (both Common and Snowy) in Tomoka State Park, Florida. Protection on southern sanctuaries may have saved these birds from extermination. (Photo by Allan D. Cruickshank.)*

OTHER SANCTUARIES

Prominent among the many sanctuaries operated primarily for non-game species are those maintained by the National Audubon Society. These number some thirty-six sanctuaries totaling 2 million acres in ten states, mainly in the south. Many of these are strategically located, often deliberately selected, to protect endangered species. A good example is Corkscrew Swamp Sanctuary in southern Florida, a 6,000-acre tract which preserves the country's largest remaining stand of virgin bald cypress and its associated fauna and flora, including alligators and orchids as well as the rare Limpkin and declining Wood Ibis.

Some state ornithological organizations, as well as more localized bird clubs, maintain sanctuaries. The Massachusetts Audubon Society operates fourteen sanctuaries with a permanent staff on some of them (Figs. 188–189). These are open the year round to the public and are visited by thousands of people annually.

*Fig. 188. Trailside Nature Museum at Pleasant Valley Sanctuary in Lenox, one of the 14 sanctuaries operated by the Massachusetts Audubon Society. (Courtesy of Alvah Sanborn.)*

*Fig. 189. Beaver ponds at Pleasant Valley Sanctuary, created by introducing beavers into a brook-fed alder swamp, now attract many water birds and even more human visitors. Ten miles of trails traverse the area. (Courtesy of Alvah Sanborn.)*

Quite unique among other types of sanctuaries are (1) Bird City at Avery Island, Louisiana, where E. A. McIlhenny built up a large rookery of water birds by constructing a dam to impound water and then introducing eight Snowy Egrets to the area; (2) the heron sanctuary at Stone Harbor, New Jersey, which has attracted to it nearly all the ardeid species that occur in North America; (3) Hawk Mountain Sanctuary in Pennsylvania (p. 269); and (4) the system of refuges maintained by the Michigan Department of Conservation for the rare Kirtland's Warbler.

## *Other Management Problems*

### PREDATOR CONTROL

A time-honored method of "managing" wildlife is some system of predator control, such as "vermin" campaigns and the payment of bounties for animals destroyed. It is probably already clear that Nature's system of predator-prey regulation is fundamentally sound, and that short-sighted attempts by man to improve things commonly result in upsets. A fairly typical example is that of a New England game reserve that envisaged improvement of conditions for nesting game birds by the elimination of predatory birds, particularly Great Horned Owls. The actual result, however, was such an increase in skunks that ground nesters were largely unsuccessful until hawks and owls were permitted to return.

A more complex example of interrelationship between predator and prey was once described by A. K. Fisher (1908). A New York marsh with a well-balanced population of ducks, skunks, and snapping turtles was heavily trapped when the market price of fur went up, so that snapping turtles, formerly held in check by the skunks eating their eggs, increased rapidly, and ducks, as a result of excessive turtles, all but disappeared. Then the market price of fur declined so that trapping was no longer profitable, skunks increased, snapping turtles decreased, and ducks were restored to normal numbers.

A more recent example of the apparent consequences of interference with basic predator-prey relationships has been reported in the outbreak of mice in the fertile Klamath basin of northern California and southern Oregon. Intensive predator control, particularly of coyotes, was followed by a buildup of mice which irrupted in the spring of 1958. To combat the plague poisoned bait (1080 and zinc phosphide) was widely distributed in an area used by 500,000 waterfowl in the spring. More than 3,000 grazing geese were said to have been poisoned, so driving parties attempted to keep the geese off the treated fields. Here it seems conceivable that the whole chain of costly events—cost of the original predator control, economic loss to crops from the mouse plague, another poisoning campaign to combat the mice, loss of valuable waterfowl resources, and man-hours involved in flushing geese from the fields—might have been averted by a policy of noninterference with the original predator-prey relationship.

There are many instances in modern management, however, where man may, with good reasons, want to favor certain species at the expense of others. It is obvious that on game farms and about fish hatcheries, or sometimes in other special projects, species that interfere with the outlined program of the area need to be controlled. But where control measures are necessary they should be in competent hands, and executed only after careful study.

## BOUNTIES

Payment of bounties as a means of encouraging people to participate in reducing the numbers of an unwanted species has repeatedly proven its inefficiency. Bounties are costly, often grossly mishandled, and usually do not produce the sort of control desired. The Goshawk bounty in some eastern states is an oft-cited example of misapplication. One of the most difficult of the hawks to identify, at least of the immatures in fall and winter, thousands of other hawks have been shot in states where the Goshawk is uncommon, or almost unknown. Young (1952) reported 9,000 shot in Virginia, where there were only ten authentic Goshawk records for the state.

A glaring example of inefficiency in administration of the bounty was that of the House Sparrow in Michigan (Barrows, 1912). In 1898 about $50,000 was paid out of county funds in one- and two-cent bounties on House Sparrows. But in the dispensation of funds, graft and fraud arose to an alarming degree; a great deal of property damage and even fatal accidents resulted from careless use of firearms; many native songbirds were needlessly destroyed; and, after the smoke of the barrage had subsided, the House Sparrows seemed to have suffered little if any reduction in numbers. Of course some bounties have accomplished their purported mission of reducing, or in some cases practically eliminating, an unwanted species, but it is seldom proven that the temporary reduction in numbers of a predator is of any long-range benefit to the prey.

### INTRODUCED SPECIES

Introduction of exotic species into a new environment often poses severe management or control problems, usually because an introduced species is relieved of contact with its natural enemies and competitors. Perhaps the worst phase of this is the accidental introduction of foreign insect pests which necessitates severe importation restrictions and subsequent control measures, if the pest secures a foothold. Among vertebrates one need only cite problems created by rabbits in Australia, goats on various islands (which cause devegetation and extinction of endemic flora and fauna on a large scale), and rats everywhere. Introduced House Sparrows and Starlings are still a problem in this country, after more than half a century of control measures.

Another aspect of introductions is the intentional stocking of game habitats with new species. This has been eminently successful with the Ring-necked Pheasant, but less so, or only on a more local scale, with Gray (Hungarian) Partridges, Chukars, Migratory Quail (*Coturnix*), Capercaillie (almost a total failure), and other species. Such importations need to be studied carefully in advance and strict regulations set up to control them.

Transplantation experiments with native species have been successful in some cases. Trumpeter Swans were moved from Red Rock Wildlife Refuge in Montana and successfully stocked in other refuges. Ruffed Grouse have been transplanted to several formerly grouseless islands in the Great Lakes, which now permit an open season, with hunter success higher than on the mainland (Ammann and Palmer, 1958).

## DISEASES AND PARASITES

Avian diseases communicable to man were discussed in Chapter 13, but perhaps a more important aspect of this topic is the effect on the birds themselves. Avian populations are sometimes regulated by diseases, which are responsible in part for periodic die-offs. Sometimes losses are severe enough to have economic significance. Among ducks, *botulism, fowl cholera,* and *lead poisoning* destroy thousands of birds annually. Botulism, or western duck sickness (Fig. 190), is a bacterial disease caused by *Clostridium botulinum* which thrives on decaying organic matter at times of low water, particularly in alkaline marshes. The best remedy known to date is control

*Fig. 190. Ducks, dead or dying from botulism on alkali flats at Bear River Refuge in Utah. Many sick birds are picked up and given antitoxin treatments at the refuge's duck hospital. Inset shows a Mallard in the final stages of the disease. (Photo by W. F. Kubichek, Fish and Wildlife Service.)*

of the water level, that is, periodic flooding or draw-down to eliminate the shallow water zone which favors the development of *Clostridium* (Kalmbach and Gunderson, 1934). Inoculations against the disease have been used successfully, but of course it is time consuming and costly to trap and inoculate the ducks. During the 1952 outbreak at Bear River Refuge in Utah, 6,233 sick ducks were treated and released, but 20,000 ducks had already died (Tinker, 1958). Fowl cholera is another bacterial disease affecting waterfowl. In the winter of 1950, 4,400 birds died of it on the Muleshoe Refuge in Texas (Petrides and Bryant, 1951).

Lead poisoning is a result of the ingestion of bullets which ducks accidentally pick up in feeding operations in areas heavily shot over in the hunting season (Fig. 191). Sometimes a few pellets in the digestive tract are sufficient to cause death, and yet many pellets, up to seventy-six or more, have been removed in postmortem examinations of single birds. In spite of considerable research, as with nonlead alloys for bullets and with stomach pumps for removing ingested lead, no practical solution to this problem is yet known. A leafy diet of pondweeds, as opposed to a corn or grain diet, seems to lessen the incidence of the disease, hence baiting

*Fig. 191. Left, lead poisoning in Mallard, showing shot in opened gizzard and rectum distended with greenish material. Right, X-ray of duck which died from lead poisoning. (Photos by Mich. Dept. of Conservation.)*

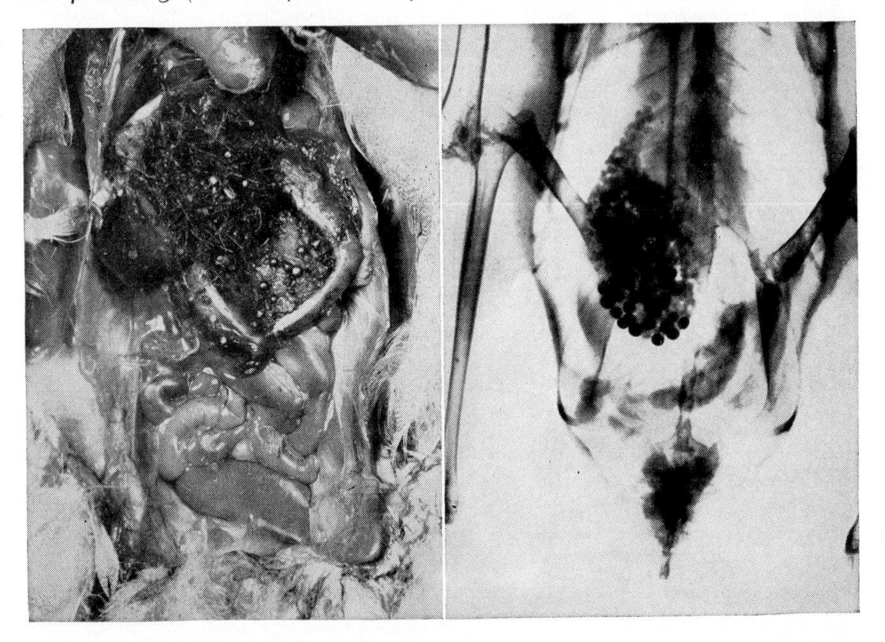

and artificial feeding may sometimes have harmful consequences. Though waterfowl losses from lead poisoning are high, Bellrose (1959), in the latest comprehensive study of the situation, concludes that the losses, which vary from one to 10 per cent of the population in different species, are not high enough to warrant drastic measures to try to curb them.

*Trichomoniasis*, a protozoan disease caused by the flagellate *Trichomonas gallinae*, has been known in doves, pigeons, turkeys, and other birds for some time. It was largely responsible for the die-off in Mourning Doves in the southeastern states in 1950 (Stabler and Herman, 1951; Haugen, 1952). The disease results in the formation of a yellowish, cheesy mass ("canker") in the posterior part of the mouth or crop, sometimes blocking off the passage of food or air and causing starvation or asphyxiation. Hawks can become infected by feeding on diseased birds (Kiel, 1960).

*Ulcerative enteritis* (quail disease), a disease of uncertain origin which causes lesions in the lower digestive tract, is of common occurrence in gallinaceous birds in captivity but also occurs in wild grouse, pheasants, and quail (Buss, *et al.*, 1958). Strict sanitation seems to be the best preventive in captives. Game birds often have to be raised on wire, so that droppings, the source of further infection, will fall through the wires. Addition of streptomycin to the drinking water was found to cut down the loss due to enteritis in adult quail from 21.4 to 4.3 per cent (Kirkpatrick and Moses, 1953).

*Ectoparasites* sometimes inflict serious harm to their hosts, though in other cases birds merely harbor the parasite without physical injury to themselves. Heavy infestations (Fig. 192), however, may cause anemia (blood-sucking types) or other run-down conditions. Lacerations in the skin may serve as portals of entry for bacteria, decrease egg production in poultry, carry more serious avian diseases to their hosts, and cause the death of nestlings (Boyd, 1951). Bird lice (Mallophaga) in particular

*Fig. 192. Head of Gray Partridge heavily infested with louse eggs. (Courtesy of Mich. Dept. of Conservation.)*

have been studied extensively by Hopkins and Clay (1952) and Malcomson (1960). Malcomson lists 800 species of Mallophaga from 500 birds in North America (including some Zoo birds not native). He reports that some 2,600 species are known and that the total may yet exceed 3,000. Ectoparasites of birds may be divided into six general types (Boyd, 1951):

1. Mallophaga (bird lice)—obligatory parasites, chewing, feather-eating types, spending complete life cycle on host.
2. Fleas—adults on birds, larvae nonparasitic.
3. Hippoboscid flies—obligatory parasites, common on many species of birds, especially nestlings.
4. Protocalliphorid flies—larvae hatched from eggs laid in nests attacking nestlings at night, sometimes causing death.
5. Ticks (Acarina)—blood-sucking types, often about the head, causing anemia and weakened condition, often vectors of disease.
6. Mites (Acarina)—blood-sucking and dermatophagous (skin and itch mites), including chiggers.

*Endoparasites,* like ectoparasites, often have serious and sometimes lethal effects on birds, although ordinarily their purpose is to find a safe home and not destroy themselves by destroying their host. Some endoparasites that seem to be important in waterfowl and game-bird management include *Leucocytozoon* in ducks (O'Roke, 1934) and grouse (Erickson, 1953; Cowan and Peterle, 1957), gizzard worms in geese (Herman and Wehr, 1954), and acanthocephalid worms in eider ducks (Clark, *et al.,* 1958). Herman (1955) gives a good review of diseases and parasites in birds, including ecto- and endoparasites, and bacterial and virus diseases.

## Wildlife Conservation in a Modern World

Chapter 10 mentioned some of the factors, natural and man-made, responsible for high mortality to birds, but did not discuss the latter. In minor ways birds and man have been in competition or conflict since man first appeared on earth, but in the last decade or two, with sharply increasing demands on the land and its resources, this conflict has become greatly accentuated. Briefly outlined below are several of the most pressing problems that birds, and sometimes man, face in the struggle for survival.

## LAND USE

One of the most critical present-day problems that threatens not only the security of birds but of man himself is the ever-increasing demand for living space and the needs that go with it. More and more wild land is being taken over for highway construction, industrial expansion, housing and suburban developments, and for food and fiber production. The advanced technology required to fulfill these needs introduces new problems—pollution of air, soil, and water on which we depend for life.

One of the many examples that might be cited to illustrate the controversy over land use is that at the heron sanctuary at Stone Harbor, New Jersey. Formerly low-value brushland, set aside as sanctuary for the herons, now its 31 acres are worth $500,000 for real estate developments. Through the intervention of several influential conservationists the herons won the first round in the conflict over the land, but as its value, and the need for it, increases, the herons may have to go, thus converting one of the most remarkable bird sanctuaries in North America into another cluster of houses.

Similar conflicts arise from the need for greater food production. There is an old saying in Turkey that the farmer sows a handful of grain for himself, another for the birds and another for the gods, but in this country the farmer must reap close to 100 per cent of the crop or he doesn't stay in business. Formerly birds and agriculture were somewhat complementary, one aiding the other, but this is no longer always true. Monocultural practices create an imbalance, favoring a buildup of grain-feeding birds, which become economic pests, at the expense of the insectivorous species whose food supply is depleted or poisoned. Several other land-use developments that imperil birds have already been mentioned (see accounts of Roseate Spoonbill, Whooping Crane, and Ivory-billed Woodpecker). A continually recurring threat to wildlife is the need for more space for military operations; one of the latest is the demand for a bombing range near Lake Mattamuskeet National Wildlife Refuge in North Carolina, where nearly 200,000 waterfowl winter annually.

## DRAINAGE

Drainage is a special type of land usage, conducted for varying purposes, but it is in a special category as far as waterfowl management is concerned.

Currently (1960–1961) the Departments of Interior and Agriculture are engaged in a struggle over the use of marsh lands, with government subsidized projects draining millions of acres of the most productive duck-breeding grounds in North America—jeopardizing a dwindling, multimillion dollar resource to produce more wheat to put into government surplus. Yet even the most ardent duck hunter may yet have to concede that wheat has greater value for more people than ducks. Animal proteins, whether in ducks on the wing or beef on the hoof, are uneconomical. Other types of drainage, as already indicated, endanger the Everglade Kite, the Limpkin, the Wood Ibis, and other rookery birds; only by setting aside parks, refuges, and sanctuaries have some of these been saved.

### OIL POLLUTION

There are many kinds and degrees of pollution, largely derived from the by-products of civilization, but it is chiefly oil pollution of coastal waters that concerns ornithologists. Though this has long posed a problem for marine life, the threat to birds was greatly accentuated by a recent spillage of oil off the coast of Newfoundland, which destroyed an estimated 250,000 water birds and wiped out a large segment of the North Atlantic Razor-billed Auk population. An earlier spillage took a similarly heavy toll of eider ducks. Oil-laden ducks, gulls, grebes, and other water birds are an increasingly common sight along the Atlantic Coast and in the Great Lakes (Fig. 193). Oil pollution is an international problem, difficult, if not impossible, to solve. Here, in addition to the menace to birds, an exceedingly valuable shellfish industry is involved.

### CEILOMETERS AND TELEVISION TOWERS

Collisions of birds with man-made structures (tall buildings, monuments, lighthouses) and moving vehicles (aircraft and automobiles) have constituted a hazard to birds for a long time, but now ceilometers and high television towers pose a new and more serious threat. Apparently birds are attracted to encircling beams of light from ceilometers and fly in and out of the beams until exhausted. The actual kill varies greatly. At the Albany airport in New York, Bartlett (1952) watched hundreds of birds flying in and out of the light, but no dead or exhausted birds were found. Later, during a heavy flight, some 300 dead or injured birds were

*Fig. 193. A Canvasback (left) that died of oil pollution in the Detroit River and a normal Canvasback (right) free from oil. An estimated 10,000–12,-000 ducks died in the Detroit River and western Lake Erie from oil pollution in the winter of 1959–60. (Photo by Mich. Dept. of Conservation.)*

retrieved (Bartlett, 1956). At three stations in Tennessee, 1,044 dead birds of 46 species were found in one night (Howell and Tanner, 1951).

High television towers are a hazard on cloudy nights with a low ceiling. In ordinary weather nocturnal migrants fly higher than the highest towers; even under cloudy skies there have been few reports of kills at towers under 800 feet, but high mortality has been recorded at some of the higher structures. The heaviest losses have been reported at Warner Robins Air Force Base in Georgia (Johnston and Haines, 1957), where 50,000 birds of 53 species were killed on October 8, 1954 (50,000 others at twenty-four other stations), and at Eau Claire, Wisconsin (Kemper, 1958), where an estimated 20,000 birds were killed in one night. Somewhat lower, but still significant, mortality has been reported by Tordoff and Mengel (1956) at Topeka, Kansas, and by Brewer and Ellis (1958) in east-central Illinois. Warblers, vireos, and thrushes usually predominate in television tower kills.

PESTICIDES

Of all the man-created hazards to bird life perhaps the most controversial is the widespread and unremitting use of chemical poisons in the control of insects and other pests. Pesticide-wildlife problems are by no means new. Lindsdale (1932), for example, summarized information on bird losses resulting from ground squirrel control with thallium-treated grain in California in the late 1920's; field workers contacted reported thousands of birds of more than 40 different species apparently dying from feeding directly on the poisoned grain, or in the case of predatory birds, from secondary poisoning. But pesticide-wildlife problems multiplied rapidly with increased use of DDT and other hydrocarbons after World War II. Control programs, some of them highly indiscriminate and often unnecessary, expanded so rapidly that by the late 1950's more than a billion pounds of formulated pesticides were being applied annually to about 100 million acres of land in this country. More than two hundred different basic pesticides had been developed, which by 1960 were listed under nearly 10,000 trade names.

A few preliminary studies indicated that some of the less toxic chemicals, when applied to small acreages in approved ways, could be used without noticeable effects on birds, but as control programs expanded, and heavier dosages or more lethal chemicals were used, reports of apparent bird mortality increased. Bird lovers in particular protested the use of such lethal materials, but their claims of bird losses were generally discredited. Many carefully conducted field studies, followed in some cases by chemical analyses of birds, have now substantiated reports of high mortality in many of the programs. The heaviest losses recorded to date have been in the fire-ant "eradication" campaign in the southeastern states, in Dutch elm disease "control" in the midwest, and in Japanese beetle programs in Illinois and Michigan.

Published data on pesticides are too numerous to document here. Rudd and Genelly (1956), in perhaps the most comprehensive report to date, detailed some of the effects on wildlife and listed nearly a thousand titles on the subject, but the three most destructive programs, mentioned above, postdated their report. Chemists in the Fish and Wildlife Service have now analyzed more than a thousand specimens, mostly birds, from the fire-ant program, substantiating earlier field reports (Allen, 1958; Lay, 1959) of an exceedingly high mortality from use of heptachlor at 2 pounds per acre. In a Japanese beetle control project in Illinois, where 3 pounds of dieldrin per acre were used, Scott, *et al.* (1959) reported virtual elimination or heavy losses for most ground-feeding birds and mammals. Similar effects on wildlife were observed in Michigan where aldrin was used.

In the Dutch elm disease program with DDT, Barker (1958) described a fatal leaf-litter-earthworm-Robin cycle in Illinois; Hunt (1960) and Hickey and Hunt (1960) compared populations of Robins and other songbirds in sprayed and unsprayed communities in Wisconsin, recording declines up to 90 per cent or more in the former; Mehner and Wallace (1959) reported simliar declines and nearly complete nesting failure in Robins at East Lansing, Michigan; and Wallace, Nickell, and Bernard (1961) reviewed the whole situation for southern Michigan. Detailed chemical analyses of more than two hundred Michigan birds verified the presence of DDT, in lethal amounts, in most of the suspected victims (Fig. 194). DDT was also found to persist through all stages of the reproductive cycle from the egg follicles in the ovaries to newly hatched nestlings.

*Fig. 194. A part of the dead and dying Robins picked up on and around the Michigan State University campus in the spring of 1961 after the spraying of the elms. All of the 69 Robins analyzed from the same area had DDT; 90 per cent of them had levels in the brain comparable to levels recovered from experimentally poisoned birds. (Photo by Robert L. Fleming, Jr.)*

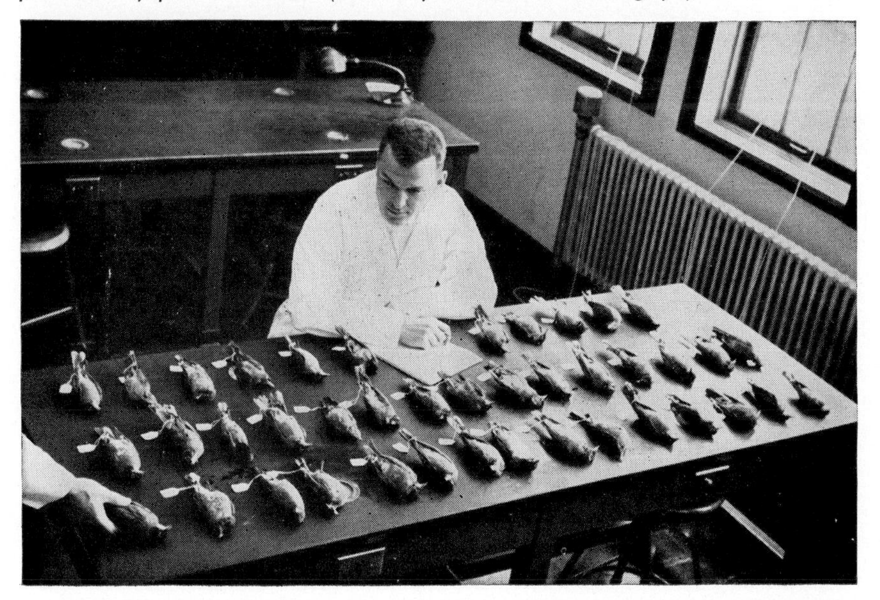

Many committees and organizations at local, state, national, and international levels are now studying and trying to evaluate sharply conflicting pest control-wildlife relationships, but the problems are still unresolved. At the meeting of the International Union for the Conservation of Nature in Poland in 1960, representatives of many nations discussed problems their countries now face in large-scale chemical contamination of plant and animal habitats. In 1961 Great Britain, after an investigation by a forty-two-member committee in the British Parliament, banned the use (for seed dressings) of aldrin, dieldrin, and heptachlor—highly toxic chemicals which we have used rather freely in this country—and asked for further restrictions and more careful supervision in the use of all agricultural poisons. Similar investigations are underway in this country, but conservationists are up against powerful opposition and vested interests.

If we are to save even appreciable remnants of our rapidly vanishing wildlife, more efforts must be made to stem the rising trend of all these man-created hazards; or else, wild animal life, as we have known it in the past, will be lost to future generations.

*Courtesy of the Cranbrook Institute of Science.*

# Selected References


TEXTBOOKS ON CONSERVATION AND MANAGEMENT

Gabrielson, Ira N. *Wildlife Refuges.* New York: Macmillan, 1943.
———. *Wildlife Conservation.* 2nd ed. New York: Macmillan, 1959.
Gustafson, A. F., Guise, C. H., Hamilton, Jr., W. J., and H. Ries. *Conservation in the United States.* Ithaca, N. Y.: Comstock, 1947.
Leopold, Aldo. *Game Management.* New York: Scribner, 1947.
Trippensee, R. E. *Wildlife Management.* Vol. I. New York: McGraw, 1948.
———. *Wildlife Management.* Vol. II. New York: McGraw, 1953.
Wing, Leonard D. *Practice of Wildlife Conservation.* New York: Wiley, 1951.

## MONOGRAPHS ON EXTINCT AND VANISHING SPECIES

Allen, Robert P. The Whooping Crane. *Research Report* (Nat. Aud. Soc., New York, 1952), **3**:1–246.

Banko, Winston E. The Trumpeter Swan. *No. Amer. Fauna* (1960), **63**:1–214.

Greenway, James C., Jr. Extinct and Vanishing Birds of the World, *Spec. Publ. No. 13*, Amer. Comm. for Intern. Wildl. Prot. (New York) 1958.

Gross, A. O. The Health Hen. *Boston Soc. Nat. Hist.* (1928), **6**:491–588.

Koford, Carl B. The California Condor. *Research Report* (Nat. Aud. Soc., New York, 1953), **4**:1–154.

Schorger, A. W. *The Passenger Pigeon; Its Natural History and Extinction.* Madison, Wisc.: Univ. Wisc. Press, 1955.

Tanner, James T. The Ivory-billed Woodpecker, *Research Report* (Nat. Aud. Soc., New York, 1942), **1**:1–111.

Walkinshaw, Lawrence H. The Sandhill Cranes. *Cranbrook Inst. Sci. Bull.*, **29** (Bloomfield Hills, Mich.) 1949.

## ATTRACTING BIRDS

Baker, John H. *The Audubon Guide to Attracting Birds.* Garden City, N. Y.: Doubleday, 1941.

Beecher, William J. *Attracting Birds to Your Backyard.* Fond du Lac, Wisc.: All-Pets Books, 1955.

Govan, Ada. *Wings at My Window.* New York: Macmillan, 1940.

Kalmbach, E. R. Homes for Birds. *Farmers' Bull.* (U.S.D.A., Washington, D. C., 1930), **1456**:1–21.

Lemmon, Robert S. *How to Attract the Birds.* Amer. Garden Guild, and Doubleday, 1947.

McKenny, Margaret. *Birds in the Garden.* New York: Reynal & Hitchcock, 1939.

Sawyer, E. J. Bird Houses, Baths, and Feeding Shelters. *Cranbrook Inst. Sci. Bull.*, **1** (Bloomfield Hills, Mich.), 4th ed., 1944.

Terres, John K. *Songbirds in Your Garden.* New York: Crowell, 1953.

## DISEASES, PARASITES, CONSERVATION PROBLEMS

Bellrose, Frank C. Lead Poisoning as a Mortality Factor in Waterfowl Populations. *Bull. Ill. Nat. Hist. Sur.*, Vol. 27, (1959) Art. **3**:233–288.

Errington, Paul L. Predation and Vertebrate Populations. *Quart. Rev. Biol.* (1946) **21**:144–177, 221–245.

Herman, Carlton M. Diseases of Birds. Chapt. 13 in *Recent Studies in Avian Biology* (ed. Albert Wolfson). Urbana, Ill.: U. of Ill., 1955.

Hopkins, G. H. E., and T. Clay. A *Check List of the Genera and Species of Mallophaga*. London: Brit. Mus., 1952.

Rothschild, M., and T. Clay. *Fleas, Flukes and Cuckoos*. London: Collins, 1952.

Rudd, Robert L., and Richard E. Gennelly. Pesticides: Their Use and Toxicity in Relation to Wildlife. *Game Bull.* 7 (Calif. Dept. Fish and Game, Sacramento, Calif.), 1956.

Wallace, G. J., Nickell, W. P., and R. F. Bernard. Bird Mortality in the Dutch Elm Disease Program in Michigan. *Cranbrook Inst. Sci. Bull.*, **41** (Bloomfield Hills, Mich.), 1961.

# PART II

# 15

# CLASSIFICATION OF BIRDS

The classification of birds from the structural standpoint—orders, families, genera, species and subspecies—was explained in Chapter 2, and a few principles of systematics and nomenclature were discussed. In this chapter there is a complete listing of the orders and families of living birds of the world, the number of species in each family, the distribution of each family, and a few distinguishing characters for the nonpasserines and for North American passerine families.

Orders and families and their arrangement (sequence) follow Wetmore's (1960) A *Classification for the Birds of the World,* which for the nonpasserine groups is essentially the same as those in Peters' *Birds of the World* and differs in only minor respects from the families listed by Mayr (1946a), Mayr and Amadon (1951), Van Tyne and Berger (1959), and Storer (1960). The arrangement of the confusing passerine families, never finished by Peters, differs considerably among these authorities, however. Still other arrangements for parts of the passerine classification have been proposed by Arvey (1951) for the waxwings and allies, by Beecher (1951, 1953) for the nine-primaried oscines, and by Tordoff (1954) for the complicated family Fringillidae.

Perhaps fortunately, the classifications of Wetmore and Van Tyne are similar for both the nonpasserine and passerine groups. They differ chiefly in Van Tyne's recognition of the musophagids as a separate order (Musophagiformes); merging of the Brachypteraciidae with the Coraciidae; separation of the wrynecks (Jyngidae) from the woodpeckers proper (Picidae);

lumping of the Paradoxornithidae (Parrotbills) and Chamaeidae (Wren-tits) with the Timaliidae (babblers); recognition of separate families for the Irenidae (leaf birds—which include Wetmore's Chloropseidae, as well as *Irena* which Wetmore put with the Oriolidae) and Neosittidae (Australian nuthatches); and dropping the family Coerebidae, whose members were assigned to other related families. Wetmore also continues to preserve the family Regulidae (kinglets) as distinct from the Sylviidae. Some juggling around of genera and subfamilies in the nine-primaried oscine complex was done by Van Tyne, but Wetmore's family names (except for the Coerebidae) are retained.

The numbers of species here indicated for each family are taken from Van Tyne and Berger (1959) which, for the nonpasserines at least, agree closely with the numbers listed by Mayr and Amadon (1951). The former edition of this book used Peters' listings for counts of species (and subspecies), but, as indicated in Chapter 2, the modern species concept tends to reduce the number of valid species (but not necessarily subspecies). This is well illustrated by the fact that Van Tyne (apparently following Mayr) reduced the number of species recognized by Peters in 31 nonpasserine families but increased the number in only 9 families (and then only by one or two species).

Peters' listings of subspecies of nonpasserines are retained here as useful indications of the amount of subspeciation taking place in various families. It is interesting to note, for instance, that the penguins, perhaps because of their long isolation on specific breeding grounds, are mostly monotypic; the 17 or 18 species include only 22 total forms. The more mobile ducks, for different reasons, have not undergone much racial differentiation in North America; some are monotypic, others have an allied race in the Old World. Dispersal habits are believed to be a reason for lack of subspecific differentiation in this case, for a duck born in the interior marshes may pair with one from the coast on common wintering grounds and go to either place for its first breeding season. Nonmigratory birds, on the other hand, probably because they form isolated populations that become more or less sedentary, with only peripheral interbreeding with nearby populations, have undergone marked racial differentiation. The North American Screech Owls, a single species, form 18 geographic races, mostly in western United States. Nonmigratory grouse (19 species into 102 subspecies) and phasianids (183 species into about 546 forms) also exhibit great racial differentiation. Mayr (1946a) says that about 75 per cent of the known species of birds are polytypic. Species, or populations, with broadly overlapping or identical breeding ranges are spoken of as *sympatric,* those with noncontiguous or completely separated ranges are *allopatric.* Such distributional arrangements are important in speciation.

In the following list, a few distinguishing characters are given for the nonpasserine families; in the passerine families, where it is often difficult to assign diagnostic differences, distinguishing characters are included for the North Amercan families only. Van Tyne and Berger (1959) give detailed descriptions of physical characteristics for all of the families, and Pettingill's *Manual* (p. 419) gives fairly complete descriptions for the North American families.

## *Orders and Families of Living Birds*

*(North American families are in boldface)*

1. SPHENISCIFORMES, Penguins.
   *1.* Spheniscidae, 17 species, 22 forms; * Antarctic, north to Galápagos; heavy-bodied (up to 94 lbs.); flightless; wings flipperlike for swimming; plumage dense of scalelike feathers completely investing the body (no apteria); body well insulated with subcutaneous fat.
2. STRUTHIONIFORMES, Ostriches.
   *1.* Struthionidae, 1 species, 6 forms; Africa, southeast Asia (Arabia); large (up to 300 lbs. in ♂), flightless, cursorial; wings degenerate, with numerous fluffy plumes; plumage loose (no interlocking), sparse on neck and absent on thighs; 2 toes.
3. RHEIFORMES, Rheas.
   *1.* Rheidae, 2 species, 6 forms; South America; large (up to 50 lbs.), flightless, cursorial; wings degenerate, with soft loose plumes; no rectrices; head and neck feathered; 3 toes.
4. CASUARIIFORMES, Cassowaries, Emus, 2 living families (another fossil); wings much reduced; plumage coarse, hairlike, drooping; long aftershafts; no real rectrices.
   *1.* Casuariidae, Cassowaries, 3 species, 30 forms; North Queensland and adjacent islands (mostly New Guinea); beak compressed; bony casque on head, often with gaudy wattles on featherless neck; remiges reduced to 4–6 stiff black quills; legs stout.
   *2.* Dromiceidae, Emus, 1 species (another extinct), 3 forms (2 others extinct); Australia; beak depressed; neck feathered, no casque or wattles; no quills on wings.
5. APTERYGIFORMES, Kiwis (*Apteryx*).
   *1.* Apterygidae, 3 species, 5 forms; New Zealand; beak long, decurved,

* "Forms," as used here, denotes total species and subspecies.

with nostril near tip; no apparent wings; plumage hairlike; legs short and stout; strong toes terminating in sharp claws.

6. Tinamiformes, Tinamous.
   *1.* Tinamidae, 45 species, 118 forms; neotropical (Mexico through South America); bobwhite to fowl size; bill usually somewhat depressed and arched; wings developed for flight, short and concave; mainly cursorial.
7. Gaviiformes, Loons.
   *1.* **Gaviidae,** 4 species, 8 forms; circumpolar; bill strong, straight, compressed; wings pointed; legs far back on body; tarsus flattened, bladelike; front toes fully webbed.
8. Podicipediformes, Grebes.
   *1.* **Podicipedidae,** 20 species, 38 forms; world-wide, all continents and larger islands; wings short (2 species flightless); plumage soft and dense, toes lobed with flattened nails; tail reduced to tuft of feathers.
9. Procellariiformes, Tube-nosed Swimmers, 4 families; nostrils tubular; hooked bill composed of horny plates; nasal glands large; wings long and narrow (large number of secondaries); plumage compact, "oily"; feet palmate.
   *1.* **Diomedeidae,** Albatrosses, 14 species, 19 forms; wide-ranging oceanic birds, breeding mainly on islands in southern hemisphere; nostrils lateral, widely separated by culmen.
   *2.* **Procellariidae,** Shearwaters, Fulmars, 56 species, 117 living forms; oceans, islands, and coasts throughout the world; nostrils dorsal, fused but imperforate.
   *3.* **Hydrobatidae,** Storm Petrels, 18 species, 40 forms; oceans, islands, and coasts throughout the world; nostrils dorsal, fused and perforate (one tube).
   *4.* Pelecanoididae, Diving Petrels, 5 species, 9 forms; southern oceans; nostrils opening vertically; wing bones shortened, flattened; alcidlike.
10. Pelecaniformes, Totipalmate Swimmers, 6 living families (6 other fossil families); totipalmate foot unique (4 toes joined in common web); nostrils rudimentary or absent; gular sac.
    *1.* **Phaëthontidae,** Tropicbirds, 3 species, 14 forms; tropical oceans; nostrils small, perforate; gular sac rudimentary; middle rectrices long and filiform.
    *2.* **Pelecanidae,** Pelicans, 6 species, 12 forms; world-wide, except polar extremes; nostrils obsolete; gular pouch very large; bill large, long and hooked; huge wingspread; legs short.
    *3.* **Sulidae,** Boobies, Gannets, 9 species, 21 forms; nearly world-wide; nostrils obsolete; gular pouch small; bill strong, conical, not hooked; lores, chin and upper throat bare.
    *4.* **Phalacrocoracidae,** Cormorants, 29 living species (1 extinct), 58 forms; world-wide; nostrils obsolete; gular sac small; bill hooked; long neck and body.
    *5.* **Anhingidae,** Snake-birds, 2 species, 6 forms; all continents, chiefly tropical or subtropical; long, narrow, finely serrate bill; long neck with

kink (eighth cervical articulates at angle); plumage glossy; tail long, fluted in ♂.

6. **Fregatidae,** Frigate-birds (Man-o'-war Birds), 5 species, 14 forms; temperate and tropical oceans; bill long and strongly hooked; throat bare with inflatable crimson pouch in ♂; wings extremely long and pointed (7-foot wingspread); tail long and deeply forked.

11. CICONIIFORMES, Long-legged Waders, 7 living families (2 fossil); neck long, often folded in flight; many species with decorative plumes or bare areas about head and neck; long legs; toes unwebbed except in flamingos (which some authors put in the next order).
    1. **Ardeidae,** Herons, Egrets, Bitterns, 58 species, 159 forms; world-wide; bill long, straight, acute; neck extremely long with lengthened sixth cervical causing kink; nuptial plumes and "aigrettes" often highly developed; powder-down tracts.
    2. Cochleariidae, Boat-billed Heron, 1 species, 3 forms; neotropical; bill broad, flat with prominent keel; head and eyes large.
    3. Balaenicipitidae, Whale-headed Stork, 1 monotypic species; Africa; large bill swollen at base, strongly hooked at tip.
    4. Scopidae, Hammerheads, 1 species, 2 forms; Africa, Arabia, Madagascar; bill moderately long, compressed; head large and crested; neck short.
    5. **Ciconiidae,** Wood Ibises, Storks, Jabirus, 17 species, 24 forms; nearly world-wide; bill variable, stout at base; bare areas about head and neck; long list of minor characters, including rudimentary penis, 2 coats of down, and neck pouches.
    6. **Threskiornithidae,** Ibises, Spoonbills, 28 species, 49 forms; nearly world-wide; bill long, slender, decurved (ibises) or straight, broad and spatulate (spoonbills).
    7. **Phoenicopteridae,** Flamingos, 6 monotypic species; mainly pantropical, also high Andes; bill large, lamellate, bent downward at middle; front toes short and fully webbed; hallux reduced or wanting.

12. ANSERIFORMES, Screamers, Waterfowl, 2 living families (1 fossil); ordinal characters chiefly internal, not very diagnostic.
    1. Anhimidae, Screamers, 3 monotypic species; South America; bill not ducklike; 2 long sharp spurs on wing; tibia partly bare; front toes with small basal webs; no uncinate processes, their absence an archaic feature found elsewhere only in *Archaeopteryx*.
    2. **Anatidae,** Ducks, Geese, Swans, 145 species, 228 forms; world-wide; bill flat and lamellate (or long and "toothed" in mergansers); plumage dense with undercoat of down (apteria reduced); front toes fully webbed.

13. FALCONIFORMES, Diurnal birds of prey, 5 living families (2 fossil); bill strong, hooked, with basal cere; nostrils usually imperforate; wings with large sail area; feet raptorial.
    1. **Cathartidae,** New World Vultures, 6 species, 11 forms; New World; nostrils large, oval and perforate; head largely bare, often colored; feet relatively weak with reduced hallux; no syringeal muscles.

2. Sagittariidae, Secretarybird, 1 monotypic species; Africa; bill without tooth, legs extremely long (hawk head with heron legs); peculiar "quills" on back of head and neck.
3. **Accipitridae,** Kites, Hawks, Eagles, Old World Vultures, Harriers, 205 species, 506 forms; world-wide; typically raptorial (strong beaks, feet, and claws); broad expanse of wings and tail.
4. **Pandionidae,** Osprey, 1 species, 5 forms; nearly world-wide (except New Zealand); set off from Accipitridae largely by tarsal and toe structure; tarsus short, stout, reticulate; toes powerful, with prickly scales, outer toe reversible.
5. **Falconidae,** Caracaras, Falcons, 58 species, 177 forms; world-wide; bill strongly hooked, with prominent tooth in true falcons; nostrils usually circular with bony tubercle in center; wings usually long and pointed (caracaras somewhat aberrant).

14. Galliformes, Megapodes, Gallinaceous Birds, Hoatzin, 7 living families (1 fossil); bill short, obtuse, culmen decurved and bent over lower; wings short, concave, with stiff remiges; aftershaft prominent; feet and claws strong; well-developed crop, gizzard, and caeca.
    1. Megapodiidae, Megapodes, 10 species, 40 forms; Australasia; feet exceptionally large and strong; aftershaft reduced; very peculiar nesting habits (p. 218).
    2. **Cracidae,** Curassows, Guans, Chachalacas, 38 species, 90 forms; Mexico (Rio Grande) through South America; bare areas about head and neck, often with crests, casques or wattles; trachea elongated and looped in some species; arboreal.
    3. **Tetraonidae,** Grouse, Ptarmigans, 18 species, 102 forms; Holarctic; nostrils feathered; tarsus feathered wholly or in part, including the toes in *Lagopus*; toes more or less pectinate; sides of neck with modified feathers and sometimes inflatable pouches.
    4. **Phasianidae,** New World Quails, Old World Partridges, Pheasants, Jungle Fowl, Peacocks, 165 species, about 545 forms, many of questionable status; mostly Old World (except New World Quail); characters very variable, but often with spectacular plumages in males; wattles, spurs, and bare areas in some species.
    5. Numididae, Guineafowl, 7 species, 35 forms; Africa and Madagascar; head and neck largely bare and colored, often with wattles, casques and hackles; plumage dense, dark, and spotted.
    6. **Meleagrididae,** Turkeys, 2 species, 6 forms; central and southern United States, Mexico, northern Central America; wattles prominent on bare head; feathers lustrous, squarish; tail broad, rounded.
    7. Opisthocomidae, Hoatzins, 1 monotypic species; South America; head crested, with scanty feathers; plumage rather loose; arboreal, with claws on wings in young; crop muscular.

15. Gruiformes, "Marsh" Birds, 12 living families (10 fossil); ordinal characters very variable and not diagnostic (group of "misfits").

1. Mesitornithidae, Roatelos, Monias, 3 monotypic species; Madagascar; weak wings, flightless or nearly so; long body, tail, and toes.
2. Turnicidae, Bustardquails, 15 species, 51 forms; Africa, Australasia; quail-like wings and body, but long tarsus; no hallux.
3. Pedionomidae, Plainwanderers (Collared Hemipodes), 1 monotypic species; Australia; short hallux, tail very short.
4. **Gruidae,** Cranes, 14 species, 23 forms; all continents except South America; large birds, with long sharp bill and long (heronlike) legs, but short toes; some with ornamental plumes or crowns on head; trachea convoluted, folded in sternum.
5. **Aramidae,** Limpkins, 1 species, 5 forms; southern United States through South America; long, slightly decurved, heavy bill; short wings and long legs (cranelike and rail-like).
6. Psophiidae, Trumpeters, 3 species, 6 forms; South America; gallinaceous bill, rail-like legs; plumage soft and fluffy.
7. **Rallidae,** Rails, Coots, Gallinules, 132 species, 324 forms; world-wide; body compressed; wings short (some species flightless); toes long with incumbent hallux.
8. Heliornithidae, Sungrebes, 3 species, 6 forms; pantropical; long bodies (neck, wings, and tail); legs short, toes lobed.
9. Rhynochetidae, Kagus, 1 monotypic species; New Caledonia; head large and crested; eyes large; powder down all over.
10. Eurypygidae, Sunbitterns, 1 species, 2 forms; neotropical; "sandpiper" with "bittern" head and neck; powder-down feathers.
11. Cariamidae, Cariamas, Seriemas, 2 monotypic species; South America; long tufts of feathers around nostrils; long legs and tail.
12. Otididae, Bustards, 23 species, 48 forms; all Old World continents; large, heavy-bodied (up to 30 lbs.), long-necked, long-legged terrestrial birds; inflatable neck pouches in some; no hallux.

16. CHARADRIIFORMES, Shorebirds, Gulls and Terns, Alcids, 16 living families (2 fossil); ordinal characters very variable; pterylosis similar throughout.
    1. **Jacanidae,** Jaçanas, 7 species, 17 forms; pantropical, north to Texas; frontal shield prominent; sharp spur or knob on bend of wing; toes extremely elongate (characters somewhat intermediate between Gruiformes and Charadriiformes; classed by some with Gruiformes).
    2. Rostratulidae, Painted Snipe, 2 species, 3 forms; southern South America and Old World tropics; bill with nerve endings; trachea looped over clavicle and breast muscles.
    3. **Haematopodidae,** Oystercatchers, 6 species, 21 forms; all continents; bill large, compressed, blunt at tip, bright red; toes partly webbed; no hallux.
    4. **Charadriidae,** Plovers, Turnstones, Surfbirds, 63 species, 102 forms; world-wide; bill short, tapering or swollen at tip; plumage often with contrasting patterns of bands, collars, rump, and wing patches.
    5. **Scolopacidae,** Sandpipers and allies, 82 species, 118 forms; world-wide;

bill usually long and slender, flexible at tip, sometimes decurved; tarsus usually scutellate (plovers usually reticulate); hallux usually present.

6. **Recurvirostridae,** Avocets, Stilts, 7 species, 12 forms; all continents; bill long, slender, straight (stilts) or recurved (avocets); legs very long.
7. **Phalaropodidae,** Phalaropes, 3 monotypic species; Holarctic in breeding distribution, wintering in southern hemisphere; bill moderate, needlelike or fairly stout; toes lobate or margined.
8. Dromadidae, Crabplovers, 1 monotypic species, shores of Indian Ocean bill deeply cleft, compressed; claw of middle toe pectinate; hallux present.
9. Burhinidae, Thick-knees, 9 species, 26 forms; all continents except North America; bill stout; eyes large (crepuscular habits); legs stout, especially at tibiotarsal joint ("thick-knees"); hallux absent.
10. Glareolidae, Pratincoles, Coursers, 17 species, 44 forms; all Old World continents, but most forms in Africa; bill short (pratincoles) or long and tapering (coursers), with oblong, impervious nostrils; wings long and pointed (pratincoles) or short and broad (coursers).
11. Thinocoridae, Seedsnipe, 4 species, 12 forms; South America; bill finchlike; legs short; tail graduated.
12. Chionididae, Sheathbills, 2 species, 5 forms; islands off South African and South American coasts; somewhat galliform; bill with horny sheath; spur on wing; legs and feet strong.
13. **Stercorariidae,** Skuas, Jaegars, 4 species, 10 forms (3 monotypic jaegars, 1 polytypic Skua); cold oceans, both hemispheres; bill complex, of 4 parts, with cere; wings and tail long and pointed; species separable by tail characters; front toes fully webbed with strong claws.
14. **Laridae,** Gulls, Terns, 82 species, 185 forms; world-wide; bill hooked (gulls) or straight and pointed (terns); tarsus moderate (gulls) or short (terns); feet small, webbed.
15. **Rynchopidae,** Skimmers, 3 species, 6 forms; pantropical; bill strongly compressed, bladelike, with upper mandible shorter; tarsus short; feet small.
16. **Alcidae,** Auks, Murres, Puffins, 22 species, 36 forms; northern hemisphere oceans; bill variable, extreme in puffins; legs far back (sit on tarsi), feet fully webbed; compact plumage.

17. COLUMBIFORMES, Pigeonlike Birds, 2 living families (1 recently extinct); ordinal characters mainly plumage peculiarities; feathers dense, loosely set in skin; well-developed crop.
    1. Pteroclidae, Sandgrouse, 16 species, 45 forms; Eurasia, Africa; bill grouselike, without operculum; tarsus short, fully feathered; toes short with hexagonal scutes, sometimes feathered; plumage noniridescent.
    2. **Columbidae,** Pigeons, Doves, 289 species, 835 forms (many questionable); world-wide, but mainly Old World; "pigeon-billed," with bare basal cere or operculum overhanging nostril; tarsus bare; plumage often iridescent. (The Raphidae, Dodos and Solitaire, consisting of

3 species, 1 each on the islands of Mauritius, Réunion, and Rodriguez, are now extinct. The extinct Raphidae were pigeonlike, but heavy-bodied, flightless forms with tufted tail.)

18. Psittaciformes, Parrots, Lories, Macaws.
    *1.* Psittacidae, 315 species, 768 forms (many of questionable status); pantropical; many peculiarities: "parrot" bill (maxilla movable, hinged to skull); tongue thick and fleshy; foot zygodactylous, with reversible fourth toe; plumage harsh, usually brightly colored.
19. Cuculiformes, Plantain-eaters, Cuckoos, 2 families; zygodactylous foot, fourth toe reversible; skin thin and tender.
    *1.* Musophagidae, Plantain-eaters, 20 species, 43 forms; Africa; crested, long-tailed arboreal birds, with stout, serrate bill; unique color pigments (turacin and turacoverdin).
    2. **Cuculidae,** Cuckoos, Anis, Roadrunners, 127 species, 359 forms; all continents; bill variable, but more or less decurved and compressed; tail long and graduated.
20. Strigiformes, Owls, 2 living families (1 fossil); well-defined order; large head with fixed eyes and facial disc, often asymmetrical ears; short neck; feathered tarsus, often including toes; raptorial foot; soft, lax plumage.
    *1.* **Tytonidae,** Barn and Grass Owls, 11 species, 60 forms; nearly world-wide; facial disc triangular, bordered by deep cleft; plumage comparatively sparse; toes bare; middle toe pectinate.
    2. **Strigidae,** Typical Owls, 123 species, 531 forms; world-wide; facial disc circular; plumage dense; notched primaries.
21. Caprimulgiformes, Goatsuckers and allies, 5 families; owllike head and plumage, but typically weak bill and feet; hind toe short; gape enormous.
    *1.* Steatornithidae, Oilbirds, 1 monotypic species; northern South America; bill hooked and notched, not especially flattened; 12 long rictal bristles on each side; large aftershaft.
    2. Podargidae, Frogmouths, 12 species, 29 forms; Australia and vicinity; enormous head and gape and wide bill; rudimentary aftershaft; powder-down patches on rump.
    3. Nyctibiidae, Potoos, 5 species, 14 forms; neotropical; bill small, narrow, decurved at tip; no rictal bristles.
    4. Aegothelidae, Owlet-frogmouths, 8 species, 17 forms; Australian region; bill small, flat; long bristles on lores.
    5. **Caprimulgidae,** Goatsuckers, 67 species, 203 forms; all continents; bill small and weak but with wide gape; usually long rictal bristles; eyes large; claw of middle toe pectinate.
22. Apodiformes, Swifts, Hummingbirds, 3 living families (1 fossil); long wings due to elongated manus (short humerus); elevator muscles (pectoralis minor) of wing large; weak feet.
    *1.* **Apodidae,** Swifts, 76 species, 219 forms; world-wide; bill short, small, wide gape; wing flat, curved, with short secondaries and long primaries; tail short, often spine-tipped; plumage dull.
    2. Hemiprocnidae, Crested Swifts, 3 species, 15 forms; Indian region;

head crested; eyes large; tail long, forked, the outer feathers attenuated.

3. **Trochilidae,** Hummingbirds, 319 species, 688 forms; neotropical; bill usually long and slender, very variable; plumage usually metallic, iridescent; sexes extremely dimorphic in many cases.

23. COLIIFORMES, Colies (Mouse-birds).

1. Coliidae, 6 species, 29 forms; Africa; long-tailed, crested, arboreal birds, with weak, rounded wings and dense, compact plumage; toes directed forward and hallux reversible.

24. TROGONIFORMES, Trogons.

1. **Trogonidae,** 34 species, 103 forms; pantropical; bill short, flat, decurved, and serrate in some species; tail long and graduated with squarish feathers; plumage soft and lax, often brilliantly colored; feet small and weak.

25. CORACIIFORMES, Kingfishers, Todies, Motmots, Bee-eaters, Rollers, Hoopoes, Hornbills, 10 families; typically large-headed, large-billed birds with metallic bright plumages; toes syndactylous, the anterior toes joined in various combinations.

1. **Alcedinidae,** Kingfishers, 87 species, 335 forms; world-wide; large heads, sometimes crested, and strong beaks; feet small and weak, with third and fourth toes joined; tarsus short, tibia partly bare.
2. Todidae, Todies, 5 monotypic species; West Indies; head smaller; bill flattened and weakly serrate; rictal bristles prominent; short wings and tail; metallic plumage.
3. Momotidae, Motmots, 8 species, 45 forms; neotropical; bill large, decurved, serrate; plumage soft, loose-webbed; tail usually long, often racquet-tipped.
4. Meropidae, Bee-eaters, 24 species, 50 forms; Old World tropics into temperate regions; bill long, decurved, pointed; tail long, central rectrices elongate.
5. Coraciidae, Rollers, 11 species, 32 forms; Old World tropics; bill short, stout, hooked; 3 anterior toes joined at base.
6. Brachypteraciidae, Groundrollers, 5 monotypic species; Madagascar; short wings, long tarsus and tail (otherwise as above).
7. Leptosomatidae, Cuckoo-rollers, 1 species, 3 forms; Madagascar and adjacent islands; wings long and pointed; tail long, square-tipped.
8. Upupidae, Hoopoes, 1 species, 9 forms; Eurasia, Africa; bill long, slender, decurved; nostrils round; head crested with long, black-tipped feathers; plumage not metallic.
9. Phoeniculidae, Woodhoopoes, 6 species, 27 forms; Africa; nostrils elongate; head not crested; tail long and graduated.
10. Bucerotidae, Hornbills, 45 species, 104 forms; Africa, southern Asia, and adjacent islands; bill enormous, with casque or helmet on culmen; tarsus short, rough and scaly; anterior toes joined for various lengths, forming broad sole.

26. PICIFORMES, Jacamars, Puffbirds, Barbets, Honeyguides, Toucans, Woodpeckers, 6 families; foot zygodactylous, with distinctive arrangement of

flexor tendons; bill very variable, but usually long, strong or well developed.

*1.* Galbulidae, Jacamars, 15 species, 38 forms; neotropical; bill long and straight, with angular gonys; plumage soft and lax, usually metallic.

*2.* Bucconidae, Puffbirds, 30 species, 76 forms; neotropical; bill shorter, stout and rounded; head large (head feathers erectile).

*3.* Capitonidae, Barbets, 72 species, 255 forms; pantropical; bill large, stout, swollen, and often bearded at base; toes with long claws; stocky, inactive birds with gaudy colors.

*4.* Indicatoridae, Honeyguides, 11 species, 36 forms; Ethiopia, Asia; bill short, finchlike with ridged and laterally swollen maxillae; nostrils with narrow membrane, not bristly; sober plumages.

*5.* Ramphastidae, Toucans, 37 species, 87 forms; neotropical; bill enormous, light and spongy, with serrate edges; face partly bare; wings weak; plumage lax.

*6.* **Picidae,** Woodpeckers, Piculets, Wrynecks, 210 species, 853 forms; world-wide; bill strong and chisel-like (except in wrynecks); nostrils concealed by bristly feathers; tongue extremely long and extensible; rectrices stiff-pointed (except in piculets and wrynecks); legs and feet strong; fourth toe permanently reversed.

27. PASSERIFORMES, Perching Birds, 70 living families (2 fossil); a large assemblage of more than 5,000 species with very variable external features (bill, wings, tail, and plumage), but "perching" foot characteristic (hallux well developed, incumbent, with long claw; 3 anterior toes directed forward). A few characters for North American families only are listed here.

*1.* Eurylaimidae, Broadbills, 14 species; India, Malaysia, Philippines, Africa.

*2.* Dendrocolaptidae, Woodhewers, 48 species; neotropical.

*3.* Furnariidae, Ovenbirds, 215 species; neotropical.

*4.* Formicariidae, Ant-thrushes, 222 species; neotropical.

*5.* Conopophagidae, Antpipits, 11 species; neotropical.

*6.* Rhinocryptidae, Tapaculos, 26 species; Costa Rica to Argentina.

*7.* **Cotingidae,** Cotingas, 90 species; southern Arizona to Argentina.

*8.* Pipridae, Manakins, 59 species; southern Mexico to Argentina.

*9.* **Tyrannidae,** Tyrant Flycatchers, 365 species; chiefly neotropical but north to Canada; bill usually flattened (wider than high at base) and slightly hooked, with prominent rictal bristles at base; tarsus short, rounded behind; feet small and weak.

*10.* Oxyruncidae, Sharpbill, 1 species; Costa Rica to Brazil.

*11.* Phytotomidae, Plantcutters, 3 species; South America.

*12.* Pittidae, Pittas, 23 species; southeastern Asia, Australia, Africa.

*13.* Acanthisittidae, New Zealand Wrens, 4 species; confined to New Zealand.

*14.* Philepittidae, Asities, False Sunbirds, 4 species; Madagascar.

*15.* Menuridae, Lyrebirds, 2 species; Australia.

*16.* Atrichornithidae, Scrubbirds, 2 species; Australia.

17. **Alaudidae,** Larks, 75 species; mainly Old World, 1 North American species; bill moderatly long and pointed, not flat; legs, feet, and toes well developed, with long, sharp, straight hind claw.
18. **Hirundinidae,** Swallows, 75 species; world-wide; bill small, flattened, with wide gape; wings long and pointed; legs short; feet and toes small and weak.
19. Dicruridae, Drongos, 20 species; Africa, southeastern Asia to Australia.
20. Oriolidae, Old World Orioles, 28 species (including 2 *Irena*); Old World.
21. **Corvidae,** Crows, Magpies, Jays, 100 species; nearly world-wide; bill rather large and strong; nostrils covered by stiff feathers; feet fairly large and strong.
22. Cracticidae, Bell Magpies, Australian Butcherbirds, 10 species; Australia.
23. Grallinidae, Magpie-larks, 4 species; Australia.
24. Ptilonorhynchidae, Bowerbirds, 18 species; Australia, New Guinea.
25. Paradisaeidae, Birds of Paradise, 43 species; New Guinea.
26. **Paridae,** Titmice, 65 species; mainly Holarctic; bill small, but stout and sharp in most species; wings rather short and rounded; nostrils concealed by feathers.
27. **Sittidae,** Nuthatches, 22 species (includes 5 Australian Neosittidae); mostly Old World; bill slender, straight or slightly recurved; tail short, not used for support; toes and claws long.
28. Hyposittidae, Coral-billed Nuthatch, 1 species, Madagascar.
29. **Certhiidae,** Creepers, 17 species; Holarctic, mostly Old World; bill long, slender and decurved in North American species; tail long and stiff-pointed for support; toes and claws long.
30. Paradoxornithidae, Parrotbills, Suthoras, 18 species; Eurasia.
31. **Chamaeidae,** Wrentits, 1 species; Oregon to Lower California; bill short and stout; wings short and tail long; plumage soft and lax.
32. Timaliidae, Babblers, 263 species; Old World tropics.
33. Campephagidae, Cuckoo-shrikes, 71 species; Old World (Africa, Asia, Australia).
34. Pycnonotidae, Bulbuls, 109 species; Old World tropics.
35. Chloropseidae, Leafbirds, 12 species; Oriental Region.
36. **Cinclidae,** Dippers, 5 species; nearly world-wide; bill straight and slender, compressed, with notch near tip; tail short; tarsus and toes long and strong; plumage dense, compact.
37. **Troglodytidae,** Wrens, 63 species; mainly New World tropics; bill slender, usually somewhat decurved; wings short and rounded, usually barred; tail barred.
38. **Mimidae,** Thrashers, Mockingbirds, 30 species; New World; bill variable, but strong, decurved in some species; tail long; rictal bristles present.
39. **Turdidae,** Thrushes, 305 species; world-wide; bill variable, but

usually straight and strong, notched near tip; tail mostly fairly short and square; tarsus "booted" (not scutellate); juvenal plumage spotted.

40. Zeledoniidae, Wrenthrushes, 1 species; Costa Rica, Panama.
41. **Sylviidae,** Old World Warblers, Gnatcatchers, 393 species; nearly world-wide; large family with very variable characters; North American species (gnatcatchers) with sharp slender bills; rounded tail longer than wings; tarsus scutellate.
42. **Regulidae,** Kinglets, 5 species; Holarctic; bill short, small; emarginate tail shorter than wings; tarsus booted.
43. Muscicapidae, Old World Flycatchers, 328 species; Old World.
44. **Prunellidae,** Accentors, Hedge-sparrows, 11 species; Europe, northern Asia to Alaska.
45. **Motacillidae,** Wagtails, Pipits, 48 species; nearly world-wide; bill sharp, slender; tail long; toes long, with long claw on hallux.
46. **Bombycillidae,** Waxwings, 3 species; Holarctic; prominently crested birds with soft, brownish plumage; secondaries (irrespective of sex or age) often tipped with red waxlike spots; tail with terminal yellow (or red) band.
47. **Ptilogonatidae,** Silky Flycatchers, 4 species; southern United States through Central America; nearly unicolored (black, brown, or gray), crested birds with short wings and long tail, and soft, silky plumage.
48. Dulidae, Palmchats, 1 species; Santa Domingo.
49. Artamidae, Woodswallows, 10 species; Africa, Asia, Australia.
50. Vangidae, Vanga Shrikes, 12 species; Madagascar.
51. **Laniidae,** Shrikes, 72 species; Old and New World; bill strong and hooked, notched near tip; feet fairly strong with sharp claws.
52. Prionopidae, Woodshrikes, 13 species; Old World.
53. Cyclarhidae, Peppershrikes, 2 species; neotropical.
54. Vireolaniidae, Shrike-vireos, Greenlets, 3 species; neotropical.
55. Callaeidae, Wattled Crows, Huias, Saddlebacks, 2 living species (Huia extinct); New Zealand.
56. **Sturnidae,** Starlings, 104 species; Old World, introduced in New World; bill fairly long, straight and strong in most species; wings long and pointed (in *Sturnus*); tail usually short and square; legs and feet strong; plumage often glossy and metallic.
57. Meliphagidae, Honey-eaters, 160 species; Australasia, Pacific Islands.
58. Nectariniidae, Sunbirds, 104 species; Old World tropics.
59. Dicaeidae, Flowerpeckers, 54 species; Asia, Australia.
60. Zosteropidae, White-eyes, 80 species; Africa, Asia to New Zealand.
61. **Vireonidae,** Vireos, 37 species; New World; bill stout (compared to parulids), slightly notched and hooked; tenth (outer) primary short.
62. **Coerebidae,** Honeycreepers, 36 species (Mayr); neotropical, to Florida.
63. Drepanididae, Hawaiian Honeycreepers, 22 species; confined to Hawaii.
64. **Parulidae,** Wood Warblers, 109 species (Mayr); New World; bill

usually slender and pointed, not notched or hooked; 9 primaries; sexual dimorphism in plumage often pronounced.

65. **Ploceidae,** Weaverbirds, 263 species (Mayr); Old World, introduced in New World; bill short, stout, conical; tenth primary rudimentary.
66. **Icteridae,** Blackbirds, Troupials, 88 species (Mayr); New World; bill very variable, but typically rather long, pointed and conical, often prolonged backward into a casque; 9 primaries; plumage with black often predominating.
67. Tersinidae, Swallowtanagers, 1 species; northern South America.
68. **Thraupidae,** Tanagers, 196 species (Mayr); New World, mainly neotropical; hard to characterize, but bill typically rather short and stout, swollen, with prominent tooth in North American species; plumage often strongly dimorphic.
69. Catamblyrhynchidae, Plush-capped Finches, 1 species; northern Andes.
70. **Fringillidae,** Grosbeaks, Finches, Buntings, Sparrows, 425 species (Mayr); world-wide except Australia; characters variable, but bill typically short and thick, often massive (grosbeaks); feet and toes strong; 9 primaries.

## *Selected References on Classification*

Arvey, M. Dale. Phylogeny of the Waxwings and Allied Birds. *Univ. Kans. Publ. Mus. Nat. Hist.* (1951), **3**:473–530.

Beecher, William J. Convergence in Coerebidae. *Wilson Bull.* (1951), **63**:274–287.

———. A Phylogeny of the Oscines. *Auk* (1953), **70**:270–333.

Mayr, Ernst. The Number of Species of Birds. *Auk* (1946a), **63**:64–69.

———, and Dean Amadon. A Classification of Recent Birds. *Amer. Mus. Novitates* (1951), **1496**:1–42.

Peters, J. L. *Check-list of Birds of the World.* Vols. 1–7. Cambridge, Mass.: Harvard U. P., 1931–1951.

Storer, Robert W. The Classification of Birds. Chapt. 3 in A. J. Marshall's *Biology and Comparative Physiology of Birds.* Vol. I. New York: Academic, 1960.

Tordoff, Harrison B. A Systematic Study of the Avian Family Fringillidae Based on the Structure of the Skull. *Univ. Mich. Mus. Zool. Misc. Publ.* (1954), **81**:1–42.

Van Tyne, Josselyn, and Andrew J. Berger. *Fundamentals of Ornithology.* New York: Wiley, 1959.

Wetmore, Alexander. A Classification for the Birds of the World. *Smithsonian Misc. Coll.* (1960), Vol. 139; **11**:1–37.

# 16

# ORNITHOLOGICAL METHODS

The purpose of this chapter is to outline some of the more elementary techniques employed in the study of birds. Often the student will need to go to the higher sources listed at the end of the chapter for a fuller explanation of the methods here so briefly described. Treatment of the subject is further minimized because it is essentially a part of laboratory, rather than textbook, instruction. Every student, however, should have some knowledge of these methods of study and know where to go for further information when it is needed.

## *Field Identification*

Learning to identify birds is the first and most important requisite of bird study. It is the foundation on which to build a hobby or a more serious study, for of course it is futile to keep migration records, to band or to photograph birds, or to pursue field or laboratory studies without knowing the birds accurately. Learning birds can be quite simple if an acquaintance with the most common kinds close to home is all that is desired, but it must be pursued almost fanatically if one hopes to become well acquainted with *all* the birds in a given region at all seasons and in all plumages.

Usually beginning classes limit their observations largely to the spring months, and learn to recognize up to 100 or more species locally available at that time; but this number could be greatly increased by continuing observations throughout the year and by expanding the area of coverage to include more diversified habitats. The quest for new birds need never end. In a lifetime of study, the ornithologist may not get thoroughly acquainted with all the birds in his home state, or if he does, there are further fields to explore.

In local field work birds are commonly divided into status groups on the basis of their seasonal distribution. Terms commonly used and definitions for them are as follows:

Permanent Residents—species present the year round in a given locality.

*a.* Nonmigratory—game birds (grouse, pheasants, quail), some owls (Great Horned, Barred, Screech), some woodpeckers, some titmice, House Sparrows, Cardinal.

*b.* Migratory—(species present in the same locality throughout the year but certain individuals at least are migratory)—some ducks, some hawks, crows and jays, Cedar Waxwing, Starling, Song Sparrow.

Summer Residents—species that come in the spring, remain for summer (breeding) and leave in the fall. Includes nearly all summer birds which are not permanent residents.

Transients—birds that pass through a given region in spring en route to more northern breeding grounds and again in fall for more southern wintering grounds. Examples (in the United States) are Arctic breeding ducks, shorebirds, and northern warblers.

Winter Residents (or Visitants)—somewhat loosely defined as birds that remain (or appear) in a given locality in winter. Some, like the Tree Sparrow, may come in the fall and remain in a small area all winter (p. 250); others, often called erratic finches (redpolls, crossbills, grosbeaks), may appear some winters for short or long periods and not show up at all in other winters.

Often these status groups are further qualified by such terms as abundant, common, uncommon, and rare, but such terms are hard to define accurately and are not used in exactly the same meaning by all observers. Widely wandering or displaced birds, such as tropical species in the north, sea birds blown inland, or Old World birds appearing in North America are called "stragglers" or "accidentals."

Fortunately for the bird student of today, there are many aids to identification. Such aids commonly include the *Audubon Bird Guides* (land birds and water birds) or Peterson's widely used *Field Guides* which feature accurate, colored illustrations and stress easily observed field characters.

More complete references, including distribution, habits, and often detailed regional status, are also widely available. Most states have at least a distributional check list; many have a rather complete reference composed of one or more elaborate volumes. In addition, some states have printed guides to the best places to look for birds, and two fairly complete guides for bird finding anywhere in the United States can be obtained. These and other useful books on identification and distribution are listed at the end of the chapter.

An almost indispensable aid to identification is some sort of field glass or binocular (Fig. 195). In common parlance all types are spoken of as field glasses or bird glasses, but technically a glass with prisms is a binocular; the nonprismatic (straight-barreled) type is a field glass. Though many a budding ornithologist has made a good start without such a glass, continued progress without one is difficult, particularly in group participation where it is usually not practicable to sit and wait for birds. Most birding groups, led by local experts who may be anxious to secure a large list, move rather rapidly, and birds are pointed out and identified at a considerable distance, making the glassless observer rather hopelessly handicapped.

*Fig. 195. Left, prism binocular, opened to show the interior mechanism of prisms and lenses; X's mark the 10 optical surfaces which in good glasses are coated to reduce undesirable reflections. (Courtesy of Robert J. and Elsa Reichert, Mirakel Repair Co., and* Audubon Magazine.*) Right, telescopes, though exceedingly helpful in identifying birds at long range, are cumbersome to carry, awkward to use, and time-consuming to set up at different stations. (Photo by Robert D. Burns.)*

Binoculars recommended for bird study range from 6 to 9 power with an objective lens (exit pupil) of 30 to 50 millimeters in diameter. The power (6x, 7x, and so on) refers to the number of magnifications. A 6x magnifies an object 6 times, or makes an object at 600 feet appear to be only 100 feet away. The diameter of the objective lens controls the amount of light admitted and thus largely determines the relative brightness with which an object is viewed. Both features are usually stamped on the glass, for example, "6x30" (or "6x, 30"), "8x30." It should be remembered, however, that a 6x30 gives a considerably brighter field than an 8x30 because of the two additional magnifications of the latter, the loss in one factor being compensated for by gain in another. Increase in magnification also reduces the field of view or *width* of the scene visible through the binocular, a factor largely determined by the interior construction. Coated lenses (treated with a coat of magnesium fluoride) also increase the brightness markedly by reducing the amount of light lost by reflection from the surface of the lenses and prisms inside the glass. The combinations of light and magnification usually preferred by ornithologists, and here recommended, are 6x30, 7x35, 8x30, 8x40, or some similar reading.

A much used glass in military service, and now often available new or second hand at reasonable prices, is the 7x50 which combines good magnification with excellent light, but is perhaps better for observations in relatively open places (as for waterfowl) than for small birds close at hand because it is usually an individual eye-focusing model. Some observers favor a glass with individual eye focus, where each eyepiece is adjusted separately and then usually left in that position; but most birders prefer central focusing. The latter necessitates constant refocusing with an index finger but enables one to follow a bird's change of position better, especially at close range. Glasses of less than 6 power (6x) are not recommended for bird study; those of 9x or more are difficult to hold steadily. The references listed on page 419 explain glasses more fully and include suggestions for selecting one.

A telescope (Fig. 195r) has a more limited use in class groups; obviously it is not a practicable piece of equipment for all individuals to carry along on a class trip. It finds its chief use for relatively stationary distant objects, such as a raft of ducks on a lake or a predatory bird on a distant perch. It is also often a great aid in identifying a troublesome shorebird. Its disadvantages are that it is cumbersome to carry afield, it is time consuming to set it up at different stations, and it can serve only one person at a time. Telescopes often have changeable eyepieces, varying from 15x to 60x, but about a 20x is commonly used for bird study. A tripod for holding the instrument is almost a necessity, though small groups in a car can often use a spotting scope to good advantage by steadying it on a car door or window.

## SONGS AND CALLS

Though a sharp eye and alertness are important in running down birds, a good ear is an equally valuable asset. It takes time, patience, and experience to become well acquainted with the songs and calls of birds, yet many students, even in a single season, become fairly expert at it. Many field men depend more on their ear than their eye for identification.

There is no royal road to learning bird songs. Most bird books give helpful descriptions; often birds sing a sufficiently simple refrain so that it can be put into suggestive words or phrases, or even closely imitated. Familiar examples are the softly whistled "fee-bee" of the Black-capped Chickadee, the "drink-your-teeeeeee" of the Rufous-sided Towhee, and the "hic-three-beers" of the Olive-sided Flycatcher. But the more complicated songs, of the thrushes and Winter Wren for example, defy description. The student should consult his bird guide frequently and make some notations of his own about each song and call.

Bird songs vary in four fundamental characteristics: (1) time or duration of a note, (2) loudness or intensity, (3) pitch, and (4) quality (including phonetics). These features can often be expressed graphically in taking notes. Time, for instance, can be represented by the length of a line (short____, long________), intensity by thickness of the bar (loud________, weak________), and pitch by a roughly estimated position on an imaginary (or real) scale (low________, high‾‾‾‾‾‾‾‾). Quality can often be aptly expressed by some phonetic rendering or word description as well as by variations in the bar ( ∿∿∿ for a quavering note or __/‾~\ for varied notes). Often such graphic expressions can be linked together into a whole song, as shown by the following examples taken from Saunders' well-known recordings of bird songs (Figs. 196–197).

One of the shortcomings in learning standardized bird songs is that many species have several distinctly different songs, or many songs if all the minor variations are taken into consideration. Aretas Saunders, in his long lifetime of study of bird music, has recorded 884 *different* Song Sparrow songs (Saunders, 1951), a species, incidentally, that gives begin-

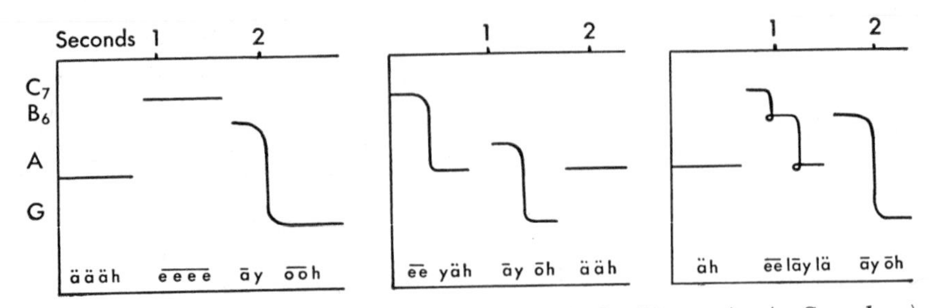


*Fig. 196. Three songs of an Eastern Meadowlark. (From A. A. Saunders.)*

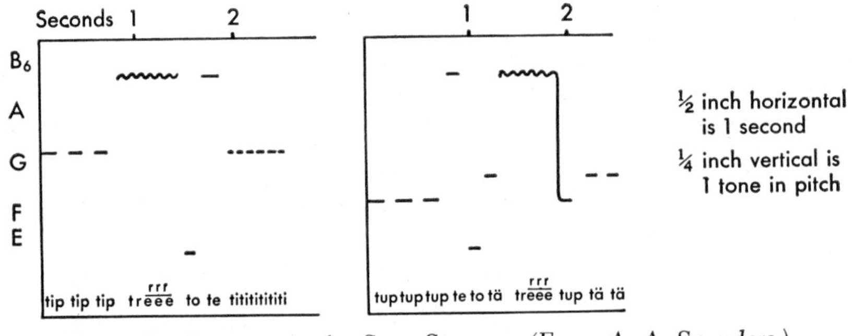


*Fig. 197. Two songs of a Song Sparrow. (From A. A. Saunders.)*

ning students a great deal of trouble. He cautions people that it is not correct to speak of "*the* song of *the* Purple Finch," but more properly "*a* song of *a* Purple Finch." A "musical ear" is helpful but by no means indispensable in recognizing bird songs; many persons not musically inclined become field experts.

In the last decade or two, the art of recording bird songs with sound equipment has seen great developments. The pioneer steps as well as much of the subsequent progress in this field has been carried out by the Laboratory of Ornithology at Cornell University. The University uses a specially equipped truck or station wagon on which a large parabolic sound-reflector with inset microphone is mounted with a swivel arrangement so that it can be turned in any direction to catch the songs of birds. This sound equipment has been taken over much of North America, even into some relatively inaccessible areas, for recording bird songs. The songs thus obtained (on the sound-track film) then have to be taken into the laboratory and transferred onto phonograph records.

More recently tape recordings have been secured in the field by many people (Fig. 198). Notable achievements of this sort, in addition to the continued work at Cornell, are those of the Federation of Ontario Naturalists (by William Gunn), the work of Ed and Ann Boyes in Michigan, and of Donald J. Borror in Ohio and other states. Records available from these and other recordings are listed on page 418.

After recordings are secured in the field, they can be taken into the laboratory and transferred to revolving drums so that the resulting graphs can be analyzed in detail as to frequency, duration, intensity, and pitch. The technical equipment required and its use is described by Borror and Reese (1953, 1954), Borror (1959), and Marler and Issac (1960).

Sound recordings of birds have been put to practical use in several ways. When played in the field, songs and calls often "attract" birds in for closer observation or for photographing, whereas playing distress or alarm calls may repel or disperse nuisance birds. Graber and Cochran (1959, 1960) describe the use of recording devices for studying calls of nocturnal migrants.

Though playing records is a helpful method of recognizing bird songs, and provides a pleasant and instructional program for classes and bird groups, it is an aid to, not a substitute for, learning songs the hard way in the field.

*Fig. 198. Recording bird songs in Mexico. The parabolic mirror with inset microphone is directed to pick up songs, which are recorded on tape by the man at the left. (Photo by Dale A. Zimmerman.)*

## Laboratory Studies

Beginning laboratory work on birds usually involves a study of the external features of a bird—topography, bills and feet, and feathers; an examination of representative skeletons, such as those of the domestic fowl or pigeon; and, less frequently in beginning courses, actual dissection. More often lab work involves mainly identification of specimens by means of pictures or keys. Though the use of keys is usually more time consuming and difficult (and often more exasperating) than merely employing picture aids, it trains students to look for diagnostic (though often artificial) characters useful in more advanced work. Slides of birds shown in class are a great aid to identification; movies are both entertaining and instructional, but not ordinarily practical for detailed identification.

### ORNITHOLOGICAL COLLECTIONS

Ornithological collections (Figs. 199–200) for study usually consist of *mounts* (birds set up on a pedestal in some lifelike pose), *skins* (specimens laid out flat), *alcoholics* (soft parts of birds preserved in alcohol or formalin), nests and eggs, and skeletons. Mounted birds are usually placed on exhibit, and in many museums and public institutions serve a widespread and useful educational purpose. Large metropolitan museums, such as the American Museum in New York, the National Museum in Washington, D.C., the Chicago Museum of Natural History, the Museum of Natural History in Denver, and several museums in California, have extremely

*Fig. 199. Collections for student use commonly include mounted birds and skins, the latter often kept in tubes for protection in handling. Here a Cardinal (mount), a Pyrrhuloxia (skin) and a Painted Bunting (in tube) illustrate these devices. (Photo by Robert L. Fleming, Jr.)*

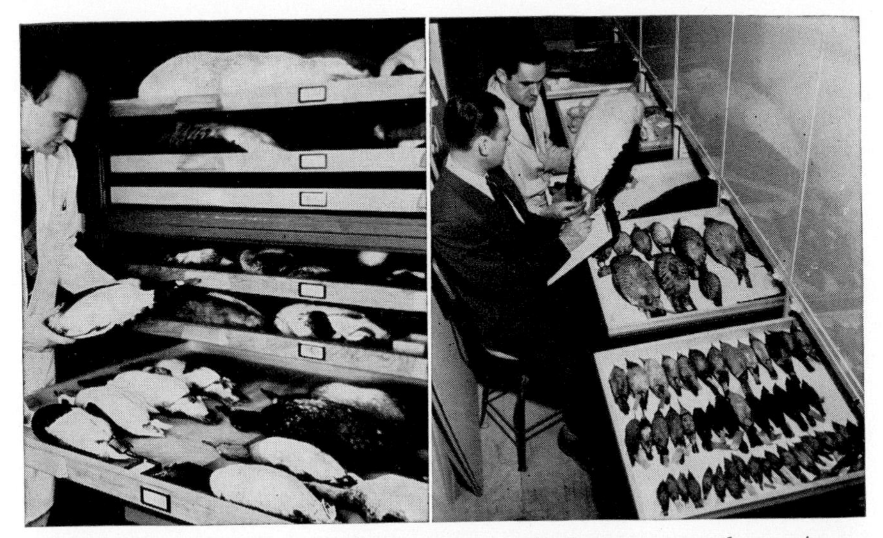

*Fig. 200. Left, scientific skin collections are usually kept in cases, the specimens arranged in phylogenetic sequence, with the names of larger categories at least on the outside of the door and names of smaller categories on the sliding trays. (Photo by Robert D. Burns.) Right, museum workers identify specimens and record pertinent data as preparatory work to cataloguing and storing the skins.*
*(From L. C. Pettit's* Introductory Zoology, *copyright 1962, by The C. V. Mosby Company, St. Louis. Photo courtesy of Mich. State Univ. Museum.)*

elaborate displays of birds from all over the world, often placed in attractive settings simulating natural habitats. Less pretentious exhibits, sometimes merely of local avifauna, are available at most institutions; if these are accessible in the laboratory, they can be used for identification purposes.

Skins are more commonly used for specimen studies, since they take up less room and are easier to prepare. Classroom specimens need to be kept in protective containers, such as glass or plastic tubes (Fig. 199), so that they can be handled by many persons without the otherwise inevitable destruction to the skins. Research collections, used by fewer students for more advanced studies, are not thus protected, yet if properly handled they may last indefinitely. Collections intended primarily for detailed taxonomic work need to be large, with numerous examples of each species, in order to show variations of age, sex, and season, as well as geographical differences. About eight museums in this country have world-wide collections numbering more than 100,000 specimens; the largest, at the American Museum of Natural History in New York City, now totals nearly a million birds. Many smaller collections, however, perhaps not world-wide in scope, are adequate for many types of studies, and a laboratory or small museum with only a few hundred to a few thousand specimens of the right selection can be very useful for instructional purposes.

Mounting birds requires special techniques, largely beyond the scope of an ornithology course, but lessons in taxidermy are available (p. 421) for those who wish to pursue this art, either as a hobby or as a profession. All advanced students, however, need to know how to prepare a bird skin. This is a fairly simple and quick method of skinning out a bird by removing the body and substituting a proper-sized filler of cotton or other suitable material.

Detailed instructions for preparing birds for study are given in Blake's and Chapin's manuals (p. 421), both currently out of print. The following condensed directions, with an instructor's guidance, should serve to get a beginning student started on the technique of making bird skins.

## DIRECTIONS FOR PREPARING BIRD SKINS

1. Relax the bird, flexing the legs, wings, and head. Sponge off any dirt or blood stains on the feathers and dry with cornmeal. Use cornmeal (or other absorbent) liberally through the whole skinning process.
2. Part the abdominal feathers and make an incision through the skin, being careful not to cut through the body wall into the viscera. Extend the cut from the posterior end of the sternum into the anus or around one side of it.
3. Loosen the skin from the abdominal wall with fingers or scalpel until the knee joint is exposed. Cut the leg at this joint, cleaning the flesh from the tibia. Rub borax over the tibia, especially at the tarsal end, wrap it tightly with cotton until it simulates the size of the original limb. Push back into natural position. Repeat with the other leg.
4. Make an incision across the base of the tail, being careful not to cut too close to the base of the tail feathers which might then be lost.
5. Invert the skin carefully, using fingers and scalpel, over the back and breast until it reaches the wings.
6. Sever each wing at the shoulder joint (proximal end of humerus) and continue pushing the skin up over the head. In most birds the skin will slip over the head easily, but in some large-headed birds (woodpeckers and ducks) it may be necessary to make a slit through the skin along the nape (or throat, if preferred) to free the head.
7. Pull the skin of the ear out of its socket with finger and thumb. Slip the skin over the eyes and remove them.
8. Make an incision across the palate between the mandibles; extend the cut along the inner margin of each mandible and across the base of the skull.

Then the body and most of the contents of the skull (brain) can be removed from the skin.

9. Clean out any remaining portions of the brain and flesh from the skull, sprinkle the interior of the skull liberally with borax, and turn the skin back carefully over the skull.
10. Clean the wing bones (humeri) of flesh and remove as much as possible of the flesh from the radius and ulna, *without* loosing the secondaries from the ulna. In large birds it is better to remove flesh and tendons from the forearm by making an incision along the underside of the wing, cleaning the bones, then sewing the slit together with a few stitches.
11. The wings can be made to lie in a natural position (in the final bird skin) by (1) tying the two radii together in a parallel position about one-half inch apart (in medium-sized birds), (2) tying the humeri in a similar manner, or (3) bringing the skin between the wings closer together (taking up the slack) by a stitch through the skin.
12. Remove the oil gland, or at least its contents, from the base of the tail. Remove any fat, flesh, or blood stains still adhering to the skin or feathers. Skins with excess fat (e.g., ducks) may have to be degreased by immersing them in benzene or carbon tetrachloride for several hours or more, then drying them with cornmeal and/or compressed air.
13. Put a small tight wad of cotton in each eye, inserting it up through the neck with forceps.
14. Prepare a pointed stick (medical applicators are ideal for small birds) and wrap it tightly with cotton to form a body roughly comparable to the size of the body removed (use excelsior or other material for large birds).
15. Insert the body into the skin, with the point of the stick pushed into the skull, or protruding into the mouth cavity.
16. Arrange the skin carefully around the cotton body and sew up the abdominal incision. Close the bill by tying a thread around it, through the nostrils if necessary.
17. Tie the crossed legs together and tie on a *correctly prepared label—with locality, date, sex, weight, collector,* and any other pertinent data on the tag. Be sure to sex the specimen by internal examination of the gonads, recording the data (a sketch to size is useful) on the label.
18. Wrap the completed specimen in strips of cotton, or pin it out on a pinning board, and allow it to dry for several days before putting it in storage.

Collecting birds needs only a brief explanation. Responsible persons who wish to collect protected birds for strictly scientific purposes can get special permits; a federal permit is required and usually one for each state in which specimens are to be taken. Collecting is usually done with shotguns of appropriate caliber, but traps and nets can also be employed to good advantage. Bullets (bird or dust shot) need to be used judiciously, because dust shot will singe or burn the feathers at close range, and shot that is too large may damage the specimens. Many collections are augmented by specimens turned in by thoughtful people who find dead birds. Our chief sources of dead birds at Michigan State University in recent years have been: (1) insecticide victims (but run heavily to Robins), (2) television towers (warblers, vireos, thrushes), (3) road kills, and (4) picture windows. Also hunters often provide us with special needs, sometimes unwittingly through the confiscation of illegal kills turned over to us by conservation officers.

Formerly many, if not most, ornithologists had a personal collection of birds; some private holdings in the past have rivaled large institutional collections, but perhaps fortunately for greater accessibility these have now largely gone over to responsible museums. The day of private egg collections, once the pride and joy of many oölogists, is also largely a thing of the past, but most ornithological collections include birds' eggs, with or without accompanying nests (the latter are hard to exhibit in an attractive way). Less common in collections, but potentially more useful, are skeletal materials. In the laboratory a few representative skeletons are essential for study, but research collections need to be much more complete. In food-habit studies, for instance, one may need to identify a skull or fragment of bone, often a difficult if not impossible task without consulting a reference collection. Preparing skeletons is usually done with the aid of *dermestids*, the carrion-feeding larvae of certain beetles which live on flesh.

## *Field Studies*

Advanced field studies (research) go beyond mere identification and listing (p. 401). In addition, the student needs to take careful notes on songs, numbers, and behavior, and—an important item sometimes overlooked—the date and place of observations should always be recorded. Some of the techniques employed in field studies are described below.

A special type of record taking is the census, widely employed by people who wish to measure a given population accurately. The game manager, for instance, may need to know how many pheasants, grouse, or quail are on a given tract at different seasons; the species can be managed properly only by knowing such data in detail. The Fish and Wildlife Service keeps a careful check on waterfowl populations on both the breeding and wintering grounds as well as on the four major flyways; regulations are based to a considerable extent on these findings. Censuses are conducted on a national scale on Mourning Doves, White-winged Doves, and several other critical species in order to determine more wisely what the hunting regulations on these birds should be. Counts are also made periodically of rare and endangered species, such as the Whooping Crane and California Condor.

Censuses are conducted in a great variety of ways, depending to some extent on the species under investigation and the type of coverage desired or feasible. Often more or less direct counts of a single species, or of all species combined, can be made on small areas. Where the area is too large for complete coverage, sample counts of small sections can be made and then applied to the whole area. Block counts (10's, 100's, or 1,000's) are often used in estimating waterfowl, either on the water or in the air. Aerial surveys are useful in estimating large birds on the ground (for example, cranes) or on the water (waterfowl). Wildlife technicians also have developed special methods for particular species, such as crowing counts for pheasants, cooing counts for doves, booming or dancing-ground counts for prairie chickens and Sharp-tailed Grouse, and drumming counts for Ruffed Grouse. The strip census employs carefully planned routes at specified intervals (distances) through an area with counts within the lanes of travel. "Sign," or any indication of the presence of animals (such as pellets, tracks, and scat deposits), can be used in an index to populations. Kill figures during the hunting season are employed in a variety of ways for an appraisal of total populations. Banding figures (ratio of banded to unbanded birds in a population) can be used in a similar way. Hickey (1955) discusses and evaluates these and other techniques employed in population research on gallinaceous birds.

Among amateur bird watchers the most popular census-taking activities are the breeding-bird censuses and the Christmas counts (p. 12). The former is based on the concept that in the breeding season the males of most species are on territories and sing or perform more or less constantly so that each one can be assumed to represent a breeding pair. Inconsistencies in this method are that some singing males may not have mates at the time of the count, that duplications may arise by recounts of particularly mobile males, and that some established pairs may be silent at least part of the time. In spite of such errors, the breeding-bird census is a fairly reliable index of the summer resident population. Such censuses may be undertaken by individual counters or by cooperating teams. In 1951 a group of cooperators, under supervision of a leader who assigned people to specific areas, made a thorough canvass of the entire breeding range of the rare Kirtland's Warbler, the first such census ever attempted for a songbird (Mayfield, 1953). The census was repeated in 1961 and is planned, in the future, for ten-year intervals. Eventually such breeding-bird censuses may enable us to calculate the breeding populations of all birds in the United States, as has been done in England for some time.

Most field observations are conducted with a mimimum of equipment, perhaps merely a glass and notebook, but more intensive studies require other materials. For close observation at a nest, either for photography or for studying life histories, some sort of blind or hide (Fig. 201l) is usually essential. This may be a crude affair of gunnysacking thrown over or around supporting vegetation, or a more elaborate canvas retreat built with a jointed pipe framework, which for observing treetop nests can be placed on an elevated platform (Fig. 201r). Birds usually become quickly adjusted to such artificial parts of the landscape and go about their family affairs unperturbed.

*Fig. 201. Left, a blind set up in a Beech-Maple Woodlot for a study of the Black-throated Blue Warbler. Right, a tower blind overlooking a marsh where a life-history study of the Common Grackle was conducted. (Photos by L. H. Walkinshaw and Lester E. Eyer.)*

Life-history studies also involve taking weights, measurements, and other checks of a bird's activities. A set of scales or balances that can be carried in the field for daily weights of the young is needed. Calipers and ruler for measurements of growth, thermometers and thermocouples for recording nestling and nest temperatures, perhaps paints, fast dyes, or color bands for marking young birds, and various other items are an essential part of the bird student's layout (Fig. 202). For more detailed studies of activities at a nest, the itograph and terragraph, which are electrical recording devices that automatically register visits of the adults to the nest, or the frequency with which the young are fed, are useful and time-saving instruments. The camera, as already pointed out, is a valuable adjunct in nearly all phases of bird study. The field worker needs to be alert to the latest techniques in trapping and marking birds (see next section) and the latest devices for studying living birds and their habits in the field.

## Bird Banding

A very fundamental operation in a great variety of bird studies is the practice of banding or marking birds in a way that facilitates subsequent recognition of the marked individuals. The idea of bird banding is old. A Gray Heron, captured in Germany in 1710, was found to be carrying

*Fig. 202. Layout of some equipment for field studies. a. Balances for daily weighings of nestlings. b. Thermometer for taking temperatures of young (oral, anal, or under wing). c. and d. Dividers and ruler for taking measurements. e. Weatherproof, aluminum-covered notebook (removable pages) for recording data. (Drawings by Homer D. Roberts.)*

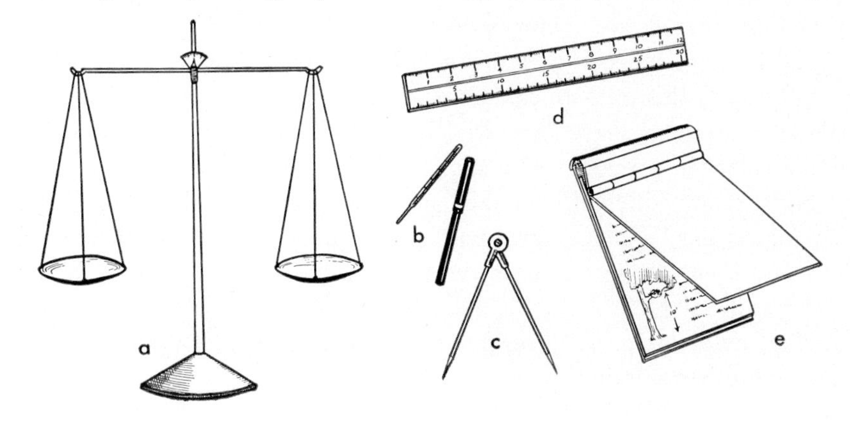

metal rings placed on its legs several years previously in Turkey. Other European projects, some of them well organized, followed at intervals during the nineteenth century.

In this country, appropriately enough, Audubon apparently pioneered in banding work by marking a brood of Eastern Phoebes with silver threads in 1803 and finding that two of them returned the following year to the same locality. One hundred years later numerous banding projects were in progress. Finally in 1920, with so many private enterprises under way, the potentialities of organized bird banding on a national scale were realized, and it was taken over by the United States Biological Survey as an official government project. Now bird banders, numbering some 2,000 cooperators in the United States and Canada (Canada has a substation at Ottawa), operate banding stations. Bands of assorted sizes (Fig. 203) are supplied to qualified permit holders (a federal and a state permit are required) by the national office, together with various instructions (*Manual for Bird Banders*) and bird-banding news. The operator provides his own equipment (traps, banding tools, bait) and must report his activities regularly to the federal office.

Since 1920 some 11 million birds have been banded; useful returns and recoveries of banded birds number more than 800,000. Many remarkable discoveries, too numerous to summarize here, have been revealed by bird banding. In the extensive bird-banding files, now kept at the Patuxent Wildlife Research Center at Laurel, Maryland, are many more pertinent data awaiting analysis. Some of the important findings of bird banding have been called to the reader's attention at appropriate places in the text.

Marking birds with serially numbered aluminum bands necessitates their recapture for subsequent identification, either by retrapping or by recovering dead birds. Many workers pursuing special studies find it helpful to mark birds so that they can be identified in the field without recapture. For this purpose colored celluloid or plastic bands, or bands of painted aluminum, have been widely used (Fig. 203I). By employing several colors in various combinations and arrangements on the two legs of birds, many differently marked individuals can be obtained. Other marking devices include clipped tail feathers, neck tags, and feathers dyed with fast-drying lacquers, either on parts of the natural plumage or by gluing artificial feathers to the bird (imping). The references on bird-banding methods (p. 420) suggest further the scope and potentiality of these and other marking systems.

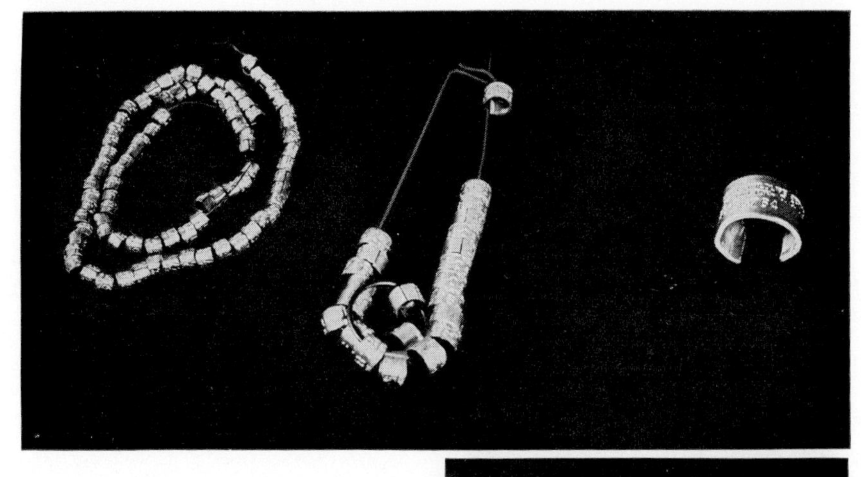

*Fig. 203. Above, U. S. Fish and Wildlife Service bands come in assorted sizes from 0–8. Shown are No. 2's, serially arranged on wire as shipped from the government office; No. 5's, placed on convenient wire holder for carrying in field box; No. 8, opened ready for placement on bird. (Photo by Philip G. Coleman.) Left, a banded bird with a numbered aluminum band on its right leg and a color band (not recommended except for detailed studies of individuals) on its left leg. (Courtesy of* National Geographic Magazine.*)*

# Selected References


AIDS TO IDENTIFICATION

Audubon Bird Cards: 50 Winter Birds, 50 Spring Birds, 50 Summer Birds. Nat. Aud. Soc. (New York). Three sets of postcard-size paintings by Allan Brooks, with biographies on back of cards.

Chapman, Frank M. *Handbook of Birds of Eastern North America.* New York: Appleton, 1930.

Headstrom, Richard. *Bird Nests.* New York: Ives Washburn, 1949. A field guide, with keys and photographs, to the identification of the nests of birds found in the United States east of the 100th meridian; a companion volume on western nests is also available.

Hoffman, Ralph. *Birds of the Pacific States.* Boston: Houghton, 1927.
Peterson, Roger T. *A Field Guide to the Birds.* 2nd ed. Boston: Houghton, 1947.
———. *A Field Guide to the Birds of Texas.* Boston, Houghton, 1960.
———. *A Field Guide to Western Birds.* 2nd ed. Boston: Houghton, 1961.
Pough, Richard H. *Audubon Bird Guide: Small Land Birds.* Garden City, N.Y.: Doubleday, 1946. 275 species illustrated in full color by Don Eckleberry.
———. *Audubon Water Bird Guide.* Garden City, N.Y.: Doubleday, 1951. Includes the species not covered by the preceding volume, the water, game, and large land birds.
Reed, Chester A. *Bird Guide: Land Birds East of the Rockies.* Completely revised. Garden City, N.Y.: Doubleday, 1951. 222 species illustrated in full color with short biographies.
Zim, Herbert S., and Ira N. Gabrielson. *Birds: A Guide to the Most Familiar American Birds.* New York: S. and S., 1949.

### BIRD SONG RECORDS

Boyes, Ed, and Ann Boyes. *Wild Bird Songs.* Long-playing record of songs of 51 species of Michigan birds; available from Michigan Audubon Society, Kalamazoo, Mich.
Cornell University Records. Cornell U. P. (Ithaca, N.Y.). Twelve records of bird songs and calls now available, including African, Mexican, Western, Florida, and American bird songs. Others on frogs, toads, and insects.
Fassett, Jim. *Symphony of the Birds.* Flicker Records (Old Greenwich, Conn.). Songs and calls of birds utilized in creating a unique symphony of sounds. Interesting but not useful for identifying bird songs.
Gunn, William W. H., and Donald J. Borror. *Sounds of Nature.* Federation of Ontario Naturalists. Vol. I: Songs of Spring; Vol. II: A Day in Algonquin Park; Vol. III: Birds of the Forest; Vol. IV: Warblers; Vol. V: A Day at Flores Morades.
Miller, Loye. *Music in Nature.* Cooper Ornith. Club, U. of C. (Los Angeles). Four 12-inch vinylite records with over 50 bird songs and animal sounds.
Peterson, R. T. *A Field Guide to Bird Songs.* Houghton (Boston). Songs and calls of more than 300 species recorded in the field by the Laboratory of Ornithology under the direction of P. P. Kellogg and A. A. Allen.
Stillwell, Jerry, and Norma Stillwell. *Bird Songs of Dooryard, Field and Forest.* (Fayetteville, Ark.). Two 12-inch vinylite, long-playing records with 275 songs of 96 species of birds.

### WHERE TO FIND BIRDS

Bailey, W. W. *Birds in Massachusetts: When and Where to Find Them.* So. Lancaster, Mass.: College Press, 1955.

Cruickshank, Allan D. *Birds Around New York City: Where and When to Find Them.* Amer. Mus. Nat. Hist. Handbook No. 13, (1942).

Morrison, Kenneth D., and Josephine Daneman Herz. *Where to Find Birds in Minnesota.* St. Paul, Minn.: Webb, 1950.

Pettingill, Olin S., Jr. *A Guide to Bird Finding East of the Mississippi.* New York: Oxford U. P., 1951.

———. *A Guide to Bird Finding West of the Mississippi.* New York: Oxford U. P., 1953. Covers the best places to look for birds, state by state, and also specialities to look for.

——— (ed.). *Enjoying Maine Birds.* Maine Audubon Society, 1960. A practical guide to Maine birds with sketches and brief biographies of 80 representative species and instructions for finding them.

Spencer, Haven H. (ed.). *Enjoying Birds in Michigan.* 2nd ed. Michigan Audubon Society. Sketches and brief biographies of 100 Michigan birds with maps and directions for finding them.

BINOCULARS AND TELESCOPES

*Binoculars and How to Choose Them.* Rochester, N. Y.: Bausch and Lomb. 32 pp., illustrated.

Hendricks, Bartlett. Some Facts about Binoculars. *Bull. Mass. Aud. Soc.* (1954), **38**:200–205.

Reichert, Robert J., and Elsa Reichert. *Binoculars and Scopes: How to Choose, Use and Photograph Through Them.* Philadelphia: Chilton, 1961. A 128-page, illustrated booklet, perhaps the most complete in this field. The booklet and reprints of shorter articles are available from Mirakel Repair Co., Mt. Vernon, N.Y.

LABORATORY MANUALS

Allen, Arthur A. *Ornithology Laboratory Notebook.* Ithaca, N.Y.: Comstock, 1947. The fifth edition of this widely used notebook is expanded to include all North American groups. Contains keys for identification and provides a place and system for recording field observations and studies.

Chiasson, Robert B. *Laboratory Anatomy of the Pigeon.* Dubuque, Iowa: Wm. C. Brown Co., 1959. Covers internal features—skeleton, muscles, arteries and veins, internal organs—quite thoroughly.

Pettingill, Olin S., Jr. *A Laboratory and Field Manual of Ornithology.* 3rd ed. Minneapolis, Minn.: Burgess, 1956. Contains detailed instructions for dissection of Common Pigeon, for laboratory identifications and field studies. Fairly complete references on nearly all topics.

CENSUS METHODS

Adams, L. Confidence Limits for the Petersen or Lincoln Index used in Animal Population Studies. *Jour. Wildl. Mngt.* (1951), **15**:13–19.

Colquhoun, M. K. The Density of Woodland Birds Determined by the Sample Count Method. *Jour. Animal Ecol.* (1940), **9**:53–67.

Cooke, May Thatcher. The Purpose of Bird Censuses and How to Make Them. *U.S.D.A. Circ.* 261 (1927).

Crissey, W. F. Counting Ducks. *Atlantic Naturalist* (1952), **8**:77–82. Describes block system of enumerating ducks, aerial surveys.

Einarsen, A. S. Quadrat Inventory of Pheasant Trends in Oregon. *Jour. Wildl. Mngt.* (1945), **9**:121–131.

Gordon, Seth. An Analysis of Methods Used to Collect Game Kill Statistics. *Penn. Game News* (1940), **11**:4–5, 22–23, 30–31.

Hayne, Don W. An Examination of the Strip Census Method for Estimating Animal Populations. *Jour. Wildl. Mngt.* (1949), **13**:145–157.

Hickey, J. J. Some American Population Research in Gallinaceous Birds. Chapt. 11 *Recent Studies in Avian Biology*, ed. Albert Wolfson. Urbana, Ill.: U. of Ill., 1955. Describes various census methods and how they are used.

Hickey, Margaret Brooks. Audubon Magazine's Sixth Breeding-Bird Census. *Aud. Mag.* (1942), **44** Sec. 2:16–32. Gives instructions for taking a breeding-bird census.

Kendeigh, S. C. Measurement of Bird Populations. *Ecol. Monographs* (1944), **14**:67–106. Gives bibliography of census taking.

Lack, David. A Review of Bird Census Work and Bird Population Problems. *Ibis* (1937). Pp. 365–395.

Leopold, Aldo. *Game Management.* New York: Scribner, 1937. Chapts. 6 and 7.

## PHOTOGRAPHY

Morris, P. A. *Nature Photography Around the Year.* New York: Appleton, 1938.

Nesbit, William. *How to Hunt with the Camera.* New York: Dutton, 1926.

Sprungman, Ormal I. *Photography Afield.* Harrisburg, Pa.: Stackpole, 1951. 499 pp., illustrated. Chapter on bird photography and making blinds.

## BIRD BANDING, TRAPPING AND MARKING

Aldrich, John W., and John H. Steenis. Neck-Banding and Other Color-Marking of Waterfowl; Its Merits and Shortcomings. *Jour. Wildl. Mngt.* (1955), **19**:317–318.

Baumgartner, A. Marguerite. Experiments in Feather Marking Eastern Tree Sparrows for Territory Studies. *Bird-Banding* (1938), **9**:124–135.

Berger, Daniel D., and Helmut C. Mueller. The Bali-Chatri: A Trap for the Birds of Prey. *Bird-Banding* (1959), **30**:18–26.

*Bird-Banding Manual.* Laurel, Md.: Patuxent Wildl. Res. Cent., U.S. Fish and Wildl. Ser., 1961. Detailed manual of instructions on nearly everything pertaining to banding.

Butts, Wilbur K. A Study of the Chickadee and White-breasted Nuthatch by Means of Marked Individuals: Part I, Methods of Marking Birds. *Bird-Banding* (1930), **I**:149–168.

Cooch, Graham. Techniques for Mass Capture of Flightless Blue and Lesser Snow Geese. *Jour. Wildl. Mngt.* (1953), **17**:460–465.

Cowan, I. McT. A Trap and Technique for the Capture of Diving Waterfowl. *Jour. Wildl. Mngt.* (1952), **16**:438–441.

Downey, Robert S., and Helmer M. Mattison. Trapping Techniques for Ruffed Grouse. *Jour. Wildl. Mngt.* (1956), **20**:47–50.

Farner, Donald S. Bird-banding in the Study of Population Dynamics. Chapt. 12 in *Recent Studies in Avian Biology*, ed. Albert Wolfson. Urbana, Ill.: U. of Ill., 1955. Good account of the use of bird-banding in the study of birds—mortality, longevity, population structure.

Kozicky, Edward L., and Henry G. Weston, Jr. A Marking Technique for Ring-necked Pheasants. *Jour. Wildl. Mngt.* (1952), **16**:223. Describes use of DuPont Duco cement and lacquer.

Low, Seth H. Banding with Mist Nets. *Bird-Banding* (1957), **28**:115–128. Perhaps the most complete of several articles that have appeared on the use of Japanese mist nets.

Mossman, Archie S. A Color Marking Technique. *Jour. Wildl. Mngt.* (1960), **24**:104. Use of water soluble dye on eggs—stain shows on breast feathers of incubating bird when wet.

Poor, Hustace H. Color-banded Immature Herring Gulls in the New York Region. *Bird-Banding* (1943), **14**:101–115. Partial results from color banding 21,561 young Herring Gulls in 11 colonies on the East Coast.

Sheldon, William G. Methods of Trapping Woodcocks on Their Breeding Grounds. *Jour. Wildl. Mangt.* (1955), **19**:109–115.

Woodbury, Angus M., and Howard Knight. Results of the Pacific Gull Color-banding Project. *Condor,* (1951), **53**:57–77.

## PREPARATION OF SPECIMENS

Blake, Emmett R. Preserving Birds for Study. *Fieldiana: Technique No. 7*, Chicago Nat. Hist. Mus.(1949). 38 pp.

Chapin, James P. The Preparation of Birds for Study. *Science Guide, No. 58*, Amer. Mus. Nat. Hist., New York (1946). 48 pp.

Moyer, John W. *Practical Taxidermy.* New York: Ronald, 1953. How to mount fish, birds, mammals, and reptiles; also illustrated instructions on heads, fur rugs, field collecting, and modern museum methods.

Van Tyne, Josselyn. Principles and Practices in Collecting and Taxonomic Work. *Auk* (1952), **69**:27–33. Some good rules to follow in preparing and labelling specimens.

# 17

# ORNITHOLOGICAL ORGANIZATIONS AND THEIR JOURNALS

Bird watchers throughout the more progressive parts of the world are a highly organized people. A common bond, an interest in birds, brings together people often otherwise engaged in very diverse occupations. The result is a large number of ornithological organizations, varying from local clubs in small communities to those that are national or international in scope. Some are organized purely for recreational outings; others, both large and small, have a more serious scientific purpose. Many, even in this comparatively young country, have now survived more than half a century; others are born in a period of enthusiasm which later subsides.

It is not feasible here to analyze or to enumerate these many organizations, but those of greater ornithological importance need to be mentioned, particularly from the standpoint of the journals they publish. Those that are national in scope and *printed* journals of the various state organizations in this country are mentioned below. The many publications issued on a more restricted geographic basis, often as mimeographed leaflets, are not included. Fisher (1954) estimates that about 250 different ornithological journals, excluding mimeographed papers, annual reports, and periodicals dealing exclusively with cage birds and poultry, have been published in the past, although many are no longer extant. The three oldest, and most important since they have published about three-fourths of the world's original literature on birds, are: (1) the *Journal für Ornithologie* (1853), (2) the *Ibis* (1859), and (3) the *Auk* (1884).

There is one international organization, known as the International Ornithological Congress, which merits mention. The Congress is a gathering of representatives of various countries, particularly of Europeans and Americans. Twelve such meetings have been held in the past, the last at Helsinki, Finland, in 1958. The 1962 meeting (thirteenth) is scheduled for Ithaca (Cornell University), New York, the first meeting of the Congress to be held in this country.

## National Organizations

The leading ornithological organizations in this country that are national in scope are listed below in alphabetical order and briefly discussed.

*American Ornithologists' Union.* Publishes the *Auk,* a quarterly journal of ornithology (Fig. 204).

The American Ornithologists' Union, popularly called the A.O.U., is the leading professional ornithological organization in this country. It is North American in scope, including Canada and Mexico, and has a total membership (all classes) of about 3,000. Most of its annual meetings are held in the eastern or midwestern states, but several meetings have been held in Canada and

*Fig. 204. Layout of four national ornithological journals. (Photo by Philip G. Coleman.)*

several in the west. Founded in 1883, largely from the stimulus of the earlier Nuttall Ornithological Club (1873), the Union has published seventy-seven volumes (through 1960) of the *Auk*, which covers all phases of technical ornithology throughout the world. The A.O.U. has published five editions of the *Check-list of North American Birds* (fifth edition in 1957), sponsored a volume on *Recent Studies in Avian Biology* (published in 1955), and is preparing a comprehensive handbook (several volumes) of North American birds.

The Union's various membership categories are more sharply divided than in most organizations. In 1960 they consisted of: (1) Patrons, twenty-six people, living and deceased, who have contributed generously in a financial way to the society; (2) Honorary Fellows, nineteen living foreign ornithologists who have been specially honored with this designation; (3) Corresponding Fellows, seventy-three additional ornithologists in foreign countries, selected in recognition of distinctive achievements in their field; (4) Fellows, eighty-three leading American ornithologists; (5) Elective members, about 200 other persons (lower ranking than Fellows) who have made substantial contributions, usually through publications, to ornithology; (6) Members, nearly 3,000 other people who belong to the organization, but who need have no special professional qualifications. Membership in all categories except members (and Patrons) is limited. All members, except the foreign ornithologists, pay dues. Election of new persons to the various membership categories is done at the Annual Meeting each year by popular vote, the Fellows electing new Fellows, the Fellows and Elective Members choosing new Elective Members.

*Bird-Banding Organizations.* Publish *Bird-Banding* magazine, a quarterly (Fig. 204).

The various bird-banding organizations in this country are divided on a regional basis into Northeastern, Eastern, Inland, and Western Bird-Banding Associations. A single journal, *Bird-Banding*, serves all of them, although some of the regional associations have their own special leaflets and newsletters (usually mimeographed) and hold regional meetings. Some states have their own local units (e.g., *Michigan Bird Banders*), separate from or more usually affiliated with the larger organizations. *Bird-Banding* magazine publishes articles based primarily on banding studies, but is also known for its outstanding reviews of foreign literature. Thirty-one volumes of the quarterly journal have been published (through 1960).

*Cooper Ornithological Society.* Publishes the *Condor*, a bimonthly (Fig. 204).

Though this organization, named for J. G. Cooper, author of the first comprehensive work on Californian birds, has members throughout North America, it serves primarily the Pacific Coast and Rocky Mountain states. The *Condor*, now (1960) in its sixty-second year, is a thoroughly scientific journal, drawing its subject matter from both field and laboratory, from Alaska to South America. The Society also publishes *Pacific Coast Avifauna*, a series of outstanding monographs.

*National Audubon Society*. Publishes *Audubon Magazine* (formerly *Bird-Lore*), a bimonthly.

The National Audubon Society, incorporated in 1905 and named after John James Audubon (Fig. 4), is a large, active, and influential organization, with its headquarters (Audubon House) at 1130 Fifth Avenue in New York City. Its membership is much greater than that of the more scientific organizations named above. Though originally founded for the protection and preservation of birds, it has since broadened its scope to include all phases of renewable natural resources. Its magazine, called *Bird-Lore* when it was devoted primarily to bird life, was changed to *Audubon Magazine* in 1941, and is a very readable, well-illustrated publication with a broad coverage designed to appeal to its many readers.

In collaboration with the United States Fish and Wildlife Service, the Society publishes *Audubon Field Notes*, which consists of six issues with detailed analyses of reported bird records for the four seasons plus the Christmas counts and breeding-bird censuses. The Society also issues a great deal of Audubon Junior Club material, sells literature and various supplies, and keeps a vigilant eye on all developments that might affect the nation's natural resources. Its Screen Tour program of colorful movies, presented in 200 cities, reaches an audience of half a million a year. Summer camps in Maine, Wisconsin, and California, and Nature Centers in Connecticut, Ohio, and California provide training courses for teachers and field workers. Still other activities of the Society have been indicated elsewhere in the text.

*The Wilson Ornithological Society*. Publishes the *Wilson Bulletin*, a quarterly (Fig. 204).

Though founded in Massachusetts in 1888, the main activities of the Society—its officers, membership, meetings, and coverage of its journal—have been largely centered in interior North America, including Mexico. Named in honor of Alexander Wilson, father of American ornithology, the Society early advocated field studies of birds as its goal, but the magazine later extended its coverage to include taxonomic and anatomical studies, especially if based on or supplementing field data. The Wilson Ornithological Society Library, housed in the University of Michigan Museum of Zoology and recently named the Josselyn Van Tyne Memorial Library in honor of the man largely responsible for it, is an outstanding collection of books, periodicals, and reprints, acquired largely by donations, for the service of members.

*Other National Organizations*. Several other organizations, not exclusively ornithological, merit mention for their contributions to bird literature. The *Journal of Wildlife Management*, published by the Wildlife Society, includes, as the name implies, findings on birds as well as on other forms of wildlife. Though major emphasis is on game species, papers cover many other aspects of bird life, with particular emphais on statistical studies, measurements of populations, and economic aspects of wildlife species. Various sportsmen's magazines occasionally have informative articles on game birds. A recent laudable trend among state conservation departments is to publish their own bulletins and magazines in which wildlife problems are analyzed and explained, usually by the department's trained personnel.

*Ecology* and *Ecological Monographs,* both published by the Ecological Society of America, are fruitful sources of bird literature in that field. The *American Midland Naturalist,* published by the University Press, Notre Dame, Indiana, sometimes has extensive papers on birds. *Natural History* magazine, published by the American Museum of Natural History, New York, features birds prominently in its popular coverage of topics. The *National Geographic Magazine* frequently carries colorfully illustrated articles on birds from various parts of the world. On the more technical side, a relatively recent journal, *Systematic Zoology,* published quarterly by the Society of Systematic Zoology since 1952, explores problems in systematics and taxonomy for both vertebrates and invertebrates.

Perhaps needless to say there are many important institutional publications, such as those of museums, colleges and universities, and various scientific societies, that contribute substantially to bird literature. Journals in allied fields (morphology, physiology, poultry, genetics), occasionally at least, feature articles which add materially to ornithological knowledge.

## *State Organizations*

It is hardly feasible here to survey all of the state ornithological organizations; some are set up on a restricted regional rather than a state-wide basis, and some locally active clubs, regional or state-wide, do not issue printed publications. The following survey, then, is limited largely to state-wide organizations that issue a magazine or journal that is mainly ornithological. Most of the journals of state societies are not very technical, but deal, often in considerable detail, with local distribution and various field studies conducted within the state, and thus serve an important local function.

Some states are situated advantageously for a state-wide organization, others are not. New York, for instance, has a Federation of Bird Clubs rather than a single unified society; the Carolinas have joined effectively to form a single club; and the Illinois Audubon Society, though ostensibly state-wide, has all of its officers and most of its members in the Chicago area and is essentially a local (Chicago) organization. Other states—Pennsylvania, California, Texas—have active local clubs but not a state-wide organization. The long-standing Delaware Valley Ornithological Club and its journal *Cassinia* include southern New Jersey and eastern Pennsylvania. Most state societies are small, with a few hundred to a thousand or so members; Massachusetts tops the list with nearly 10,000. The following is an alphabetical listing of selected states and the journals they publish.

*District of Columbia. The Atlantic Naturalist* (formerly called the *Wood Thrush*), published five times a year by the Audubon Society of the District of Columbia. Though founded in 1897, the Society has been issuing its magazine for only about fifteen years (up to 1960). It is an attractive, artistically illustrated journal of 50 or more pages. As the new name of the publication implies, it is not limited to ornithology, but features articles on a wide variety of natural-history subjects, drawing on the abundant talent available in the Washington region for authorship. It often takes a strong stand on conservation issues.

*Florida.* The *Florida Naturalist,* a quarterly published by the Florida Audubon Society. Founded in 1900, the Society has been issuing its present journal since 1927. Though formerly largely ornithological, the journal has recently broadened its coverage to include related fields.

*Georgia.* The *Oriole,* a quarterly published by the Georgia Ornithological Society, which was founded in 1936. Its aims are somewhat more technical than those of other state societies, and there is no concerted attempt to increase its relatively small membership by popularizing the magazine, which is devoted almost exclusively to Georgia ornithology.

*Illinois.* The *Audubon Bulletin,* a quarterly published by the Illinois Audubon Society, which was founded in 1897. The *Bulletin* deals mainly with local distributional records and affairs of the Society, which is centered largely in the Chicago area.

*Indiana.* The *Indiana Audubon Quarterly* (formerly the *Indiana Audubon Society Yearbook*), published by the Indiana Audubon Society, which was founded in 1898 and incorporated in 1939. This also deals principally with local records and society affairs.

*Iowa.* The *Iowa Bird Life,* a quarterly published by the Iowa Ornithologists' Union, which was founded in 1923 for the study and protection of native birds. It has been issued under its present title since 1931, having been preceded by the *Bulletin* and by mimeographed newsletters. It is devoted almost exclusively to Iowa ornithology.

*Kentucky.* The *Kentucky Warbler,* a quarterly published by the Kentucky Ornithological Society which was founded in 1923. It deals quite thoroughly with local bird records and observations.

*Maine.* The *Bulletin* (Fig. 205), a quarterly published by the Maine Audubon Society at Brunswick. Its twenty or so pages are devoted primarily to further observations on the birds of Maine, which have been well documented in the past.

*Massachusetts.* The *Massachusetts Audubon,* now a quarterly though formerly (the *Bulletin*—Fig. 205) published monthly except for summer, is perhaps the largest and most pretentious of the state ornithological magazines, and is issued by the oldest (founded in 1896) and by far the largest of the state societies. Its magazine is well illustrated and designed to keep its many subscribers informed on conservation education as well as Massachusetts ornithology. Considerable magazine space, however, is devoted to business affairs within the Society and to advertising. *Records of New England Birds,* a monthly report of records of New England observers, is published separately. Unlike most other state groups, the Society has a salaried staff, with a headquarters, library, and salesroom, and a coordinated group of educational workers distributed throughout the state. It also maintains 12 sanctuaries (Fig. 188–189), with year-round resident directors on some of them.

*Michigan.* The *Jack-Pine Warbler* (Fig. 205), a quarterly published by the Michigan Audubon Society. The magazine is named in honor of Michigan's unique bird, the Kirtland's Warbler (Fig. 144). The Society, founded in 1904, is one of the largest and most active of the state societies, and is well organized as to officers and committees. It maintains a library, a bookshop, and one developed and two undeveloped sanctuaries. The magazine, originating as a mimeographed newsletter in 1923, has been issued in substantially its present form since 1939. Currently its 40 or more pages feature leading articles on Michigan birds, summarize the seasonal records of the state's many observers, and publish other material pertaining to society affairs. A *Newsletter* keeps members posted on items not pertinent to the more permanent journal. "Camp-outs," get-togethers of members and guests at some field station, are held at least twice yearly in addition to the regular Annual Meeting.

*Minnesota.* The *Flicker* (Fig. 205), a quarterly published by the Minnesota Ornithologists' Union, which has its headquarters at the Museum of Natural History in Minneapolis. Eight or more local Minnesota clubs are affiliated with the Union. The magazine is a fairly substantial one, sometimes running to more than 50 pages. It deals mainly with Minnesota bird life, including notes from adjacent Ontario (the Canadian Lakehead) and North Dakota.

*Nebraska.* The *Nebraska Bird Review,* a quarterly of the ornithology of the Nebraska region, published by the Nebraska Ornithologists' Union. Though small with respect to members and the size of its journal, the Union is one of the older societies (1899) and has been active for a long time.

*New York.* The *Kingbird* is issued four times a year by the Federation of New York Bird Clubs, which is composed of the many bird clubs scattered throughout the state. Some of the local groups have their own literature also (e.g., *Feathers* published by the Schenectady Bird Club and the *Goshawk* by the Genesee Ornithological Society), and active bird clubs are found at Buffalo (Buffalo Academy of Natural Science), Ithaca (Cornell University), Rochester, Albany, and of course in and around the New York City region.

*Fig. 205. Layout of selected state journals. (Photo by Philip G. Coleman.)*

*North and South Carolina.* The *Chat,* a quarterly published by the Carolina Bird Club. The Club was preceded by the North Carolina Bird Club (1937) which joined with several South Carolina natural-history groups in 1948 to form the broader organization. The *Chat* is a 20-to-30-page, illustrated journal devoted primarily to bird life in the Carolinas.

*Rhode Island.* The *Bulletin,* published five times a year by the Audubon Society of Rhode Island which was founded in 1897. The *Bulletin* is a small printed leaflet of 5 to 10 or more pages distributed to members to inform them of the activities of the Society. Recent reorganization with a paid executive director has considerably increased both membership and activities. The Kimball Bird Sanctuary maintained by the Society is well known locally.

*South Dakota.* The *South Dakota Bird Notes,* issued quarterly, is the official publication of the South Dakota Ornithologists' Union. Though small (of 10 to 20 pages), it is attractively prepared and contains ornithological notes of interest to its small but active membership.

*Tennessee.* The *Migrant,* a quarterly published by the Tennessee Ornithological Society. It also is devoted primarily to records and observations of Tennessee's varied bird life.

*Wisconsin.* The *Passenger Pigeon,* a quarterly of Wisconsin bird study, published by the Wisconsin Society for Ornithology. It is one of the more pretentious of the various state journals, is well edited, well illustrated, and serves as an efficient medium for the observations and local studies of a large corps of active and enthusiastic Wisconsin observers.

# BIBLIOGRAPHY

## *Foreign and Regional Publications*

### *Foreign Journals*

Perhaps it hardly needs to be added that the more progressive countries throughout the world have well-developed ornithological programs; this is particularly true in northern and central Europe. Unfortunately, the foreign journals usually are not readily available in the smaller schools and libraries, although they are almost indispensable for doing advanced work with birds. Some of the better known or accessible ones are listed below, alphabetically by countries.

Australia. *The Emu,* a quarterly official organ of the Australasian Ornithologists' Union, Melbourne. Deals with ornithology of Australia and surrounding islands.

Belgium. *Le Gerfaut* (The Falcon), Revue de Belge d'ornithologie.

Denmark. *Dansk Ornithologisk Forenings Tidsskrift.*

England. *The Ibis; British Birds; Bird Study; Avicultural Magazine* (serves also for Avicultural Society of America); the *Oologists' Record* (world-wide oölogy).

Finland. *Ornis Fennica; Suomen Riista,* Finnish Game Foundation, Helsinki. Articles in Finnish, Swedish and English.

France. *Alauda; L'Oiseau* et la Revue Française d'ornithologie.

Germany. *Journal für Ornithologie; Die Vogelwarte; Die Vogelwelt.*

India. *Journal of the Bombay Natural History Society,* a quarterly devoted to natural history, but is the leading Indian journal dealing with birds.

Japan.*Tori; Yacho.*

Netherlands. *Ardea* (some articles in English); *Limosa.*

New Zealand. *Notornis,* a quarterly bulletin of the Ornithological Society of New Zealand.

South Africa. The *Bokmakierie,* South African Ornithological Society and Wikwatersprand Bird Club (popular magazine for bird watchers); the *Ostrich,* South African Ornithological Society.

Sweden. *Vår Fågelvärld.*

Switzerland. *Nos Oiseaux,* Bulletin de la Société Romande pour l'étude et protection des oiseaux; *Der Ornithologische Beobachter.*

## *Systematic and Regional Publications*

Something of the nature and extent of ornithological literature has been suggested in other parts of this text. Chapter-end references list some of the more comprehensive works on the subject matter of the various chapters and the "Literature Cited" section indicates the many additional references consulted. Little has been said, however, about some of the monumental projects in systematic ornithology, such as catalogues of birds and elaborate regional works. Some of the larger and more comprehensive of these are listed below.

### BIRDS OF THE WORLD

Alexander, W. B. *Birds of the Ocean.* 2nd ed. New York: Putnam, 1954. xxiii plus 428 pp.; 88 plates of photographs.

Austin, Oliver L., Jr. *Birds of the World.* New York: Golden, 1961. 316 pp.; 300 paintings. An elaborate, informative, and up to date volume treating all orders and families, lavishly illustrated with paintings of more than 700 birds by Arthur Singer.

Gilliard, E. Thomas. *Living Birds of the World.* Garden City, N.Y.: Doubleday, 1958. 400 pp.; 400 illustrations, 217 in full color. A magnificent volume treating all families of living birds, with an admirable selection of photographs both in black and white and in color. Text material is fresh and up to date.

Knowlton, Frank H. *Birds of the World.* New York: Holt, 1909. 886 pp.; 16 color plates, and 236 illustrations. An old and classic work, now out of print.

Peters, J. L. *Check-list of Birds of the World.* Cambridge, Mass.: Harvard U. P., 1931–1960. Six volumes list all known species and subspecies of nonpasserine birds and their ranges. Vol. 7, the first on the passerines, issued in 1951 before the author's death. Vols. 8 to 14 are being prepared under the editorship of Ernst Mayr, but only Vol. 9 had appeared by 1961.

## SYSTEMATIC AND REGIONAL WORKS IN THE AMERICAS

(exclusive of state bird books which are in the next list)

A.O.U. *Check-list of North American Birds.* 5th ed. 1957. Standard distributional list of all birds known to occur in North America north of Mexico.

Blake, Emmet Reid. *Birds of Mexico: A Guide for Field Identification.* Chicago: U. of Chicago, 1953. Includes keys, descriptions, distribution, and remarks on each of the 967 species and approximately 2,000 forms of Mexican birds; 644 pages, with more than 325 illustrations by Douglas E. Tibbitts.

Bond, James. *Birds of the West Indies.* Boston: Houghton, 1961. Replaces an earlier *Field Guide to Birds of the West Indies*, which is out of print. Retains most of the original drawings by Earl Poole and adds 8 new color plates by Don R. Eckelberry. Describes 429 birds.

de Schauensee, Rudolphe M. Birds of Colombia. *Caldasia* (1948–1952), 5(22):251–380; 5(23):381–644; 5(24):645–871; 5(25):873–1112; 5(26): 1115–1214. A very comprehensive distributional list, published serially in a Colombian journal, of the 1,532 species and 2,558 forms recorded in Colombia.

Eisenmann, Eugene. The Species of Middle American Birds. Vol. VII. *Trans. Linn. Soc.* (New York) (1955). vi plus 128 pp. A list of the 1,424 species recorded from Mexico to Panama, with suggested English names, outlines of range, and distributional bibliography.

Forbush, E. H., and John B. May. *Natural History of the Birds of Eastern and Central North America.* Boston: Houghton, 1939. Mainly a condensed reprinting of Forbush's *Birds of Massachusetts* (see list of state bird books) with the elimination of considerable descriptive matter and the addition of some birds occurring outside of New England.

Gabrielson, Ira N., and F. C. Lincoln. *Birds of Alaska.* Norrisburg, Pa.: Stockpole, 1959. xiii plus 922 pp.; 10 color plates. The only comprehensive account of Alaskan bird life. Lists 321 species and 414 forms.

Hellmayr, C. E. (with C. B. Cory and Boardman Conover). Catalogue of the Birds of the Americas. *Field Mus. Nat. Hist. Zool. Ser.* 13 (1918–1949). Parts 1–15. A standard reference, the only one of its kind, for the birds of both continents. A long-term project begun by C. B. Cory (2 vols.) in 1918 and 1919, continued by Hellmayr (9 vols.) until his death in 1944 and completed by Conover (4 vols.) before his death in 1950.

Munro, George C. *Birds of Hawaii.* Rutland, Vt.: Tuttle, 1960. 189 pp.; illustrated in color and black and white. Replaces the 1944 edition.

Murphy, Robert Cushman. *Oceanic Birds of South America.* Amer. Mus. of Nat. Hist. (New York, 1936). A monumental work in two volumes, 1,245 pages with 16 paintings by Francis L. Jaques, and 72 plates of photographs.

———, and Dean Amadon. *Land Birds of America.* New York: McGraw, 1953. 240 pp.; 264 photographs (221 in color). Primarily a picture book, but with running commentary on North American bird groups, and considerable introductory matter on the history of ornithology and related subjects.

Pearson, T. Gilbert (ed.) *Birds of America.* Garden City, N.Y.: Garden City, 1936. xliv plus 289 pp.; 106 color plates by Louis Aggasiz Fuertes and many additional photographs.

Peters, Harold S., and Thomas D. Burleigh. *The Birds of Newfoundland.* Prov. of Nfld., St. Johns: Dep't. Nat. Resources, 1951. 450 pp. Illustrated with 32 color plates and 40 line drawings by Roger Tory Peterson.

Rand, Austin L. *American Water and Game Birds.* New York: Dutton, 1956. 239 pp.; 130 photographs in full color and 70 other illustrations. Beautiful color plates of birds and informative up-to-date text.

Ridgway, Robert, and Herbert Friedmann. The Birds of North and Middle America. *Bull.* 50 National Museum (Washington, D.C., 1901–1950). Parts I–XI, 7,990 pp. A descriptive catalogue of the higher groups, genera, species, and subspecies of birds known to occur in North America, from the Arctic lands to the Isthmus of Panama, including the West Indies and Galápagos Islands. A monumental project, begun by Robert Ridgway, formerly Curator of Birds at the National Museum, and continued by his successor, Herbert Friedmann. The last two parts are long overdue. The completed work will be a meticulous compilation of data totaling nearly 10,000 pages.

Salomonsen, Finn. *The Birds of Greenland.* Copenhagen: Ejnar Munksgaard, 1950–1951. Three volumes totaling 609 pages, set up in two columns, in English and Danish, and 52 color plates by Gitz-Johansen. A complete and modern account of the bird life of Greenland, including general habits, breeding biology, food, migration, and distribution.

Sturgis, B. B. *Field Book of Birds of the Panama Canal Zone.* New York: Putnam, 1928. A useful guide to identification, but nomenclature is out of date and species list is incomplete.

Taverner, P. A. *Birds of Canada.* Toronto, Ont.: Musson, 1938. A useful, attractive, and authoritative work on Canadian birds, illustrated with small color plates by Allan Brooks and Hennessey and by many text figures by the author; a single volume combining and revising two earlier volumes on the birds of eastern and western Canada.

## *State Bird Books*

It has already been mentioned that every state has at least a checklist of the birds known to occur within its boundaries and that many states have rather elaborate works with detailed descriptions of species and their distribution and habits. A fairly complete list of these, conveniently alphabetized by states, can be found in Pettingill's *Manual* (p. 419); listed here are only those of considerable magnitude.

Bailey, Florence Merriam. *Birds of New Mexico.* Santa Fe, N.M.: N.M. Dept. of Fish and Game, 1928. 807 pp., with illustrations by Allan Brooks and Fuertes.

Barrows, Walter. *Michigan Bird Life.* East Lansing, Mich.: Mich. Agr. Coll., 1912. Reprinted without change by Mich. St. Coll. in 1932. 822 pp.; 222 illustrations in black and white. Though the classification and some distributional data are out of date, this comprehensive volume remains the only bird book of the state that gives detailed species accounts of life histories and habits. N. A. Wood's Birds of Michigan (*Univ. of Mich. Mus. of Zool. Misc. Publ.* **75**:1–559) gives revised distributional data and status up through 1943.

Brandt, Herbert. *Arizona and Its Bird Life.* Cleveland, Ohio: Bird Res. Found., 1951. A deluxe edition of 740 pages with 20 color plates on the bird life of Arizona's rather unique southeastern corner, which boasts an unusual variety of nesting land birds.

Burleigh, Thomas D. *Georgia Birds.* Norman, Okla.: U. of Okla., 1958. xix plus 746 pages; 35 color plates by G. M. Sutton; 13 plates of photographs, text figures, and maps. A sumptuous volume in the traditional state-bird book style, mainly a systematic account but with a good history of Georgia ornithology and description of physiographic and biogeographic regions.

Dawson, W. L. *The Birds of Ohio.* Columbus, Ohio: Wheaton, 1903. Two vols.

———. *The Birds of Washington.* Seattle, Wash.: Occidental, 1909. Two vols. With J. H. Bowles, co-author. (See Jewett also.)

———. *The Birds of California.* San Diego, Calif.: Smith Moulton, 1923. Four vols., 2121 pp. Detailed comprehensive volumes on the birds of these three states, but out of date in many respects. More recent publications in all of these states bring distribution and status up to date. The magnificent California work, published under great difficulties at a cost of approximately $250,000, appeared in about 10 different editions or formats, mostly in four volumes, although the largest students' edition appeared in three volumes (Chambers, 1939).

Eaton, E. H. *Birds of New York.* Albany, N.Y.: N.Y. State Mus., 1910–1914. Two vols. One of the early comprehensive state works, illustrated with 106 full-page color plates by Fuertes, containing 1,220 pages of text, maps, and illustrations.

Forbush, Edward Howe. *Birds of Massachusetts and Other New England States.* Boston: Mass. Dept. of Agr., 1925–1929. Three vols. Elaborate volumes on the birds of Massachusetts with data for the other New England states; 1,408 pages illustrated with full-page color plates by Fuertes and Allan Brooks.

Gabrielson, Ira. N., and Stanley G. Jewett. *Birds of Oregon.* Corvallis, Ore.: Ore. St. Coll., 1940. 650 pp.; 97 halftone plates.

Howell, Arthur H. *Florida Bird Life.* New York: Coward-McCann, 1932. Revised and republished by Alexander Sprunt, Jr., and the National Audubon Society in 1954. xlii plus 527 pp.; 40 color plates, 16 pages of black-and-white photographs, and 65 text figures. There are 473 species and subspecies described, with an additional 36 forms listed as hypothetical.

Jewett, Stanley G., Taylor, W. P., Shaw, W. T., and J. W. Aldrich. *Birds of Washington State*. Seattle, Wash.: U. of Wash., 1953. 767 pp. More than 450 birds are included.

Lowery, George H., Jr. *Louisiana Birds*. Baton Rouge, La.: La. St. U. P., 1955. xxix plus 556 pp. Well illustrated with line drawings, black and white photographs and some color plates. A useful combination of ornithological text and annotated species accounts of the birds of the state.

Palmer, Ralph S. *Maine Birds*. Bull. Mus. Comp. Zool. (Cambridge, Mass.) (1949), **102**:1–656. Earlier works on the birds of this state are brought up to date in this comprehensive volume, which is mainly a compilation of former records.

Pearson, T. G., Brimley, G. S., and H. H. Brimley. *Birds of North Carolina*. Raleigh, N.C.: N.C. St. Mus., 1959. Revised by David L. Wray and Harry T. Davis. With illustrations in color and black and white by Rex Brasher, Robert Horsfall, and R. T. Peterson of the 396 species and subspecies found in the state.

Roberts, Thomas Sadler. *The Birds of Minnesota*. Minneapolis, Minn.: U. of Minn., 1932. Two comprehensive, classic volumes with 92 color plates by 6 famous artists, 606 text figures, and 1,512 pages of text.

Sprunt, Alexander, Jr., and E. Burnham Chamberlain. *South Carolina Bird Life*. Columbia, S.C.: U. of S.C., 1949. Nearly 600 pages of text, with 35 color plates and 48 photographs, that describe and illustrate 442 species and subspecies.

Stewart, Robert E., and Chandler S. Robbins. *Birds of Maryland and the District of Columbia*. Washington, D.C.: N.A. Fauna No. 62, Gov. Print. Off., 1958. vi plus 401 pp. An annotated list of 333 species, plus 19 hypothetical. Includes many ecological and quantitative data.

## Other Regional Publications

Some regional works, covering areas smaller than a state, have taken on the aspect and magnitude of state publications. Some of the more notable books of this sort are described below.

Bagg, Aaron C., and Samuel A. Eliot, Jr. *Birds of the Connecticut Valley in Massachusetts*. Northampton, Mass.: The Hampshire Bookshop, 1937. A detailed systematic account (over 800 pages) of bird records and observations in a limited region of central Massachusetts—a 50-mile stretch of a single river valley, based mainly on the field records of the two authors.

Cruickshank, Allan D. Birds Around New York City. *Am. Mus. Nat. Hist.*, Handbook Series, No. 13 (1942). xvii plus 489 pp. The latest of several comprehensive listings of the birds of the New York City area, with 35 plates of photographs by the author.

Stone, Witmer. *Bird Studies at Old Cape May.* Philadelphia: Acad. Nat. Sci., 1937. An outstandingly comprehensive and readable account in two volumes (nearly one thousand pages) of the many observations by the author and other members of the Delaware Valley Ornithological Club at one of the East Coast's most famous birding spots. Illustrated with 119 plates of photographs and 270 text figures.

Todd, W. E. C. *Birds of Western Pennsylvania.* Pittsburgh, Pa.: U. of Pittsburgh, 1940. A sumptuous volume with detailed species accounts of the birds found in the western mountainous part of the state, including the narrow stretch of Lake Erie that abuts on Pennsylvania. Represents a half-century of observation by the author as well as the contributions of other observers. Twenty-two color plates by G. M. Sutton depict 118 species.

Trautman, Milton B. The Birds of Buckeye Lake, Ohio. *Univ. of Mich. Mus. Zool. Misc. Publ.* (1940), 44:1–466. An unusual and thorough analysis of the distribution and status, past and present, of the birds of an inland lake and its borders—an area of about 44 square miles.

# Literature Cited

*(See also chapter-end references which usually are not repeated here.)*


Abbott, Herschel G. Application of Avian Repellents to Eastern White Pine Seed. *Jour. Wildl. Mngt.* (1958), **22**:304–306.

Abbott, Waldo G. Leaf Bathing of the Mockingbird. *Condor* (1954), **56**:163–164.

Agee, C. Phillip. The Fall Shuffle in Central Missouri Bob-whites. *Jour. Wildl. Mngt.* (1957), **21**:329–335.

Aldrich, Elmer C. Pterylography and Molt of the Allen Hummingbird. *Condor* (1956), **58**:121–133.

Allen, Francis H. The Quails of the Sinai Peninsula—Another Interpretation. *Auk* (1948), **65**:451–452.

———. Audubon on Territory. *Wilson Bull.* (1951), **63**:206.

Allen, Ralph H., Jr. Wildlife Losses in the Southern Fire Ant Program. *Pass. Pigeon* (1958), **20**:144–147.

Allen, Robert P. Bird Colonies along the Texas Coast. *Aud. Mag.* (1952), **54**:254–259, 270–272.

———. Do We Want to Save the Whooping Crane? *Aud. Mag.* (1960), **62**:122–125, 134–135.

Altmann, Stuart A. Avian Mobbing Behavior and Predator Recognition. *Condor* (1956), **58**:241–253.

Ammann, G. A. Number of Contour Feathers of *Cygnus* and *Xanthocephalus*. *Auk* (1937), **54**:201–202.

———, and Walter L. Palmer. Ruffed Grouse Introductions on Michigan Islands. *Jour. Wildl. Mngt.* (1958), **22**:322–325.

Armstrong, Edward A. Counterfeit Terror. *Outdoors Illustrated* (1953), **5**:10–13.

Austin, Oliver L., Jr. *Birds of the World*. New York: Golden, 1961.

Bagg, Aaron M. Airborne from Gulf to Gulf. *Bull. Mass. Aud. Soc.* (1955), **39**:106–110, 159–168.

———, *et al.* Barometric Pressure-patterns and Spring Bird Migration. *Wilson Bull.* (1950), **62**:5–19.

Bailey, Robert E. The Incubation Patch of Passerine Birds. *Condor* (1952), **54**:121–136.

Baird, James, and Ian C. T. Nisbet. Observations of Diurnal Migration in the Narragansett Bay Area of Rhode Island in Fall 1958. *Bird-Banding* (1959), **30**:171–181.

———. Northward Fall Migration on the Atlantic Coast and Its Relation to Offshore Drift. *Auk* (1960), **77**:119–149.

Baker, John H. Better Protection for the California Condor. *Aud. Mag.* (1950), **52**:348–354.

———. Wild Bird Plumage Amendment Adopted. *Aud. Mag.* (1952), **54**:240.

Bakus, Gerald J. Observations on the Life History of the Dipper in Montana. *Auk* (1959), **76**:190–207.

Barker, Roy J. Notes on Some Ecological Effects of DDT Sprayed on Elms. *Jour. Wildl. Mngt.* (1958), **22**:269–274.

Barnes, Irston R. Persecution or Freedom. *Aud. Mag.* (1951), **53**:282–289.

Barrows, Walter B. *Michigan Bird Life.* Spec. Bull. Mich. Agr. College (East Lansing, Mich., 1912), pp. 1–822.

Barth, Edward K. Incubation Period and Loss of Weight of Eggs of the Common Gull, *Larus canus canus,* and of the Lesser Black-backed Gull, *L. fuscus intermedius. Papers on Game Research* (Helsinki) (1952), **8**:111–121.

Bartholomew, George A., Jr., and Tom J. Cade. The Body Temperature of the American Kestrel, *Falco sparverius. Wilson Bull.* (1957), **69**:149–154.

Bartholomew, George A., Jr., and William R. Dawson. Body Temperatures in Nestling Western Gulls. *Condor* (1952), **54**:58–60.

Bartlett, Guy. A Wholesale Attraction, but not Destruction, of Migrating Birds by the Albany (N. Y.) Airport Ceilometer. *Feathers* (1952), **14**:61–66.

———. Albany's Ceilometer—Killer of Migrants. *Feathers* (1956), **18**:57–60.

Barton, A. J. A Releaser Mechanism in the Feeding of Nestling Chimney Swifts. *Auk* (1958), **75**:216–217.

Batts, H. Lewis, Jr. The Distribution and Population of Nesting Birds on a Farm in Southern Michigan. *Jack-Pine Warbler* (1958), **36**:131–149.

Beals, Marie V. New Age Record for a Blue Jay. *Bird-Banding* (1952), **23**:168.

Beddall, Barbara G. Historical Notes on Avian Classification. *Syst. Zool.* (1957), **6**:129–136.

Beebe, Frank L. The Marine Peregrines of the Northwest Pacific Coast. *Condor* (1960), **62**:145–189.

Beecher, William J. Adaptations for Food-getting in the American Blackbirds. *Auk* (1951), **68**:411–440.

Beer, James R., Frenzel, Louis D., and Norman Hansen. Minimum Space Requirements of Some Nesting Passerine Birds. *Wilson Bull.* (1956), **68**:200–209.

Beer, James R., and Douglas Tibbitts. Nesting Behavior of the Red-winged Blackbird. *Flicker* (1950), **22**:61–77.

Beer, James R., and Wayne Tidyman. The Substitution of Hard Seeds for Grit. *Jour. Wildl. Mngt.* (1942), **6**:70–82.

Bellrose, Frank C. Celestial Orientation by Wild Mallards. *Bird-Banding* (1958), **29**:75–90.

Bené, Frank. The Feeding and Related Behavior of Hummingbirds, with Special Reference to the Black-chin. *Memoirs Boston Soc. Nat. Hist.* (1947), **19**:403–478.

Berger, Andrew J. Nesting Density of Virginia and Sora Rails in Michigan. *Condor* (1951a), **53**:202.

———. Ten Consecutive Nests of the Song Sparrow. *Wilson Bull.* (1951b), **63**:186–188.

———. Protracted Incubation of a Female American Goldfinch. *Condor* (1953a), **55**:151.

———. Three Cases of Twin Embryos in Passerine Birds. *Condor* (1953b), **55**:157–158.

———. Nesting Behavior of the House Sparrow. *Jack-Pine Warbler* (1957), **35**:86–92.

Bergstrom, E. Alexander. Extreme Old Age in Terns. *Bird-Banding* (1952), **23**:72–73.

———. Extreme Old Age in Birds. *Bird-Banding* (1956), **27**:128–129.

Biehn, Earl R. Crop Damage by Wildlife in California. *Game Bull.* 5, Dept. Fish & Game (Calif.) (1951), 71 pp.

Bissonnette, T. H. Sexual Photoperiodicity in the Blue Jay *(Cyanocitta cristata)*. *Wilson Bull.* (1939), **51**:227–232.

Black, Glenn A. The Use of Birds Among the Prehistoric Indians of the Ohio Valley. *Kent. Warb.* (1953), **29**:3–7.

Blackwelder, R. E. The Present Status of Systematic Zoology. *Syst. Zool.* (1959), **8**:69–75.

Blake, Charles H. Raised Ear Coverts. *Auk* (1950), **67**:105–106.

———. Respiration Rates. *Bird-Banding* (1958), **29**:38–40.

———. Terminal Migrants and Transmigrants. *Bird-Banding* (1959), **30**:233.

Bleitz, Don. Nest of Pygmy Nuthatches Attended by Four Parents. *Condor* (1951), **53**:150–151.

Bock, Walter J. Salivary Glands in the Gray Jays *(Perisoreus)*. *Auk* (1961), **78**:355–365.

Bond, James. *Field Guide to Birds of the West Indies.* New York: Macmillan, 1947.

Bond, Richard R. Ecological Distribution of Breeding Birds in the Upland Forests of Southern Wisconsin. *Ecol. Monog.* (1957), **27**:351–384.

Borgmeier, Thomas. Basic Questions of Systematics. *Syst. Zool.* (1957), **6**:53–69.

Borror, Donald J. Variation in the Songs of the Rufous-sided Towhee. *Wilson Bull.* (1959), **71**:54–72.

———, and Carl R. Reese. The Analysis of Bird Songs by Means of a Vibralizer. *Wilson Bull.* (1953), **65**:271–276.
———. Analytical Studies of Henslow's Sparrow Songs. *Wilson Bull.* (1954), **66**:243–252.
Bowers, Darl E. A Study of Variation in Feather Pigments of the Wrentit. *Condor* (1959), **61**:38–45.
Boyd, Elizabeth M. The External Parasites of Birds: A Review. *Wilson Bull.* (1951), **63**:363–369.
———. Birds and Some Human Diseases. *Bird-Banding* (1958), **29**:34–38.
Brackbill, Hervey. Light Intensity and Waterfowl Flight; Pre-flight Activities. *Wilson Bull.* (1952), **64**:242–244.
———. Observations on Remating in the American Robin, *Turdus migratorius*. *Auk* (1952), **69**:465–466.
———. Foot-Quivering by Foraging Hermit Thrushes. *Auk* (1960), **77**:477–478.
Brand, Albert. Vibration Frequency of Passerine Bird Song. *Auk* (1938), **55**:263–268.
———, and P. Paul Kellogg. Auditory Responses of Starlings, English Sparrows, and Domestic Pigeons. *Wilson Bull.* (1939a), **51**:38–41.
———. The Range of Hearing of Canaries. *Science* (1939b), **90**:354.
Brauner, Joseph. Reactions of Poor-wills to Light and Temperature. *Condor* (1952), **54**:152–159.
———. Observations on the Behavior of a Captive Poor-will. *Condor* (1953), **55**:68–74.
Brewer, Richard, and Jack A. Ellis. An Analysis of Migrating Birds Killed at a Television Tower in East-Central Illinois, September 1955–May 1957. *Auk* (1958), **75**:400–414.
Brodkorb, Pierce. The Number of Feathers in Some Birds. *Quart. Jour. Fla. Acad. Sci.* (1949), 1951, **12**(4):1–5.
———. Number of Feathers and Weights of Various Systems in a Bald Eagle. *Wilson Bull.* (1955), **67**:142.
———. How Many Species of Birds Have Existed? *Bull. Fla. State Mus.* (1960), **5**:41–53
Broley, C. L. Migration and Nesting of Florida Bald Eagles. *Wilson Bull.* (1947), **59**:3–20.
———. The Plight of the American Bald Eagle. *Aud. Mag.* (1958), **60**:162–163.
Broun, Maurice. *Hawks Aloft: The Story of Hawk Mountain.* New York: Dodd, 1949.
———, and Ben V. Goodwin. Flight-Speeds of Hawks and Crows. *Auk* (1943), **60**:487–492.
Brown, Jerram L. Method of Head Scratching in the Wrentit and Other Species. *Condor* (1959), **61**:53.
Buchheister, Carl W. What About Problem Birds? *Aud. Mag.* (1960), **62**:116–118.

Burton, John H., II. Some Population Mechanics of the American Coot. *Jour. Wildl. Mngt.* (1959), **23**:203–210.

Buss, Irven O., Conrad, Robert D., and James R. Reilly. Ulcerative Enteritis in the Pheasant, Blue Grouse and California Quail. *Jour. Wildl. Mngt.* (1958), **22**:446–449.

Cade, Tom J., and John L. Buckley. A Mass Emigration of Sharp-tailed Grouse from the Tanana Valley, Alaska, in 1934. *Condor* (1953), **55**:313.

Cahalane, Victor H. A Nutcracker's Search for Buried Food. *Auk* (1944), **61**:643.

———. Some Effects of Exotics on Nature. *Atlantic Nat.* (1955), **10**:176–185.

Cahn, Alvin R. The Migration of Animals. *Amer. Nat.* (1925), **59**:539–556.

Cardinell, H. A. Protecting Cherries from Birds. *Mich. State Coll. Agr. Exp. Sta. Circ. Bull.* (1937), **160**: 1–22.

———, and D. W. Hayne. Corn Injury by Red-Wings in Michigan. *Mich. State Coll. Agr. Exp. Sta. Tech. Bull.* (1945), **198**:1–59.

Carnie, S. Kent. Food Habits of Nesting Golden Eagles in the Coast Ranges of California. *Condor* (1954), **56**:3–12.

Chamberlain, B. R. Safety Factor in a Hanging Nest. *The Chat* (1954), **18**:48–50.

Chambers, W. Lee. Biographical Notes on Dawson's Birds of California. *Condor* (1939), **41**:231–243.

Chapin, James P., and Leonard W. Wing. The Wideawake Calendar, 1953 to 1958. *Auk* (1959), **76**:153–158.

Chettleburgh, M. R. Observations on the Collection and Burial of Acorns by Jays in Hainault Forest. *Brit. Birds* (1952), **45**(10):359–364.

Childs, Henry E., Jr., and Archie S. Mossman. Notes on the Sexual Behavior of Two Falcons. *Condor* (1952), **54**:207–208.

Clark, Gordon M., O'Meara, David, and James W. Van Weelden. An Epizootic Among Eider Ducks Involving an Acanthocephalid Worm. *Jour. Wildl. Mngt.* (1958), **22**:204–205.

Cobb, Stanley. On the Angle of the Cerebral Axis in the American Woodcock. *Auk* (1959), **76**:55–59.

Cole, Leon J., and William F. Kirkpatrick. Sex Ratios in Pigeons, Together with Observations on the Laying, Incubation, and Hatching of the Eggs. *Bull. 162, Agr. Exp. Sta.* (R. I. State College, 1915), 463–512.

Collias, Nicholas S., and Richard D. Taber. A Field Study of Some Grouping and Dominance Relations in Ring-necked Pheasants. *Condor* (1951), **53**:265–275.

Cooch, Graham. Observations on the Autumn Migration of Blue Geese. *Wilson Bull.* (1955), **67**:171–174.

Cook, David B., and E. W. Littlefield. Grosbeak Damage to Scotch Pine. *Jour. Forestry* (1945), **43**:269–272.

Cottrell, V. May. Strange Is the Kiwi. *Nat. Mag.* (1955), **48**:41–43, 52.

Cowan, Archibald B., and Tony J. Peterle. *Leucocytozoon bonasae* in Michigan Sharp-tailed Grouse. *Jour. Wildl. Mngt.* (1957), **21**:469–471.

Cowles, Raymond B., and William R. Dawson. A Cooling Mechanism of the Texas Nighthawk. *Condor* (1951), **53**:19–22.

Cox, George W. A Life History of the Mourning Warbler. *Wilson Bull.* (1960), **72**:5–28.

Crooks, Malcolm P., and George O. Hendrickson. Field Sparrow Life History in Central Iowa. *Iowa Bird Life* (1953), **23**:10–13.

Cruickshank, Allan D. Sixtieth Christmas Bird Count. *Aud. Field Notes* (1960), **14**:80–280.

Cuthbert, Nicholas L. A Nesting Study of the Black Tern in Michigan. *Auk* (1954), **71**:36–63.

Dambach, C. A., and D. L. Leedy. Ohio Studies with Repellent Materials with Notes on Damage to Corn by Pheasants and Other Wildlife. *Jour. Wildl. Mngt.* (1948), **12**:392–398.

Daniel, Joseph Carl, Jr. An Embryological Comparison of the Domestic Fowl and the Red-winged Blackbird. *Auk* (1957), **74**:340–358.

Davis, David E. Number of Eggs Laid by Herring Gulls. *Auk* (1942), **59**:549–554.

———. Determinate Laying in Barn Swallows and Black-billed Magpies. *Condor* (1955), **57**:81–87.

———. Observations on Territorial Behavior of Least Flycatchers. *Wilson Bull.* (1959), **71**:73–85.

Davis, John. Comparative Foraging Behavior of the Spotted and Brown Towhees. *Auk* (1957), **74**:129–166.

———. Singing Behavior and the Gonad Cycle of the Rufous-sided Towhee. *Condor* (1958), **60**:308–326.

———, and Laidlaw Williams. Irruptions of the Clark Nutcracker in California. *Condor* (1957), **59**:297–307.

Dawn, Walter. Cattle Egrets Provoke Cattle to Move and Pick Flies off Bulls. *Auk* (1959), **76**:97–98.

Dawson, William R., and Francis C. Evans. Relation of Growth and Development to Temperature Regulation in Nestling Vesper Sparrows. *Condor* (1960), **62**:329–340.

de Kiriline, Louise. The Voluble Singer of the Treetops. *Aud. Mag.* (1954), **56**:109–111.

Dennis, John V. A Balanced Diet for Birds. *Aud. Mag.* (1951–1952), **53**:398–403; **54**:52–57.

———. Food Distributors in Tree Trunk and Tree Top. *Aud. Mag.* (1957), **59**:36–41.

———. Some Aspects of the Breeding Ecology of the Yellow-breasted Chat (*Icteria virens*). *Bird-Banding* (1958a), **29**:169–183.

———. Death on the Highway. *Aud. Mag.* (1958b), **60**:159.

de Schauensee, Rodolphe M. Birds of Colombia. *Caldasia* (1948–1952), **5**:251–380; **5**:381–644; **5**:645–871; **5**:873–1112; **5**:1115–1214.

Dexter, Ralph W. Extra-parental Cooperation in the Nesting of Chimney Swifts. *Wilson Bull.* (1952), **64**:133–139.

Dexter, Ralph W. Two 13-year-old Age Records for the House Sparrow. *Bird-Banding* (1959), **30**:182.

———. Analysis of Chimney Swift Returns at Kent, Ohio, 1956–1959. *Bird-Banding* (1960), **31**:87–89.

Dice, L. R. Minimum Intensities of Illumination under which Owls can Find Dead Prey by Sight. *Amer. Nat.* (1945), **79**:385–416.

Dilger, William C. Electrocution of Parakeets at Agra, India. *Condor* (1954), **56**:102–103.

———. Hostile Behavior and Reproductive Isolating Mechanisms in the Avian Genera *Catharus* and *Hylocichla. Auk* (1956), **73**:313–353.

———. The Loss of Teeth in Birds. *Auk* (1957), **74**:103–104.

———. Agonistic and Social Behavior of Captive Redpolls. *Wilson Bull.* 1960), **72**:115–132.

Dixon, James B. The Golden Eagle in San Diego County, California. *Condor* (1937), **39**:49–56.

Dixon, Keith L. Ecological and Distributional Relations of Desert Scrub Birds of Western Texas. *Condor* (1959), **61**:397–409.

Douville, Clayton H., and Charles E. Friley, Jr. Records of Longevity in Canada Geese. *Auk* (1957), **74**:510.

Downs. Wilbur G. Little Egret Banded in Spain Taken in Trinidad. *Auk* (1959), **76**:241–242.

Dreis, Robert E., and George O. Hendrickson. Wood Duck Production from Nest-Boxes and Natural Cavities in the Lake Odessa Area, Iowa, in 1951. *Iowa Bird Life* (1952), **22**:19–22.

Dykstra, Walter W. Nuisance Bird Control. *Aud. Mag.* (1960), **62**:118–119.

Eaton, Stephen W. A Life History Study of the Louisiana Waterthrush. *Wilson Bull.* (1958), **70**:211–236.

Edwards, Ernest P. Hearing Ranges of Four Species of Birds. *Auk* (1943), **60**:239–241.

Edwards, J. Gordon. What Should We Mean by "Subspecies"? *Turtox News* (1956), **34**:200–202.

Eisenmann, Eugene. Northern Birds Summering in Panama. *Wilson Bull.* (1951), **63**:181–185.

Eklund, Carl R. Antarctic Ornithological Studies During the IGY. *Bird-Banding* (1959), **30**:114–118.

Elder, William H., and Charles M. Kirkpatrick. Predator Control in the Light of Recent Wildlife Management Concepts. *Wilson Bull.* (1952), **64**:126–128.

Elder, William H., and Milton W. Weller. Duration of Fertility in the Domestic Mallard Hen after Isolation from the Drake. *Jour. Wildl. Mngt.* (1954), **18**:495–502.

Emanuel, Victor L. Another Probable Record of an Eskimo Curlew on Galveston Island, Texas. *Auk* (1961), **78**:259–260.

Emerson, Guy. The Lure of the List. *Bird-Lore* (1940), **42**:37–39.

Emlen, John T., Jr. Bird Damage to Almonds in California. *Condor* (1937), **39**:192–197.

———. An Experimental Analysis of the Breeding Cycle of the Tri-colored Red-wing. *Condor* (1941), **43**:209–219.

———. Social Behavior in Nesting Cliff Swallows. *Condor* (1952a), **54**:177–199.

———. Flocking Behavior in Birds. *Auk* (1952b), **69**:160–170.

———. Territory, Nest Building, and Pair Formation in the Cliff Swallow. *Auk* (1954), **71**:16–35.

———. Display and Mate Selection in the Whydahs and Bishop Birds. *The Ostrich* (1957), 202–213.

Erickson, Arnold B. *Leucocytozoon bonasae* in Ruffed Grouse; Its Possible Relationship to Fluctuations in Numbers of Grouse. *Jour. Wildl. Mngt.* (1953), **17**:536–538.

Evenden, Fred G. Observations on Nesting Behavior of the House Finch. *Condor* (1957), **59**:112–117.

Eyer, Lester E. A Study of a Nest of a Ruby-throated Hummingbird. *Jack-Pine Warbler* (1949), **27**:148–158.

Farner, Donald S. Age Groups and Longevity in the American Robin: Comments, Further Discussion, and Certain Revisions. *Wilson Bull.* (1949), **61**:68–81.

———, and D. L. Serventy. Body Temperature and the Ontogeny of Thermoregulation in the Slender-billed Shearwater. *Condor* (1959), **61**:426–433.

Ferry, Philip. The Battle of the Eggs. *Nat. Hist.* (1952), **61**:176–181.

Fichter, Edson. Mourning Dove Production in Four Idaho Orchards and Some Possible Implications. *Jour. Wildl. Mngt.* (1959), **23**:438–447.

Fisher, A. K. Economic Value of Predaceous Birds and Mammals. Yearbook, U. S. Dep't. Agr. (1908).

Fisher, Harvey I. The Function of M. Depressor Caudae and M. Caudofemoralis in Pigeons. *Auk* (1957), **74**:479–486.

———. The "Hatching Muscle" in the Chick. *Auk* (1958), **75**:391–399.

Fisher, James. *The Birds of Britain*. London: Collins, 1942.

———. A History of Birds. Boston: Houghton, 1954.

French, Norman R. Notes on Breeding Activities and on Gular Sacs in the Pine Grosbeak. *Condor* (1954), **56**:83–85.

Friedmann, Herbert. Notes on Differential Threshold of Reaction to Vitamin D Deficiency in the House Sparrow and the Chick. *Biol. Bull.* 69 (1925), **1**:71–74.

———. The Instinctive Emotional Life of Birds. *Psychoanal. Rev.* 21 (1934), **384**:1–57.

———. The Honey-Guides. *Bull. 208 U. S. Nat. Mus.* (Washington, D.C.), 1955.

Frings, Hubert, and William A. Boyd. Evidence for Olfactory Discrimination by the Bobwhite Quail. *Amer. Midl. Nat.* (1952), **48**:181–184.

Frings, Hubert, and Mable Frings. Observations on Salt Balance and Behavior of Laysan and Black-footed Albatrosses in Captivity. *Condor* (1959), **61**: 305–314.

Frings, Hubert, and Joseph Jumber. Preliminary Studies on the Use of a

Specific Sound to Repel Starlings (*Sturnus vulgaris*) from Objectional Roosts. *Science* (1954), **119**:318–319.

Frings, Hubert, and Betty Slocum. Hearing Ranges for Several Species of Birds. *Auk* (1958), **75**:99–100.

Frith, H. J. Breeding Habits in the Family Megapodiidae. *Ibis* (1956), **98**: 620–640. See *C.S.I.R.O. Wildlife Research* (1956–1957), **1**:79–95; **2**:101–110, for other papers.

Fritsch, Lee E., and Irven O. Buss. Food of the American Merganser in Unakwik Inlet, Alaska. *Condor* (1958), **60**:410–411.

Geis, Aelred D. Annual and Shooting Mortality Estimates for the Canvasback. *Jour. Wildl. Mngt.* (1959), **23**:253–261.

Geis, Mary Barraclough. Productivity of Canada Geese in the Flathead Valley, Montana. *Jour. Wildl. Mngt.* (1956), **20**:409–419.

George, J. C., and R. M. Naik. Intramuscular Fat Store in the Pectoralis of Birds. *Auk* (1960a), **77**:216–217.

———. Some Observations on the Distribution of the Blood Capillaries in the Pigeon Breast Muscle. *Auk* (1960b), **77**:224–226.

Gier, H. T. The Air Sacs of the Loon. *Auk* (1952), **69**:40–49.

Glenny, Fred H. Antarctica as a Center of Origin of Birds. *Ohio Jour. Sci.* (1954), **54**:307–314.

———. Modifications of Pattern in the Aortic Arch System of Birds and Their Phylogenetic Significance. *Proc. U. S. Nat. Mus.* (1955), **104**:525–621.

Goodge, William R. Locomotion and Other Behavior of the Dipper. *Condor* (1959), **61**:4–17.

Goodman, Jeanne Moore. *Aves Incendiaria. Wilson Bull.* (1960), **72**:400–401.

Gower, Carl. The Cause of Blue Color as Found in the Bluebird (*Sialia sialis*) and the Blue Jay (*Cyanocitta cristata*). *Auk* (1936), **53**:178–185.

———. The Use of the Bursa of Fabricius as an Indication of Age in Game Birds. *N. A. Wildl. Conf. Trans.* (1939), **4**:426–430.

Graber, Richard R. Artificial Incubation of Some Non-galliform Eggs. *Wilson Bull.* (1955), **67**:100–109.

Graber, Richard R., and William W. Cochran. An Audio Technique for the Study of Nocturnal Migration of Birds. *Wilson Bull.* (1959), **71**:220–236.

———. Evaluation of an Aural Record of Nocturnal Migration. *Wilson Bull.* (1960), **72**:253–273.

Greenhalgh, Clifton M. Food Habits of the California Gull in Utah. *Condor* (1952), **54**:302–308.

Gregory, Joseph T. The Jaws of the Cretaceous Toothed Birds, *Ichthyornis* and *Hesperornis*. *Condor* (1952), **54**:73–88.

Griffin, Donald R. Homing Experiments with Leach's Petrels. *Auk* (1940), **57**:61–73.

———. Acoustic Orientation in the Oil Bird, *Steatornis*. *Proc. Nat. Acad. Sci.* (1953), **39**:884–893.

Griscom, Ludlow. *Modern Bird Study*. Cambridge, Mass.: Harvard U. P., 1945.

Gross, A. O. Nesting of Hicks' Seedeater at Barro Colorado Island, Canal Zone. *Auk* (1952), **69**:433–446.

———. Life History of the Bananaquit of Tobago Island. *Wilson Bull.* (1958), **70**:257–279.

Grzimek, Bernhard. The Last Great Herds of Africa. *Nat. Hist.* (1961), **70**: 8–21.

Grzimek, Michael, and Bernhard Grzimek. Census of Plains Animals in the Serengeti National Park, Tanganyika. *Jour. Wildl. Mngt.* (1960), **24**:27–37.

Gullion, Gordon W. The Frontal Shield of the American Coot. *Wilson Bull.* (1951), **63**:157–166.

———. The Displays and Calls of the American Coot. *Wilson Bull.* (1952), **64**:83–97.

———. Observations on Molting of the American Coot. *Condor* (1953a), **55**: 102–103.

———. Territorial Behavior in the American Coot. *Condor* (1953b), **55**:169–186.

Hailman, Jack P. Convergence in Passerine Alarm Calls. *Bird-Banding* (1959), **30**:232.

———. A Field Study of the Mockingbird's Wing-Flashing Behavior and Its Association with Foraging. *Wilson Bull.* (1960), **72**:346–357.

Hamerstrom, Frances. Dominance in Winter Flocks of Chickadees. *Wilson Bull.* (1942), **54**:32–42.

Hamilton, William J., III, and Merrill C. Hammond. Oriented Overland Spring Migration of Pinioned Canada Geese. *Wilson Bull.* (1960), **72**: 385–391.

Hamrum, Charles L. Experiments on the Senses of Taste and Smell in the Bob-white Quail (*Colinus virginianus virginianus*). *Amer. Midl. Nat.* (1953), **49**:872–877.

Hann, Harry W. Polyandry in the Oven-bird. *Wilson Bull.* (1940), **52**:69–72.

———. *An Introduction to Ornithology.* Ann Arbor, Mich.: Edwards Brothers, 1945.

———. *The Biology of Birds.* Ann Arbor, Mich.: Edwards Brothers, 1953.

Hanson, Harold C. Aids for Exploration of the Avian Cloaca for Characters of Sex and Age. *Jour. Wildl. Mngt.* (1953a), **17**:89–90.

———. Inter-family Dominance in Canada Geese. *Auk* (1953b), **70**:11–16.

———, and Charles W. Kossack. Weight and Body-Fat Relationships of Mourning Doves in Illinois. *Jour. Wildl. Mngt.* (1957), **21**:169–181.

Hartman, Frank A. Heart Weight in Birds. *Condor* (1955), **57**:221–238.

———. Sparrow Hawks Attempting to Breed in the Laboratory. *Wilson Bull.* (1959), **71**:384–385.

Haugen, A. O. Trichomoniasis in Alabama Mourning Doves. *Jour. Wildl. Mngt.* (1952), **16**:164–169.

Hauser, Doris C. Some Observations on Sun-bathing in Birds. *Wilson Bull.* (1957), **69**:78–90.

Haverschmidt, F. Observations on the Breeding Habits of the Little Owl. *Ardea* (1946), **34**:214–246.

Haverschmidt, F. Notes on the Breeding Habits of *Panyptila cayennensis*. *Auk* (1958), **75**:121–130.

Hayne, D. W., and H. A. Cardinell. Damage to Blueberries by Birds. *Mich. State Coll. Agr. Exp. Sta. Quart. Bull.* (1949), **32**:213–219.

Hazelhoff, E. H. Structure and Function of the Lung of Birds. *Poultry Science* (1951), **30**:3–10.

Hecht, William Robert. Nesting of the Marsh Hawk at Delta, Manitoba. *Wilson Bull.* (1951), **63**:167–176.

Helms, Carl W., and William H. Drury, Jr. Winter and Migratory Weight and Fat Field Studies on Some North American Buntings. *Bird-Banding* (1960), **31**:1–40.

Hensley, M. Max, and James B. Cope. Further Data on the Removal and Repopulation of the Breeding Birds in a Spruce-Fir Forest Community. *Auk* (1951), **68**:483–493.

Herman, Carlton M., and Everett E. Wehr. The Occurrence of Gizzard Worms in Canada Geese. *Jour. Wildl. Mngt.* (1954), **18**:509–513.

Hess, Eckhard H. Imprinting. *Science* (1959), **130**:133–141.

Heydweiller, A. Marguerite. A Comparison of Winter and Summer Territories and Seasonal Variations of the Tree Sparrow. *Bird-Banding* (1935), **6**:1–11.

Hickey, Joseph J., and L. Barrie Hunt. Initial Songbird Mortality Following a Dutch Elm Disease Control Program. *Jour. Wildl. Mngt.* (1960), **24**:259–265.

Hindwood, K. A. The Nesting of Birds in the Nests of Social Insects. *The Emu* (1959), **59**:1–36.

Hobson, Mrs. Randolph L. Wrens and Skulls. *Kent. Warb.* (1952), **28**:36.

Hochbaum, H. Albert. Sex and Age Determination of Waterfowl by Cloacal Examination. *N. A. Wildl. Conf. Trans.* (1942), **7**:299–307.

———. The Canvasback on a Prairie Marsh. *Amer. Wildl. Inst.* (Washington, D. C.), 1944.

Hoffmeister, Donald F., and Henry W. Setzer. The Postnatal Development of Two Broods of Great Horned Owls. *Univ. Kans. Publ.* (1947), **1**:157–173.

Hofslund, Pershing B. The Hawk Pass at Duluth. *Flicker* (1954), **26**:96–99.

———. Fall Migration of Herring Gulls from Knife Island, Minnesota. *Bird-Banding* (1959), **30**:104–114.

Höglund, Nels. Capercaillie Reproduction and Climate. *Papers on Game Research* (Helsinki, 1952), **8**:78–81.

Holstein, Vagn. Duehøgen *Astur gentilis dubious* (Sparrman) *Biologiske Studier over Danske Rovfugle* (1942), **I**:1–55. English summary.

Homberg, Lars. Fishing Crows. *Fauna och Flora* (1957), **5**:182–185.

Hopkins, Milton, Jr. The Black Vulture as a Predator in Southern Georgia. *Oriole* (1953), **18**:15–17.

Hou, H. C. Relation of the Preen Gland (Glandula uropygialis) of Birds to Rickets. *Chinese Jour. Physiol.* (1929–1931), **3**:171–182; **4**:79–92; **5**:11–18.

Howard, Hildegarde. The Prehistoric Avifauna of Smith Creek Cave, Nevada, with a Description of a New Gigantic Raptor. *Bull. So. Calif. Acad. Sci.* (1952), **51**:50–54.

———. A Gigantic "Toothed" Marine Bird from the Miocene of California. *Bull. 1, Santa Barbara Mus. Nat. Hist.* (1957).

Howell, Joseph C., and James T. Tanner. An Accident to Migrating Birds at the Knoxville Airport. *Migrant* (1951), **22**:61–62.

Howell, Thomas R. A Southern Hemisphere Migrant in Nicaragua. *Condor* (1955), **57**:188–189.

———, and Tom J. Cade. The Birds of Guadalupe Island in 1953. *Condor* (1954), **56**:283–294.

———, and William R. Dawson. Nest Temperatures and Attentiveness in the Anna Hummingbird. *Condor* (1954), **56**:93–97.

Hrubant, H. Everett. An Analysis of the Color Phases of the Eastern Screech Owl, *Otus asio*, by the Gene Frequency Method. *Amer. Nat.* (1955), **89**: 223–230.

Huggins, Russel A. Egg Temperatures of Wild Birds under Natural Conditions. *Ecology* (1941), **22**:148–157.

Humphrey, Philip S. Diving of a Captive Common Eider. *Condor* (1958), **60**:408–410.

Hunt, L. Barrie. Songbird Breeding Populations in DDT-Sprayed Dutch Elm Disease Communities. *Jour. Wildl. Mngt.* (1960), **24**:139–146.

Hutchinson, G. Evelyn. Survey of Contemporary Knowledge of Biogeochemistry: The Biogeochemistry of Vertebrate Excretion. *Bull. Amer. Mus. Nat. Hist.* (1950) XVIII plus 554 pp.

Hutt, F. B., and Lelah Ball. Number of Feathers and Body Size in Passerine Birds. *Auk* (1938), **55**:651–657.

Ingram, Collingwood. The Importance of Juvenile Cannibalism in the Breeding Biology of Certain Birds of Prey. *Auk* (1959), **76**:218–226.

Inoue, Yosoichi. The Swallows Are Remembered. *Bull. Mass. Aud. Soc.* (1954), **38**:57–58.

Irving, Laurence. Nutritional Condition of Water Pipits on Arctic Nesting Grounds. *Condor* (1960), **62**:469–472.

Jaeger, Edmund C. Further Observations on the Hibernation of the Poor-will. *Condor* (1949), **51**:105–109.

Jickling, Lee. Mr. Bob-white Sticks It Out. *Jack-Pine Warbler* (1940), **18**: 114–115.

Johnsgard, Paul A. Courtship Activities of the Anatidae in Eastern Washington. *Condor* (1955), **57**:19–27.

———. A Quantitative Study of Sexual Behavior of Mallards and Black Ducks. *Wilson Bull.* (1960), **72**:133–155.

Johnson, R. A. Nesting Behavior of the Atlantic Murre. *Auk* (1941), **58**:153–163.

Johnston, David W. Sex and Age Characters and Salivary Glands of the Chimney Swift. *Condor* (1958), **60**:73–84.

———, and T. P. Haines. Analysis of Mass Bird Mortality in October, 1954. *Auk* (1957), **74**:447–458.

Kalmbach, E. R., and M. G. Gunderson. Western Duck Sickness: A Form of Botulism. *Tech. Bull.* 411, U.S.D.A. (Washington, D. C.), 1934.

Kalmbach, E. R., and J. F. Welch. Colored Rodent Baits and Their Value in Safeguarding Birds. *Jour. Wildl. Mngt.* (1946), **10**:353–360.

Keith, Stuart. A New North American Bird Record. *Aud. Mag.* (1961), **63**: 264–265, 296.

Kemper, Charles A. Bird Destruction at a TV Tower. *Aud. Mag.* (1958), **60**:270–271, 290–293.

Kendeigh, S. Charles. A Study of Merriam's Temperature Laws. *Wilson Bull.* (1932), **44**:129–143.

———. Factors Affecting Length of Incubation. *Auk* (1940), **57**:499–513.

———. Bird Population Studies in the Coniferous Forest Biome during a Spruce Budworm Outbreak. *Biol. Bull.*, Dept. Lands and Forests (Ontario, Can., 1947), **1**:1–100.

———, and S. P. Baldwin. Development of Temperature Control in Nestling House Wrens. *Amer. Nat.* (1928), **62**:249–278.

Kenyon, Karl W., and James W. Brooks. Birds of Little Diomede Island, Alaska. *Condor* (1960), **62**:457–463.

Kenyon, Karl W., and Dale W. Rice. Homing of Laysan Albatrosses. *Condor* (1958), **60**:3–6.

Kessel, Brina. Distribution and Migration of the European Starling in North America. *Condor* (1953), **55**:49–67.

Kessler, Francis W. Egg Temperatures of the Ring-necked Pheasant Obtained with a Self-recording Potentiometer. *Auk* (1960), **77**:330–336.

Kiel, William H., Jr. (compiler). *Mourning Dove Newsletter—1960,* U. S. Dept. Int., Fish and Wildl. Serv. (1960).

Kilham, Lawrence. Sealed-in Winter Stores of Red-headed Woodpeckers. *Wilson Bull.* (1958a), **70**:107–113.

———. Territorial Behavior of Wintering Red-headed Woodpeckers. *Wilson Bull.* (1958b), **70**:347–358.

———. Eating of Sand by Blue Jays. *Condor* (1960), **62**:295–296.

Kirkpatrick, C. M., and Harold E. Moses. The Effects of Streptomycin Against Spontaneous Quail Disease in Bobwhites. *Jour. Wildl. Mngt.* (1953), **17**: 24–28.

Kluijver, H. N., Ligtovoet J., Van den Ouwelant, C., and F. Zegwaard. De Levenwijze van den Winterkoning, *Troglodytes t. troglodytes* (L.). *Limosa* (1940), **13**:1–51.

Knappen, Phoebe. Number of Feathers on a Duck. *Auk* (1932), **49**:461.

Knorr, Owen A. Communal Roosting of the Pygmy Nuthatch. *Condor* (1957), **59**:398.

Kramer, G. Experiments in Bird Orientation. *Ibis* (1952), **94**:265–285.

Lack, David. The Significance of Clutch-Size. *Ibis* (1947–1948), **89**:302–352; **90**:25–45.

———. The Influence of Weather on Passerine Migration. A Review. *Auk* (1960), **77**:171–209.

———, and Lambert Lack. Territory Reviewed. *Brit. Birds* (1933), **27**:179–199.

Lanyon, Wesley E. The Motivation of Sun-bathing in Birds. *Wilson Bull.* (1958), **70**:280.

Laskey, Amelia R. A Study of Nesting Eastern Bluebirds. *Bird-Banding* (1939), **10**:23–32.

Law, J. Eugene. The Function of the Oil Gland. *Condor* (1929), **31**:148–156.

Lawrence, Louise de Kiriline. Jays of a Northern Forest. *Aud. Mag.* (1960), **62**:266–267, 286–287.

Lay, Dan. Aftermath of Waste. *Texas Game and Fish* (1959), 4 pp.

Leopold, A. Starker. Intestinal Morphology of Gallinaceous Birds in Relation to Food Habits. *Jour. Wildl. Mngt.* (1953), **17**:197–203.

Lewis, Brother Hubert, F.S.C. Thistle-nesting Goldfinches. *Flicker* (1952), **24**:105–109.

Lewis, John B. Sight and Scent in the Turkey Vulture. *Auk* (1928), **45**:467–470.

Lincoln, Frederick C. *The Migration of American Birds.* Garden City: Doubleday, 1939.

———. Migration of Birds. *Circ. 16:1–102, U. S. Fish and Wildl. Serv.* (Washington, D. C.), 1950.

Lindsdale, Jean M. Further Facts Concerning Losses to Wild Animal Life Through Pest Control in California. *Condor* (1932), **34**:121–135. See also *Condor* (1931), **33**:92–106.

Lovell, Harvey B. Black Vulture Depredations at Kentucky Woodlands. *Wilson Bull.* (1952), **64**:48–49.

———. Baiting of Fish by a Green Heron. *Wilson Bull.* (1958), **70**:280–281.

Low, Jessop B., Kay, Lee, and D. I. Rasmussen. Recent Observations on the White Pelican on Gunnison Island, Great Salt Lake, Utah. *Auk* (1950), **67**:345–356.

Lowe, Percy R. On the Primitive Characters of the Penguins, and Their Bearing on the Phylogeny of Birds. *Proc. Zool. Soc.* (London, 1933), Pt. **2**:483–538.

———. On the Relationship of the Struthiones to the Dinosaurs and to the Rest of the Avian Class, with Special Reference to the Position of *Archaeopteryx. Ibis* (1935), **5**(13th ser.):398–432.

Lowery, George H., Jr. Trans-Gulf Spring Migration of Birds and the Coastal Hiatus. *Wilson Bull.* (1945), **57**:92–121.

———. Evidence of Trans-Gulf Migration. *Auk* (1946), **63**:175–211.

Ludwig, C. C. Banding Returns of Michigan Mourning Doves. *Jack-Pine Warbler* (1960), **38**:29–33.

MacMullan, R. A., and L. L. Eberhardt. Tolerance of Incubating Pheasant Eggs to Exposure. *Jour. Wildl. Mngt.* (1953), **17**:322–330.

Madura, Marilu. Feathered Observations. *Pass. Pigeon* (1952), **14**:65–68.

Makkink, G. T. Contribution to the Knowledge of the Behavior of the Oystercatcher (*Haematopus ostralegus* L.). *Ardea* (1942), **31**:23–74.

Malcomson, Richard O. Mallophaga from Birds of North America. *Wilson Bull.* (1960), **72**:182–197.

Marler, Peter, and Donald Isaac. Physical Analysis of a Simple Bird Song as Exemplified by the Chipping Sparrow. *Condor* (1960), **62**:124–135.

Marshall, Hubert. Longevity of the American Herring Gull. *Auk* (1947), **64**: 188–198.

Mayer, Winnifred. The Matin Song of the Eastern Kingbird. *Pass. Pigeon* (1952), **14**:91–94.

Mayfield, Harold. A Census of the Kirtland's Warbler. *Auk* (1953), **70**:17–20.

Mayhew, Wilbur W. Spring Rainfall in Relation to Mallard Production in the Sacramento Valley, California. *Jour. Wildl. Mngt.* (1955), **19**:36–47.

Mayr, Ernst. Birds of Paradise. *Sci. Guide* 127, Am. Mus. Nat. Hist. (New York), 1945.

———. The Number of Species of Birds. *Auk* (1946a), **63**:64–69.

Mazzeo, Rosario. Homing of the Manx Shearwater. *Auk* (1953), **70**:200–201.

McAllister, Nancy M. Courtship, Hostile Behavior, Nest-Establishment, and Egg Laying in the Eared Grebe (*Podiceps caspicus*). *Auk* (1958), **75**:290–311.

McAtee, W. L. The Local Suppression of Agricultural Pests by Birds. *Ann. Report Smithsonian Inst.* (1920), 411–438.

———. The Relation of Birds to Woodlots in New York State. *Roosevelt Wild Life Bull.* (1926), **4**:7–152.

———. Comparative Abundance of Birds in the District of Columbia Region 1861–1942. *Atlantic Nat.* (1951), **7**:66–82.

McCabe, Robert A. The Song and Song-Flight of the Alder Flycatcher. *Wilson Bull.* (1951), **63**:89–98.

———. The Selection of Colored Nest Boxes by House Wrens. *Condor* (1961), **63**:322–329.

———, and Harold F. Deutsch. The Relationship of Certain Birds as Indicated by their Egg White Proteins. *Auk* (1952), **69**:1–18.

McCabe, T. T. Types of Shorebird Flight. *Auk* (1942), **59**:110–111.

McClure, H. Elliott. Protecting Grain Fields in Japan from Pilferage by Birds. *Jour. Wildl. Mngt.* (1956), **20**:462–464.

McDowell, Sam. The Bony Palate of Birds. Part I: The Palaeognathae. *Auk* (1948), **65**:520–549.

McIlhenny, E. A. Life History of the Boat-tailed Grackle in Louisiana. *Auk* (1937), **54**:274–295.

———. Feeding Habits of Black Vulture. *Auk* (1939), **56**:472–474.

McKinley, Daniel. The Carolina Parakeet in Pioneer Missouri. *Wilson Bull.* (1960), **72**:274–287.

McLaughlin, Charles L., and David Grice. The Effectiveness of Large-scale Erection of Wood Duck Boxes as a Management Procedure. *N. A. Wildl. Conf. Trans.* (1952), **17**:242–259.

Meanley, Brooke. Notes on the Ecology of the Short-billed Marsh Wren in the Lower Arkansas Rice Fields. *Wilson Bull.* (1952), **64**:22–25.

———. A Nesting Study of the Little Blue Heron in Eastern Arkansas. *Wilson Bull.* (1955), **67**:84–99.

———, and Johnson A. Neff. Food Habits of the Bobolink in Arkansas Rice Fields. *Auk* (1953), **70**:211–212.

Mehner, John F., and George J. Wallace. Robin Populations and Insecticides. *Atlantic Nat.* (1959), **14**:4–9.

Mengel, Robert M. Certain Molts and Plumages of Acadian and Yellow-bellied Flycatchers. *Auk* (1952), **69**:273–283.

Mewaldt, L. Richard. The Incubation Patch of the Clark Nutcracker. *Condor* (1952), **54**:361.

———. Pterylography and Natural and Experimentally Induced Molt in Clark's Nutcracker. *Condor* (1958), **60**:165–187.

Meyerriecks, Andrew J. Foot Stirring Feeding Behavior in Herons. *Wilson Bull.* (1959a), **71**:153–158.

———. "Foot-Paddling" Feeding Behavior in a Semipalmated Sandpiper. *Wilson Bull.* (1959b), **71**:277.

Michener, Josephine R. Territorial Behavior and Age Composition in a Population of Mockingbirds at a Feeding Station. *Condor* (1951), **53**:276–283.

Middleton, Raymond J. Banding Robins at Norristown. *Bird-Banding* (1960), **31**:136–139.

Miller, Alden H. Response to Experimental Light Increments by Andean Sparrows from an Equatorial Area. *Condor* (1959), **61**:344–347.

Miller, W. T. A Bird that Walks on Water. *Nat. Mag.* (1952), **45**:69–71.

Milne, Lorus J., and Margery J. The Eyes of Birds. *Nat. Mag.* (1950), **43**: 121–123.

Miskimen, Mildred. Sound Production in Passerine Birds. *Auk* (1951), **68**: 493–504.

———. Absence of Syrinx in the Turkey Vulture (*Cathartes aura*). *Auk* (1957), **74**:104–105.

Moreau, R. E. Clutch-size: A Comparative Study with Special Reference to African Birds. *Ibis* (1944), **86**:286–347.

Morgan, Allen H. Your Executive Vice-President Reports. *Mass. Aud.* (1960), **44**:141–144.

Morrison, Alva. The Greater Snow Goose—A Story of Survival. *Mass. Aud.* (1960), **45**:57–63.

Mountfort, Guy. Nest-Hole Excavation by the Bee-Eater. *Brit. Birds* (1957), **50**:263–267.

Mueller, Helmut C., and Daniel D. Berger. Some Long-Distance Barn Owl Recoveries. *Bird-Banding* (1959), **30**:182.

Munro, J. A. Observations of the Loon in the Cariboo Parklands, British Columbia. *Auk* (1945), **62**:38–49.

Murphy, Dean A., and Thomas S. Baskett. Bobwhite Mobility in Central Missouri. *Jour. Wildl. Mngt.* (1952), **16**:498–510.

Murphy, Robert Cushman. *Oceanic Birds of South America.* New York: Macmillan, 1936.

———, and Louis S. Mowbray. New Light on the Cahow, *Pterodroma cahow.* *Auk* (1951), **68**:266–280.

Mussehl, Thomas W. Blue Grouse Production, Movements, and Populations in the Bridger Mountains, Montana. *Jour. Wildl. Mngt.* (1960), **24**:60–68.

Musselman, T. E. Three Years of Eastern Bluebird Banding and Study. *Bird-Banding* (1935), **6**:117–125.

Nair, K. K. A Comparison of the Muscles in the Forearm of a Flapping and a Soaring Bird. *Jour. Animal Morph. Physiol.* (1954), **1**:26–34.

Nelson, Arnold L., and Alexander C. Martin. Gamebird Weights. *Jour. Wildl. Mngt.* (1953), **17**:36–42.

Nero, Robert W. A Behavior Study of the Red-winged Blackbird. *Wilson Bull.* (1956), **65**:5–37, 129–150.

———, and John T. Emlen, Jr. An Experimental Study of Territorial Behavior in Breeding Red-winged Blackbirds. *Condor* (1951), **53**:105–116.

Nice, L. B., Nice, M. M., and R. M. Kraft. Erythrocytes and Hemoglobin in the Blood of Some American Birds. *Wilson Bull.* (1935), **47**:120–124.

Nice, Margaret M. The Question of Ten-day Incubation Periods. *Wilson Bull.* (1953), **65**:81–93.

———. Problems of Incubation Periods in North American Birds. *Condor* (1954), **56**:173–197.

———. Nesting Success in Altricial Birds. *Auk* (1957), **74**:305–321.

———, and W. E. Schantz. Head-scratching Movements in Birds. *Auk* (1959), **76**:339–342.

Nickell, Walter P. Studies of Habitats, Territory, and Nests of the Eastern Goldfinch. *Auk* (1951), **68**:447–470.

———. Variations in Engineering Features of the Nests of Several Species of Birds in Relation to Nest Sites and Nesting Materials. *Butler Univ. Bot. Studies* (1958), **13**:121–140.

Noble, G. K. Courtship and Sexual Selection of the Flicker (*Colaptes auratus luteus*). *Auk* (1936), **53**:269–282.

Norris, Robert A. Density, Racial Composition, Sociability, and Selective Predation in Nonbreeding Populations of Savannah Sparrows. *Bird-Banding* (1960), **31**:173–216.

Norris, Robert A., and Gordon L. Hight, Jr. Subspecific Variation in Winter Populations of Savannah Sparrows: A Study in Field Taxonomy. *Condor* (1957), **59**:40–52.

Norris, Robert A., and Francis S. L. Williamson. Variation in Relative Heart Size of Certain Passerines with Increase in Altitude. *Wilson Bull.* (1955), **67**:78–83.

Norris-Elye, L. T. S. Heat Insulation in the Tarsi and Toes of Birds. *Auk* (1945), **62**:455.

Odum, Eugene P. Circulatory Congestion as a Possible Factor in Regulating Incubation Behavior. *Wilson Bull.* (1944), **56**:48–49.

Odum, Howard T. The Bird Navigation Controversy. *Auk* (1948), **65**:584–597.

Olson, Harold. Beetle Rout in the Rockies. *Aud. Mag.* (1953), **55**:30–32.

O'Roke, E. C. A Malaria-like Disease of Ducks Caused by *Leucocytozoon anatis* Wickware. *Bull. 4, Univ. Mich. School for Forest. and Conserv.* (Ann Arbor, Mich.), 1934.

Owen, D. F. Mortality of the Great Blue Heron as Shown by Banding Recoveries. *Auk* (1959), **76**:464–470.

Parkes, Kenneth C. The Incubation Patch in Males of the Suborder Tyranni. *Condor* (1953), **55**:218–219.

Parmalee, Paul W. The Vultures: Their Movements, Economic Status, and Control in Texas. *Auk* (1954), **71**:443–453.

Parmelee, David F. The Breeding Behavior of the Painted Bunting in Southern Oklahoma. *Bird-Banding* (1959), **30**:1–18.

Payne, Roger S., and William H. Drury, Jr. Marksman of the Darkness. *Nat. Hist.* (1958), **67**:316–323.

Pearson, Anita K., and Oliver P. Pearson. Natural History and Breeding Behavior of the Tinamou, *Nothoprocta ornata. Auk* (1955), **72**:113–127.

Pearson, Oliver P. The Metabolism of Hummingbirds. *Scient. Amer.* (Jan. 1953), Vol. 188, **1**:69–72.

Peterle, Tony J. An Extended Incubation Period of the Ruffed Grouse. *Wilson Bull.* (1953), **65**:119.

Peterson, Roger T. Bird's-eye View—Japan's Glamour Birds. *Aud. Mag.* (1960a), **62**:204–205; 217.

———. Bird's-eye View: Rediscovery on Kauai. *Aud. Mag.* (1960b), **62**:258–261.

Petrides, George A. Notes on Determination of Sex and Age in the Woodcock and Mourning Dove. *Auk* (1950), **67**:357–360.

———. Competition for Food Between Five Species of East African Vultures. *Auk* (1959), **76**:104–106.

———, and Charles R. Bryant. An Analysis of the 1944–1950 Fowl Cholera Epizootic in Texas Panhandle Waterfowl. *N. A. Wildl. Conf. Trans.* (1951), **16**:193–216.

Pettingill, Olin S., Jr. The Birds of a Bull's Horn Acacia. *Wilson Bull.* (1942), **54**:89–96.

Phillips, Allan R. Complexities of Migration: A Review with Original Data from Arizona. *Wilson Bull.* (1951), **63**:129–136.

———. The Molts of the Rufous-winged Sparrow. *Wilson Bull.* (1951), **63**:323–326.

Phillips, Richard E., and Hugh C. Black. A Winter Population Study of the Western Winter Wren. *Auk* (1956), **73**:401–410.

Pimentel, Richard A. Mendelian Infraspecific Divergence Levels and Their Analysis. *Syst. Zool.* (1959), **8**:139–159.

Pitelka, Frank A. Territoriality and Related Problems in North American Hummingbirds. *Condor* (1942), **44**:189–204.

———. Numbers, Breeding Schedule, and Territoriality in Pectoral Sandpipers of Northern Alaska. *Condor* (1959), **61**:233–264.

Pittman, James A. Direct Observation of the Flight Speed of the Common Loon. *Wilson Bull.* (1953), **65**:213.

Poole, Earl L. Weights and Wing Areas in North American Birds. *Auk* (1938), **55**:511–517.

Ramsay, A. Ogden. Seasonal Patterns in the Epigamic Displays of Some Surface-feeding Ducks. *Wilson Bull.* (1956), **68**:275–281.

Rand, A. L. Factors Affecting Feeding Rates of Anis. *Auk* (1953a), **70**:26–30.

———. Use of Snake Skins in Bird's Nests. *Chicago Acad. Sci. Nat. Hist. Misc.* (1953b), **125**:1–5.

———. On the Spurs on Birds' Wings. *Wilson Bull.* (1954), **66**:127–134.

———, and R. M. Rand. Breeding Notes on the Phainopepla. *Auk* (1943), **60**:333–341.

Reeder, William G. Stomach Analysis of a Group of Shorebirds. *Condor* (1951), **53**:43–45.

Rice, Dale W. Birds and Aircraft on Midway Islands. *Spec. Scient. Report: Wildlife No. 44* (Washington, D. C.), 1959.

Richdale, L. E. Supplementary Notes on the Royal Albatross. *Emu* (1942), **41**:169–184; 253–264.

———. *Notornis* Is Found. *Nat. Mag.* (1951a), **44**:127–129.

———. *Sexual Behavior in Penguins.* Lawrence, Kans.: U. of Kans., 1951b.

Riney, Thane. Relationships between Birds and Deer. *Condor* (1951), **53**: 178–185.

Ripley, Dillon. Strange Courtship of Birds of Paradise. *Nat'l. Geog. Mag.* (1950), **97**(2):247–278.

Rivolier, Jean. Polar Realm of the Emperors. *Nat. Hist.* (1959), **68**:66–81.

Robson, F. D. *Kiwis in Captivity.* Bull. Hawkes Bay Art Gallery and Mus., Napier (New Zealand) (1948), 1–8.

Rodger, George, and Jinx Rodger. The Last Great Animal Kingdom: A Portfolio of Africa's Vanishing Wildlife. *Nat'l. Geog. Mag.* (1960), **118**:390–409.

Rudbeck, Gustaf. Studies on Bird Migration. Based on Field Studies in Southern Sweden. *Vår Fagelvörld* (1950), Suppl. **1**:1–148.

Ryder, Ronald A. Interspecific Intolerance of the American Coot in Utah. *Auk* (1959), **76**:424–442.

Sabine, Winifred S. The Winter Society of the Oregon Junco: The Flock. *Condor* (1955), **57**:88–111.

———. The Winter Society of the Oregon Junco: Intolerance, Dominance and the Pecking Order. *Condor* (1959), **61**:110–135.

Salt, George W. Observations on Fox, Lincoln, and Song Sparrows at Jackson Hole, Wyoming. *Auk* (1957), **74**:258–259.

———, and Erik Zeuthen. The Respiratory System. Chapt. X in A. J. Marshall's *Biology and Comparative Physiology of Birds.* New York: Academic, 1960.

Salyer, J. C., and Karl Lagler. The Food and Habits of American Merganser during Winter in Michigan, Considered in Relation to Fish Management. *Jour. Wildl. Mngt.* (1940), **4**:186–219.

Sargent, Theodore David. Winter Studies on the Tree Sparrow, *Spizella arborea. Bird-Banding* (1959), **30**:27–37.

Saunders, Aretas A. The Song of the Song Sparrow. *Wilson Bull.* (1951), **63**:99–109.

———. Forty Years of Spring Migration in Southern Connecticut. *Wilson Bull.* (1959), **71**:208–219.

Savile, D. B. O. The Flight Mechanism of Swifts and Hummingbirds. *Auk* (1950), **67**:499–504.

———. The Primaries of *Archaeopteryx*. *Auk* (1957), **74**:99–101.

Sawyer, Edmund J. Unusual Adaptations of Wildlife. *Aud. Mag.* (1959), **61**:212–213.

Schaefer, Ernst. Contribution to the Life History of the Swallow-Tanager. *Auk* (1953), **70**:403–460.

———. Zur Biologic des Steisshuhnes, *Nothocercus bonapartei*. *Jour. für Ornith.* (1954), **95**:219–232.

Schmidt-Nielsen, Knut, and Ragnar Fange. The Function of the Salt Gland in the Brown Pelican. *Auk* (1958), **75**:282–289.

Schnell, Jay H. Nesting Behavior and Food Habits of Goshawks in the Sierra Nevada of California. *Condor* (1958), **60**:377–403.

Schorger, A. W. The Deep Diving of the Loon and Old-squaw and Its Mechanism. *Wilson Bull.* (1947), **59**:151–159.

———. The Crushing of *Carya* Nuts in the Gizzard of the Turkey. *Auk* (1960), **77**:337–340.

Schwartzkopff, Johann. On the Hearing of Birds. *Auk* (1955), **72**:340–347.

Scott, F. R. Middle Atlantic Coast Region. *Aud. Field Notes* (1960), **14**:373–376.

Scott, John W. Mating Behavior of the Sage Grouse. *Auk* (1942), **59**:477–498.

Scott, Thomas G., Willis, Yuell L., and Jack A. Ellis. Some Effects of a Field Application of Dieldrin on Wildlife. *Jour. Wildl. Mngt.* (1959), **23**:409–427.

Scott, W. E. (ed.). *Silent Wings: A Memorial to the Passenger Pigeon.* Madison: Wisc. Soc. for Ornith., 1947, 42 pp.

Seibert, Henri C. Light Intensity and the Roosting Flight of Herons in New Jersey. *Auk* (1951), **68**:63–74.

Selander, Robert K. Sex Ratio of Nestlings and Clutch Size in the Boat-tailed Grackle. *Condor* (1960a), **62**:34–44.

———. Failure of Estrogen and Prolactin Treatment to Induce Brood Patch Formation in Brown-headed Cowbirds. *Condor* (1960b), **62**:65.

———, and D. K. Hunter. On the Functions of Wing-flashing in Mockingbirds. *Wilson Bull.* (1960), **73**:341–345.

Sharp, Ward M. Social and Range Dominance in Gallinaceous Birds—Pheasants and Prairie Grouse. *Jour. Wildl. Mngt.* (1957), **21**:242–244.

Shelford, Victor E. Life Zones, Modern Ecology and the Failure of Temperature Summing. *Wilson Bull.* (1932), **44**:144–157.

Shepard, Paul, Jr. Eyes—Clues to Life Habits. *Nat. Mag.* (1951), **44**:457–460.

Shivrajkumer of Jasdan, Naik, R. M., and K. S. Lavkumar. A Visit to the Flamingos in the Great Rann of Kutch. *Jour. Bombay Nat. Hist. Soc.* (1960), **57**:465–478.

Sibley, Charles G. Notes on the Birds of New Georgia, Central Solomon Islands. *Condor* (1951), **53**:81–92.

———. The Abbreviated Inner Primaries of Nestling Woodpeckers. *Auk* (1957), **74**:102–103.

———. The Electrophoretic Patterns of Avian Egg-White Proteins as Taxonomic Characters. *Ibis* (1960), **102**:215–284.

Skutch, Alexander F. Helpers at the Nest. *Auk* (1935), **52**:257–273.

———. Social and Sleeping Habits of Central American Wrens, *Auk* (1940), **57**:293–312.

———. Do Tropical Birds Rear as Many Young as They Can Nourish? *Ibis* (1949a), **91**:430–455.

———. Life History of the Ruddy Quail-Dove. *Condor* (1949b), **51**:3–19.

———. The Royal Flycatcher. *Aud. Mag.* (1952a), **54**:227–231.

———. Life History of the Chestnut-tailed Automolus. *Condor* (1952b), **54**:93–100.

———. Kingfishers—Sovereigns of the Watercourses. *Nat. Mag.* (1952c), **45**:461–464, 500.

———. Life History of the Ruddy Ground Dove. *Condor* (1956), **58**:188–205.

———. Life History of the Amazon Kingfisher. *Condor* (1957), **59**:217–229.

———. Helpers Among Birds. *Condor* (1961), **63**:198–226.

Slud, Paul. The Song and Dance of the Long-Tailed Manakin, *Chiroxiphia linearis*. *Auk* (1957), **74**:333–339.

Smith, Robert Leo. The Songs of the Grasshopper Sparrow. *Wilson Bull.* (1959), **71**:141–152.

Smith, W. John. Movements of Michigan Herring Gulls. *Bird-Banding* (1959), **30**:69–104.

Snow, D. W., and B. K. Snow. Northern Waterthrush Returning to Same Winter Quarters in Successive Winters. *Auk* (1960), **77**:351–352.

Snyder, Dana P., and J. Frank Cassel. A Late Summer Nest of the Red Crossbill in Colorado. *Wilson Bull.* (1951), **63**:177–180.

Snyder, Dorothy E. Dovekie Flights and Wrecks. *Mass. Aud.* (1960), **44**:117–121.

Snyder, L. L. Additional Instances of Paired Ovaries in Raptorial Birds. *Auk* (1948), **65**:602.

Sokolowski, Jan. *The Mute Swan in Poland.* Warsaw: State Council for Conserv. of Nat., 1960, 28 pp.

Southern, William E. Homing of Purple Martins. *Wilson Bull.* (1959), **71**:254–261.

Speirs, J. Murray. Flight Speed of the Old-squaw. *Auk* (1945), **62**:135–136.

Spencer, O. Ruth. Nesting Habits of the Black-billed Cuckoo. *Wilson Bull.* (1943), **55**:11–22.

Sprunt, Alexander, Jr. Bird Boarders in the Southeast. *Aud. Mag.* (1960), **62**:236–239.

Sprunt, Alexander, IV, and M. Philip Kahl, Jr. Mysterious Mycteria—Our American Stork. *Aud. Mag.* (1960), **62**:206–209, 234, 252.

Stabler, Robert M., and Carlton M. Herman. Upper Digestive Tract Trichomoniasis in Mourning Doves and Other Birds. N. A. *Wildl. Conf. Trans.* (1951), **16**:145–163.

Staebler, Arthur E. Number of Contour Feathers in the English Sparrow. *Wilson Bull.* (1941), **53**:126–127.

Stallcup, William B. Relationships of Some Families of the Suborder Passeres (Songbirds) as Indicated by Comparisons of Tissue Proteins. *Jour. Grad. Research Center* (1961), **29**:43–65.

Stamm, Anne L. The Breeding of the House Wren in Kentucky. *Kent. Warb.* (1951a), **27**:47–56.

———. Four Species Choose Same Nesting Tree. *Kent. Warb.* (1951b), **27**:23–24.

Stewart, Paul A. Dispersal, Breeding Behavior, and Longevity of Banded Barn Owls in North America. *Auk* (1952), **69**:227–245.

———. Locomotion of Wood Ducks. *Wilson Bull.* (1958), **70**:184–187.

Stewart, Robert E. Ecology of a Nesting Red-shouldered Hawk Population. *Wilson Bull.* (1949), **61**:26–35.

———. Clapper Rail Populations of the Middle Atlantic States. *N. A. Wildl. Conf. Trans.* (1951), **16**:421–430.

———. Breeding Populations of Clapper Rail at Chincoteague, Virginia (p. 55 in *Special Scient. Report: Wildlife* No. 18), 1952a.

———. Molting of Northern Yellow-throat in Southern Michigan. *Auk* (1952b), **69**:50–59.

———. A Life-History Study of the Yellow-throat. *Wilson Bull.* (1953), **65**:99–115.

Stewart, Robert E., and John W. Aldrich. Removal and Repopulation of Breeding Birds in a Spruce-Fir Forest Community. *Auk* (1951), **68**:471–482.

Stewart, Robert E., Geis, Aelred D., and Charles D. Evans. Distribution of Populations and Hunting Kill of the Canvasback. *Jour. Wildl. Mngt.* (1958), **22**:333–370.

Stewart, Robert E., and Joseph H. Manning. Distribution and Ecology of Whistling Swans in the Chesapeake Bay Region. *Auk* (1958), **75**:203–212.

Stine, Perna M. Changes in the Breeding Birds of Bird Haven Sanctuary Over a Period of Forty-five Years. *Wilson Bull.* (1959), **71**:372–380.

Storer, Robert W. The Fossil Loon, *Colymboides minutus*. *Condor* (1956), **58**:413–426.

Stresemann, Erwin. The Status of Avian Systematics and Its Unsolved Problems. *Auk* (1959), **76**:269–280.

Suomalainen, Heikk, and Evi Arhimo. On the Microbial Decomposition of Cellulose by Wild Gallinaceous Birds (Family Tetraonidae). *Ornis Fennica* (1945), **22**:21–23.

Suthers, Roderick A. Measurement of Some Lake-Shore Territories of the Song Sparrow. *Wilson Bull.* (1960), **72**:232–237.

Sutton, George M. Roadrunner. In A. C. Bent's *Life Histories of North American Cuckoos, Goatsuckers, Hummingbirds, and Their Allies.* Bull. 176, U. S. Nat. Mus. (Washington, D. C.) 1940.

———. Dispersal of Mistletoe by Birds. *Wilson Bull.* (1951), **63**:235–237.

Sutton, George M., and David F. Parmelee. Nesting of the Greenland Wheatear on Baffin Island. *Condor* (1954a), **56**:295–306.

———. Nesting of the Snow Bunting on Baffin Island. *Wilson Bull.* (1954b), **66**:159–179.

Svardson, Gunnar. The "Invasion" Type of Bird Migration. *Brit. Birds* (1957), **50**:314–343.

Tabler, Fan Boswell. Notes on the Barn Swallow. *Kent. Warb.* (1956), **32**:43–46.

Tanner, James T. Black-capped and Carolina Chickadees in the Southern Appalachian Mountains. *Auk* (1952), **69**:407–424.

Tevis, Lloyd, Jr. Effect of Vertebrate Animals on Seed Crop of Sugar Pine. *Jour. Wildl. Mngt.* (1953), **17**:128–131.

Thompson, William L. Agonistic Behavior in the House Finch. Part I: Annual Cycle and Display Patterns. *Condor* (1960), **62**:245–271; Part II: Factors in Aggressiveness and Sociability. *Condor* (1960), **62**:378–402.

Thomson, A. L., and E. P. Leach. Report on Bird-Ringing for 1951. *Brit. Birds* (1952), **45**:265–277.

Tillinghast, D. A. A Beef Cattle and Bluebird Farm. *The Chat* (1952), **16**:4–5.

Tinbergen N. The Function of Sexual Fighting in Birds; and the Problem of the Origin of "Territory." *Bird-Banding* (1936), **7**:1–8.

Tinker, Frank A. Avian Botulism—The Battle at Bear River. *Aud Mag.* (1958), **60**:116–119, 140, 174–177, 224–227.

Tooke, Alfred I. The Birds that Helped Columbus. *Aud. Mag.* (1961), **63**:252–253, 287, 296.

Tordoff, Harrison B. Social Organization and Behavior in a Flock of Captive Nonbreeding Red Crossbills. *Condor* (1954), **56**:346–358.

———. Food-storing in the Sparrow Hawk. *Wilson Bull.* (1955), **67**:139–140.

———, and Robert M. Mengel. Studies of Birds Killed in Nocturnal Migration. *Univ. Kans. Publ.* (1956), **10**:1–44.

Tucker, Richard. Taxonomy of the Salivary Glands of Vertebrates. *Syst. Zool.* (1958), **7**:74–83.

Turček, F. J. On Bird Banding in the USSR. *Bird-Banding* (1958), **29**:111–112.

Udvardy, Miklos D. F. Ecological and Distributional Analysis of North American Birds. *Condor* (1958), **60**:50–66.

Van Tyne, Josselyn. Winter Returns of the Indigo Bunting in Guatemala. *Bird-Banding* (1932), **3**:110.

———. A Cardinal's, *Richmondena cardinalis,* Choice of Food for Adult and for Young. *Auk* (1951), **68**:110.

Vogt, William. *Road to Survival.* New York: William Sloane, 1948.

Wagner, H. O. Variation in Clutch Size at Different Latitudes. *Auk* (1957), **74**:243–250.

Walkinshaw, Lawrence H. Aortic Rupture in Field Sparrow Due to Fright. *Auk* (1945), **62**:141.

———. Chipping Sparrow Notes. *Bird-Banding* (1952), **23**:101–108.

———. Life History of the Prothonotary Warbler. *Wilson Bull.* (1953), **65**:152–168.

Wallace, George J. Bicknell's Thrush, Its Taxonomy, Distribution and Life History. *Proc. Boston Soc. Nat. Hist.* (1939), **41**:211–402.

———. Winter Studies of Color-banded Chickadees. *Bird-Banding* (1941), **12**:49–67.

———. Returns and Survival Rate of Wintering Tree Sparrows. *Bird-Banding* (1942), **13**:81–83.

———. The 1940 Nesting Population at Pleasant Valley Sanctuary, Lenox, Massachusetts. *Auk* (1943), **60**:403–407.

———. The Barn Owl in Michigan. *Mich. State Coll. Agr. Exp. Sta. Tech. Bull.* (1948), **208**:1–61.

———. A Case of Microphthalmia in the American Robin. *Wilson Bull.* (1956), **68**:151–152.

Warburton, Frederick E. Sparrow Hawk, *Falco sparverius,* Eats Bread. *Auk* (1952), **69**:85.

Watson, J. B., and K. S. Lashlay. An Historical and Experimental Study of Homing. *Marine Biol. Papers,* Carnegie Inst. (Washington, D. C., 1915), **7**:1–60.

Weaver, Richard L. Reproduction in English Sparrows. *Auk* (1943), **60**:62–74.

Weller, Milton W. Growth, Weights, and Plumages of the Redhead, *Aythya americana. Wilson Bull.* (1957), **69**:5–38.

———. Observations on the Incubation Behavior of a Common Nighthawk. *Auk* (1958), **75**:48–59.

Welter, Wilfred A. The Natural History of the Long-billed Marsh Wren. *Wilson Bull.* (1935), **47**:3–34.

Westerskov, Kaj. The Nesting Habitat of the Royal Albatross on Campbell Island. *Proc. N. Z. Ecol. Soc.* (1959), **6**:16–20.

Wetherbee, David K. Unilateral Microphthalmia in *Quiscalus quiscula* and Synophthalmia in *Mimus polyglottos. Auk* (1958), **75**:101–103.

Wetmore, Alexander. The Number of Contour Feathers in Passeriform and Related Birds. *Auk* (1936), **53**:159–169.

———. Recent Additions to Our Knowledge of Prehistoric Birds. *Proc. 10th Internatl. Ornith. Congr.* (1950), **51**:74.

Wharton, William P. Homing by a Female Cowbird. *Bird-Banding* (1959), **30**:228.

Whitaker, Lovie M. Lark Sparrow Oiling Its Tarsi. *Wilson Bull.* (1957b), **69**:179–180.

———. Behavior of Birds on Warm Surfaces. *Wilson Bull.* (1960), **72**:403–404.

Whittle, C. H., and L. B. Fletcher. Group Habit Among Birds. *Auk* (1924), **41**:327–333.

Wible, Mary. Notes on Feeding and Fecal-Sac Disposal of Sapsuckers. *Wilson Bull.* (1960), **72**:399.

Wilcox, Harry H. The Pelvic Musculature of the Loon, *Gavia immer. Amer. Midl. Nat.* (1952), **48**:513–573.

Williams, George G. The Nature and Causes of the "Coastal Hiatus." *Wilson Bull.* (1950), **62**:175–182.
———. Birds on the Gulf of Mexico. *Auk* (1952), **69**:428–432.
Williams, Gordon R. The California Quail in New Zealand. *Jour. Wildl. Mngt.* (1952), **16**:460–483.
———. The Dispersal from New Zealand and Australia of Some Introduced European Passerines. *Ibis* (1953), **95**:676–692.
Williamson, Francis S. L., and Robert A. Norris. Data on Relative Heart Size of the Warbling Vireo and Other Passerines from High Altitudes. *Wilson Bull.* (1958), **70**:90–91.
Willis, Edwin. A Study of the Foraging Behavior of Two Species of Ant-Tanagers. *Auk* (1960), **77**:150–170.
Wilson, A. C., and Donald S. Farner. The Annual Cycle of Thyroid Activity in White-crowned Sparrows of Eastern Washington. *Condor* (1960), **62**:414–425.
Wilson, Nancy, Preston, Eric J., and F. W. Preston. The Gloss of Eggs. *Auk* (1958), **75**:456–464.
Wing, Leonard W. Number of Contour Feathers on a Cowbird, *Molothrus ater*. *Auk* (1952), **69**:90.
———. *Natural History of Birds*. New York: Ronald, 1956.
Wolfe, L. R. Notes of the Birds of Korea. *Auk* (1950), **67**:433–455.
Wolfson, Albert. Bird Migration and the Concept of Continental Drift. *Science* (1948), **108**:23–30.
Wood, Harold B. Homing Ability of Female Cowbirds. *Wilson Bull.* (1952), **64**:46–47.
Woodbury, Angus M. Animal Migration—Periodic Response Theory. *Auk* (1941), **58**:463–505.
Woodgerd, Wesley. Food Habits of the Golden Eagle. *Jour. Wildl. Mngt.* (1952), **16**:457–459.
Woolfenden, Glen E. Comparative Breeding Behavior of *Ammospiza caudacuta* and *A. maritima*. *Univ. Kans. Publ. Mus. Nat. Hist.* (1956), **10**:45–75.
Worth, C. Brooke. Birds and Human Disease. *Wilson Bull.* (1949), **61**:183–186.
———, Hamparian, Vincent, and Geoffrey Rake. A Serological Survey of Ornithosis in Bird Banders. *Bird-Banding* (1957), **28**:92–97.
Wright, Bruce S. The Relation of Bald Eagles to Breeding Ducks in New Brunswick. *Jour. Wildl. Mngt.* (1953), **17**:55–62.
———. Predation on Big Game in East Africa. *Jour. Wildl. Mngt.* (1960), **24**:1–15.
Wynne-Edwards, V. C. Zoology of the Baird Expedition (1950) I: The Birds Observed in Central and South-east Baffin Island. *Auk* (1952), **69**:353–391.
Yeagley, H. L. A Preliminary Study of a Physical Basis of Bird Navigation. *Jour. Applied Physics* (1947), **18**:1035–1036; (1951), **22**:746–760.
Yocom, Charles F. Techniques Used to Increase Nesting of Canada Geese. *Jour. Wildl. Mngt.* (1952), **16**:425–428.
Young, Stanley P. The Bounty System. *Atlantic Nat.* (1952), **8**:10–17.

# INDEX